DYNAMICS

in

MACHINES

By

F. R. ERSKINE CROSSLEY, M.A.,D.Eng.

ASSOCIATE PROFESSOR OF MECHANICAL ENGINEERING
YALE UNIVERSITY

THE RONALD PRESS COMPANY ◢ NEW YORK

Library of Congress Catalog Card Number: 54-7644

PRINTED IN THE UNITED STATES OF AMERICA

PREFACE

This book is intended as a text for the intermediate course in dynamics given to junior or senior mechanical engineering students as a sequel to their introductory courses in statics, dynamics, and strength of materials. It provides the student with an opportunity to apply these fundamental skills to the analysis of dynamic problems in machine design, with the aim of developing in him an appreciation of the tremendous importance of the mass, the inertia forces, and the flexibility of machine members in motion.

After an initial chapter which reviews some basic dynamics, attention is given in Chapter 2 to the fact that many students have difficulty in transposing mechanical situations into mathematical equation form. In this it is assumed that the student has acquired a reasonable facility with the calculus and no peculiar effort is made to avoid it; however, the presentation is always as simple as possible. No previous knowledge of differential equations is expected and an Appendix to the chapter lists the solutions of the few necessary types.

Since every mechanical engineer should know and understand the phenomena of natural frequency, resonance, and critical speeds, Chapters 3, 4, and 5 are devoted to the theory of vibration. This is developed only for a single degree of freedom, which is taken to include the Rayleigh method for shafts with distributed mass. A more complete treatment would be suitable only for more specialized or more advanced study. In Chapter 4 the whirling of shafts is shown to modify the otherwise precise matter of the balance of rotors, and the juxtaposition of these two aspects presents the first opportunity to emphasize the drastic nature of the usual assumption of the "rigid body." The subject of rotation is completed in Chapter 6 with a study in three dimensions, including the gyroscope and some applications. It is felt that a real understanding of the gyroscope comes only through comprehension of the behavior of the angular momentum vector, although some will find that a reading of the second half of the chapter satisfies them.

The effects of inertia forces in machines and further balancing problems are considered in Chapters 7, 8, and 9. First it is desired to show that these problems are often only slightly more difficult than are problems in the static equilibrium of forces in frameworks, provided of course that the kinematical analysis is mastered. In Chapters 7 and 8, for the sake of the kinematics, the rigid body assumption is allowed.

iii

Here the simple engine mechanism is prominent because it is of such common occurrence and because, although it is so simple, it contains the connecting rod as an example of the most general type of plane motion. In Chapter 9 the rigid body assumption is discarded and the accompaniment of strain with stress is examined. The second half of this chapter, dealing with cam-actuated motion, is a new presentation which is a final challenge to those who still cling to the use of "rigid body" kinematics universally. The last chapter is devoted to governors, which have a traditional place in this subject field and which are of interest also as an introduction to automatic control.

Sufficient material is included to occupy a full-year course. The author recognizes however that in many colleges only one semester is available for this study, and for this reason a considerable independence between chapters has been established, permitting selective coverage of the topics. It is hoped that the student will find here a stimulation to further pursuit of the theory of vibrations, of mechanical servomechanisms, and of general dynamics.

In the acquisition of technical knowledge, the solution of many problems plays an important part. Problems of varying difficulty and length are to be found at the end of each chapter; the answers to the majority of odd-numbered ones are listed at the end of the book. Some problems emphasize the mathematical side, while others are drawn directly from actual practical machines; some are presented in simplified form with exactly the right amount of data, while others are more like those encountered in practice with too much or too little data available, thus necessitating selection or intelligent approximation. Those problems which carry the notation "C.U." or "U.L." are reproduced, by kind permission, from final examinations set by the Cambridge University Engineering Department and by the University of London, to whom the author makes acknowledgment.

Further grateful acknowledgment is made to the many authors whose works are referred to throughout the book, and to Dean S. W. Dudley and Professor H. L. Seward for their encouragement. A book of mimeographed notes, first written by Professors C. F. Smith and C. T. Porter in 1917, rewritten and enlarged many times by Professor Dudley, and then in the last ten years by the author, has really been the *sine qua non* of the present work.

F. R. E. CROSSLEY

New Haven, Connecticut
March, 1954

CONTENTS

.

DYNAMICS IN MACHINES

Chapter 1

INTRODUCTORY KINETICS

1–1. Newton's Laws. The science of dynamics originated with the experiments of Galileo (1564–1642). Before his time the confusion of thought about dynamics is demonstrated by citing the contention current in those days that in order for a body to keep moving it was necessary to have some force continually acting on it from behind. This is not so irrational, for it was observed that all unaided motions soon stopped. Galileo experimented with dropping stones and with motion on an inclined plane and advanced the hypothesis that a force produces in a body a proportional acceleration.

Sir Isaac Newton, however, first formulated the three fundamental laws of mechanics. Published in his *Principia* in 1687, the laws may be expressed as follows:

1. Every body continues in its state of rest, or of uniform motion in a straight path, unless the application of a force compels a change in that state.
2. An (unbalanced) force causes a proportional rate of change of momentum that takes place in the direction in which the force is impressed.
3. For every action between two contiguous bodies there is a reaction which is equal, opposite, and simultaneous.

The first law may be regarded as merely a special case of the second, and both are concerned with particles rather than bodies, although it will be shown how, by reckoning any body to consist of an agglomeration of particles, the laws may be developed to deal adequately with these also. The extra considerations arise when a body rotates; but it should take no great stretch of the imagination to see that what applies to particles will apply equally to any large body which has a motion of translation—that is, where all particles in the body move together in identical manner.

The second law may be expressed mathematically as

$$\frac{d}{dt}(mv) = F \tag{1-1}$$

where F and v are assumed to have the same direction and sense; then

3

if the mass is to remain constant, this becomes

$$m \frac{dv}{dt} = F$$

or

$$F = ma \qquad (1\text{--}2)$$

In reality this is a definition of mass. It arises from the observed proportionality, that as in a free fall the weight W of a body produces an acceleration g due to gravity, so any other force F acting on the same body will produce an acceleration a in direct proportion:

$$\frac{F_1}{a_1} = \frac{F_2}{a_2} = \cdots = \frac{W}{g} \qquad (1\text{--}3)$$

Furthermore, from the second law (eq. 1–1) the fundamental laws of the momentum and energy of a particle can be derived. Acceleration can be written in two alternate forms:

$$a = \frac{dv}{dt} \quad \text{or} \quad = \frac{dv}{ds} \cdot \frac{ds}{dt} = v \frac{dv}{ds}$$

where s is a displacement. Thus by integration of the first form, with m constant, in eq. 1–1,

$$m \int_{v_1}^{v_2} dv = \int_{t_1}^{t_2} F \, dt$$

$$mv_2 - mv_1 = \int_{t_1}^{t_2} F \, dt \qquad (1\text{--}4)$$

which is the law of momentum; or by integration, using the second form,

$$m \int_{v_1}^{v_2} v \, dv = \int_{s_1}^{s_2} F \, ds$$

$$\tfrac{1}{2} mv_2^2 - \tfrac{1}{2} mv_1^2 = \int_{s_1}^{s_2} F \, ds \qquad (1\text{--}5)$$

which is the law of energy. The time integral of force occurring in eq. 1–4 is the *impulse* of the applied force, and the space integral of the force in eq. 1–5 is the *work* done on the body. They are left in integral form in case the force should vary during the interval considered.

1-2. Systems of Units, Gravitational and Absolute. Through the relation in eq. 1–3, mass is expressed as a ratio

$$m = W/g$$

and this is the cause of some trouble in defining terms. In engineering, the weight W of a body is usually encountered first, and mass is then defined through weight: for a weight measured in pounds, we can divide by $g = 32.2$ ft/sec^2 and obtain the mass measured in lb sec^2 per ft, or a unit sometimes called a slug. This is a gravitational system of units, and there is a similar system used by European engineers in metric measure, in terms of kilograms, meters, and seconds. We shall use the gravitational system throughout this book. However, the objection to this is that the acceleration g is not a constant in all parts of the world, and therefore if we are to start with a weight and divide by a variable g the mass will appear as if it were a variable.

The acceleration g due to the attraction of the earth appears purely only at the poles, where it has the value 32.26 ft/sec^2 at sea level. At lesser latitudes its value is less, due primarily to the centrifugal forces caused by the earth's rotation; so that at latitude 45° (north or south) it has the value 32.17, and at the equator it is 32.09 ft/sec^2. It also diminishes with altitude because of the inverse-square law of the attraction between two bodies.

In the absolute system of dimensions mass is the starting point, and weight is then regarded as the product $W = mg$. In English units, the standard mass is the mass of a platinum cylinder which weighs a pound in London; it is defined as a pound mass. Then the unit of force (or weight) is defined as that force which gives this mass a unit acceleration (1 ft/sec^2) instead of g ft/sec^2; consequently it is of a magnitude approximately half an ounce and is called a poundal. This system is used very seldom, but the metric absolute system is used by physicists everywhere; the gram mass is a thousandth part of the mass of a platinum bar weighing a kilogram where it is kept in Paris, and the unit of force is such as will produce in this an acceleration of one centimeter per sec^2. Since g is around 986 cm/sec^2, this unit force, the dyne, is only about one tenth of one per cent of a gram weight, a very tiny force.

To engineers the total variation in g appears as of small account: although for various places on the earth and for altitudes up to 50,000 ft, the variation is as much as from 32.06 to 32.26 ft/sec^2, yet most objects do not move around much. So 32.2 is a value normally used.

However, herein lies a danger of which the student is warned, that this number carries the dimensions feet and seconds with it. It is better when solving numerical problems to remember two values, and then, in a problem concerning inches, a moment's hesitation will help in making the correct decision:

$$g = 32.2 \text{ ft/sec}^2$$
$$g = 386 \text{ in./sec}^2$$

1–3. D'Alembert's Principle. Inertia Forces.

In solving problems in dynamics there are three methods of attack at our disposal. They are the methods of inertia, of momentum, and of energy. Here we shall take these up in succession.

The inertia method is developed directly from Newton's second law and eq. 1–2. It applies to all bodies at rest or in motion that have a

(a)   (b)

Fig. 1–1.

constant mass, and this is common enough. Suppose a body as in Fig. 1–1a is set upon a table. A force P is applied horizontally, and a frictional force f opposes it. The net horizontal force, by which P exceeds f, will produce an acceleration a, and resolution of horizontal forces yields the relation

$$P - f = \frac{W}{g}a \qquad (1\text{–}6)$$

An alternative manner of regarding this equation (in many problems) is due to d'Alembert.* He suggested that a fictitious force F be assumed to be added to the applied forces, a force equal in magnitude to that required for the acceleration $\left(\text{i.e., } \frac{W}{g}a\right)$ but opposite in direction. This is then a "reversed effective force," and with it (Fig. 1–1b) the body appears to be in equilibrium. The equation of the equilibrium of forces is

$$P - f - \frac{W}{g}a = 0$$

which is the same as eq. 1–6.

Newton's law states that for any number of actual forces F acting on a body, the sum of their components F_x in any chosen direction x will produce an acceleration a_x in that direction

$$\Sigma F_x = \frac{W}{g}a_x \qquad (1\text{–}7)$$

D'Alembert's Principle, on the other hand, is stated

$$\Sigma F_x - \frac{W}{g}a_x = 0$$

and by this simple device we have extended the idea of static equilibrium to apply to dynamic cases. We shall freely make use of this extended sense of the word equilibrium.

* Jean d'Alembert, *Traité de Dynamique*, 1743.

Take the example of a boy holding a string to which is tied a stone, and whirling it around his head. The stone requires a normal (centripetal) acceleration to hold it in a circular path.

The Newtonian style of analysis would proceed: the boy must pull on the string to produce a tension which is transmitted to the stone to give it the required normal acceleration. Therefore

$$\text{Tension} = \frac{W}{g}r\omega^2$$

By d'Alembert's method, a reversed effective force is added. Since the acceleration is toward the center, this reversed effective force is outward; it goes by the common name of "centrifugal force." With this extra hypothetical force the stone may be regarded as being in equilibrium, and we state that the tension inward balances the "centrifugal force" outward, or

$$\text{Tension} = \frac{W}{g}r\omega^2$$

We shall feel free to use whichever of these two approaches seems easier in any problem.

These reversed effective forces are seen to be proportional to the mass (or inertia) of a body; hence they are grouped under the general name *inertia forces*.

Example. Fig. 1–2 shows a device called the Atwood Machine. Two unequal weights, A and B, are held by a light string which passes over a fixed pulley C, and it is assumed that the surface of the pulley is perfectly frictionless.

When the weights are released from rest, find the tension in the string.

Assume that A is the heavier weight (for convenience) and that T is the tension in the string, which will act on both weights upward. Assume A will accelerate downward with an acceleration a. Resolving forces downward first for A, then for B, treating them as free bodies, obtain the equations

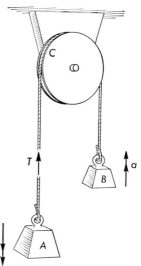

FIG. 1–2.

$$W_A - T = \frac{W_A}{g}a$$

$$W_B - T = -\frac{W_B}{g}a$$

Eliminate a by multiplying respectively by W_B, and W_A:

$$W_A W_B - W_B T = W_A T - W_A W_B$$
$$T = \frac{2 W_A W_B}{W_A + W_B}$$

Note that if C is assumed to be a rotating pulley, a term for its moment of inertia and angular acceleration must enter the analysis. We shall look into this in Art. 1–5.

1–4. Rigid Body — Plane Rotation. As considered so far, Newton's law and d'Alembert's Principle apply to a particle. Let us investigate their application to a rigid body, by regarding that body as a group of elemental particles to each of which the law applies.

But first let it be recalled that by the principle of static moments, the center of gravity of any rigid body is defined mathematically by the equations

$$\Sigma x \cdot \delta w = \Sigma y \cdot \delta w = \Sigma z \cdot \delta w = 0 \qquad (1\text{–}8)$$

where x, y, and z are the coordinate distances of any element weighing δw, measured from the center of gravity. This is apparent in Fig. 1–3

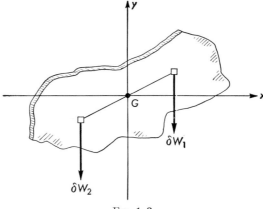

Fig. 1–3.

where some irregularly shaped rigid body has its center of gravity G as shown. A section on the xy plane shows that for every particle δw_1 with moment $x \cdot \delta w_1$ there must be another particle δw_2 with moment $-x \cdot \delta w_2$.

Now in Fig. 1–4 we have a body rotating about an axis through its center of gravity, and the body has symmetry about the plane of rotation. It could be a lamina (thin sheet), a right cylinder, or a sphere. On the element at P is acting the centrifugal force $r\omega^2 (\delta w/g)$ where r is the distance GP and ω the angular velocity in radians per second. The x

and y components of this force are $x\omega^2(\delta w/g)$ and $y\omega^2(\delta w/g)$. Thus, for the whole body all the centrifugal inertia forces add up to

$$\Sigma F_x = (\omega^2/g)\Sigma x\, \delta w \quad \text{and} \quad \Sigma F_y = (\omega^2/g)\Sigma y\, \delta w$$

and by eq. 1–8 these sums are both zero.

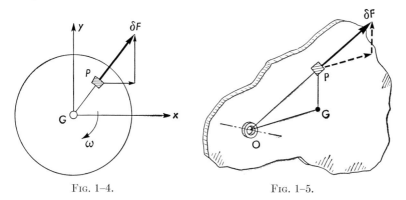

FIG. 1–4.   FIG. 1–5.

Next consider the same sort of symmetrical body rotating about an axis through O other than the center of gravity G (Fig. 1–5). The centrifugal force acting on the element P of weight δw is

$$\delta F = \overline{OP}\cdot\omega^2(\delta w/g)$$

This vector is regarded as the vector sum of two

$$\overline{OP} = \overline{OG} + \!\!\!+\, \overline{GP}$$
$$\delta F = \overline{OG}\omega^2(\delta w/g) +\!\!\!+ \overline{GP}\omega^2(\delta w/g)$$

So the sum effect of all elements of centrifugal force is

$$\Sigma F = \overline{OG}(\omega^2/g)\Sigma\delta w +\!\!\!+ (\omega^2/g)\Sigma\overline{GP}\, \delta w$$

For all the elements such as P, the first term is the same containing the radius OG. On the other hand, the sum of forces represented by the second term presents exactly the same problem as that just analyzed, so that by breaking $\overline{GP}$ into x and y for each particle the sum is seen to vanish, with the result that

$$\Sigma F = \overline{OG}(\omega^2/g)\Sigma\delta w = (W/g)\, \overline{OG}\omega^2 \qquad (1\text{–}9)$$

where $W = \Sigma\delta w$ refers to the weight of the whole body.

We therefore have the theorem: that in any two-dimensional system the sum of all centrifugal inertia forces is the same as it would be if the mass were concentrated at the center of gravity.

Example 1. A penny remains as set upon the revolving table of a phonograph, which rotates at a constant speed of 78 rpm. The maximum coefficient of friction between the surfaces is 30 per cent. Find the amount of the area of table on which this is possible.

Note the forces that are acting. There is centrifugal force radially outward, acting at the center of gravity, but under the condition of constant speed no tangential forces at all. Therefore friction acts radially inward.

The weight of the penny is not given, so that the magnitudes of inertia force and friction are not determinable until a general value W is assumed for the weight. Equilibrium of radial forces gives

$$\frac{W}{g}R\omega^2 = f\cdot W$$

The W assumed drops out, showing that the result is independent of the weight. Solving for the radius R

$$R = \frac{fg}{\omega^2} \quad \text{where} \quad \omega = \frac{2\pi}{60}78 = 2.6\pi \text{ rad/sec}$$

At small values of the radius, friction will be less than 30 per cent; but the maximum radius at which the penny can be placed will be found with the maximum possible friction. For R to be found in inches, g must be in inch units also.

$$R_{\max} = \frac{0.3 \times 386}{(2.6\pi)^2} = 1.74 \text{ in.}$$

Hence the center of the penny must be within a circle of this radius on the table.

Example 2. A half-dollar remains set on the same turntable. Within what area is this possible?

It is possible if the center of the half-dollar is within the same radius as in Example 1 because the answer was independent of the weight.

1–5. Inertia Couple. A flywheel is rotating about a shaft. If then (neglecting friction) a torque is applied to the shaft, an angular acceleration will result. To find the relation between the torque and the acceleration, let P be an element of weight δw at radius r (Fig. 1–6). If the body has an angular acceleration α, then the point P will have a tangential acceleration $r\alpha$, and this requires a force $\frac{\delta w}{g}\cdot r\alpha$ at P or a moment $\left(\frac{\delta w}{g}r\alpha\right)r$ around G. Thus the total torque needed to produce the angular acceleration and overcome the inertia opposing the motion is

$$T = \sum \frac{\delta w}{g}r^2\alpha$$
$$= \alpha\Sigma r^2\delta m = I_G\alpha \tag{1-10}$$

I_G is the moment of inertia* of the body about G by definition, when the elements δm are reduced to the limit. The units, as can be seen from the definition, will be lb ft sec², lb in. sec², or similar varieties. If the slug is used as the unit of mass, then the units are slug ft².

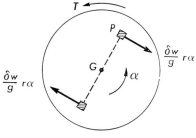

Fig. 1–6.

The more general case in two dimensions is that of any rigid body (Fig. 1–5) rotating about any fixed axis O perpendicular to its plane. For the element at P the inertia force $(\delta w/g)\rho\alpha$ is resolved into two components: $(\delta w/g)r\alpha$ is proportional to and perpendicular to the radius r from the center of gravity G, and $(\delta w/g)a_G$ is parallel to the acceleration a_G of G.

Now the sum effect of all inertia will be the effect of all forces of the former kind, and all of the latter kind. The system of forces $(\delta w/g)r\alpha$ are all in circulation around G, and thus they form a couple about G of magnitude

$$T = \Sigma(\delta w/g)r\alpha \cdot r$$
$$= \alpha\Sigma r^2 \,\delta m = I_G\alpha$$

This is exactly as in eq. 1–10. But there is also the sum of all forces of the second kind, which is a parallel system. They therefore produce a single force

$$F = \Sigma(\delta w/g)a_G = Ma_G$$

and since the moment of these forces about G is zero, since

$$T = (\Sigma r \,\delta m)a_G = 0$$

the line of action passes through G.

The conclusion, then, is that with such a body rotating about a fixed axis O, there are two inertia effects:

    a) *a reversed inertia force* $F = Ma$ acting at the center of gravity, where M is the mass of the whole body and a is the acceleration of the center of gravity, and

---

* Note: In certain problems, such as the bending of beams, another sort of moment of inertia occurs, which is defined as $\int r^2 \, dA$ (instead of $\int r^2 \, dm$). The units of this are usually in.⁴. Distinction between them is important. Where both occur, we shall call one *mass* moment of inertia, the other, *area* moment of inertia.

b) *a reversed inertia couple* $T = I_G \alpha$ acting around the center of
gravity, where I_G is the moment of inertia of the whole body
about an axis through the center of gravity.

The direction of the force (a) is opposite to the acceleration a and
the sense of the moment (b) is opposite to the acceleration α.

Example 1. A free-running cylindrical spool, with moment of inertia
1.20 lb in. sec^2 and diameter 6 in., is wound with thread. The free end
falls vertically and is pulled down by a force $F = 10$ lb. Find the angular
acceleration of the spool, and compare with that of the same spool
when a weight $W = 10$ lb is attached to the thread to apply the force
instead. The weight of the thread is negligible. The axis of the spool is
held fixed horizontally as in Fig. 1–7.

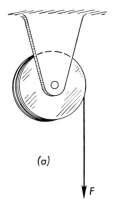
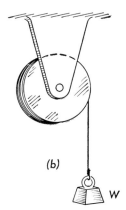

(a)   (b)

F W

FIG. 1–7.

Case (a): The moment applied by force F causes the acceleration

$$Fr = I\alpha_1 \quad \text{(lb in.)}$$

There is no inertia *force* effect, for the center of mass of the spool is
unmoved. Thus,

$$\alpha_1 = \frac{Fr}{I} = \frac{10 \times 3}{1.20} = 25 \text{ rad/sec}^2$$

Or the linear acceleration of the free end of the thread is $a_1 = r\alpha_1 = 75$
in./sec^2.

Case (b): The moment on the spool is less than 30 lb in., because the
weight W drops with acceleration $a_2 = r\alpha_2$.

$$\left(W - \frac{W}{g}r\alpha_2\right)r = I\alpha_2 \quad \text{(lb in.)}$$

$$\alpha_2 = \frac{Wr}{I + (W/g)r^2} = \frac{10 \times 3}{1.20 + 0.233} = 20.9 \text{ rad/sec}^2$$

since $Wr^2/g = (10 \times 9)/386 = 0.233$. The downward acceleration of W is $a_2 = 62.8$ in./sec².

Example 2. A spool of cylindrical shape, radius r, has a string attached and wound around it; it is then released to fall by unwinding the string (as a "Yo-yo" toy), Fig. 1–8. Find the acceleration.

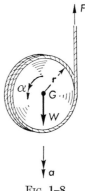

Realize first that since there is always the pull upward on the string, the spool is not free to fall, and its acceleration will be less than the free-falling gravity. However, the acceleration will be constant, since the forces producing it are all constant.

We assume therefore some general value a for the acceleration, and also an angular acceleration α radians per sec, and enter on the figure the two inertia effects, the reversed effective force $\dfrac{W}{g}a$ and the reversed effective couple $I_G\alpha$ around the center of gravity.

Fig. 1–8.

Neglect friction and the possibility of the spool tipping sideways; assume the thickness of the string is negligible compared to the radius of the spool, and write down the equations of equilibrium:

1. By resolving forces vertically

$$\Sigma F_V = F - W + \frac{W}{g}a = 0 \qquad \text{where } F \text{ is the string tension;}$$

2. By taking moments about the center of gravity

$$\Sigma M_G = Fr - I_G\alpha = 0$$

Eliminate F as unwanted, by multiplying the first by r and substituting the second for Fr:

$$Wr(1 - a/g) = I_G\alpha$$

To solve this we need a relation between a and α, which is provided by geometry:

$$a = r\alpha$$

since the tangent point of the string is the instantaneous center of rotation. Then if we take the spool to be a cylinder we may write its moment of inertia about G as

$$I_G = \frac{1}{2}\frac{W}{g}r^2$$

and so

$$Wr(1 - a/g) = \left(\frac{1}{2}\frac{W}{g}r^2\right)\left(\frac{a}{r}\right)$$

$$a = \frac{2}{3}g$$

If the moment of inertia were more than the above (which would be the case if there were large flanges and smaller center) the acceleration would be less than this.

1–6. Some Values of Moment of Inertia. Since most objects that occur in engineering are of regular geometric shapes, their moments of inertia (whether of mass or of area) may be calculated easily or found in a handbook. A very convenient formula for remembering many of them is known as Routh's Rule:*

$$\left.\begin{array}{l}\text{Moment of iner-}\\\text{tia about an ax-}\\\text{is of symmetry}\end{array}\right\} = \text{Mass} \times \frac{\text{(Sum of the squares of the perpendicular semi-axes)}}{3, 4, \text{ or } 5}$$

$$(1\text{--}11)$$

where the denominator is

3 in the case of a rectangular lamina, rods of negligible section, rectangular blocks, and cubes

4 in the case of elliptical and circular bodies

5 in the case of ellipsoidal and spherical bodies

For cylinders, see Example 4 below.

For area moments, cross-sectional area may be substituted for mass above, without other change, although for an area there is never a second perpendicular axis.

Example 1. Moment of inertia of a rod. The axes of symmetry are through the center. Let the length be L, the diameter negligible, but the weight W.

Then about a transverse axis, the two perpendicular axes are along the rod and transverse the other way. The lengths of the semi-axes are $\frac{1}{2}L$ and half the diameter (negligible). So

$$I = \frac{W}{g} \cdot \frac{(\frac{1}{2}L)^2 + 0^2}{3} = \frac{1}{12}\frac{W}{g}L^2 \qquad (1\text{--}12)$$

Example 2. A circular lamina about a diameter. The semi-axes perpendicular to the diameter are half the thickness (negligible) and the radius. For weight W measured in pounds and radius in inches, the mass moment of inertia

$$I = \frac{W}{g} \cdot \frac{r^2 + 0}{4} = \frac{W}{4}\frac{r^2}{386} \text{ lb in. sec}^2 \qquad (1\text{--}13a)$$

And the *area* moment (needed for the bending of round shafts)

$$I = \frac{Ar^2}{4} = \left(\frac{\pi}{4}d^2\right)\frac{d^2}{16} = \frac{\pi}{64}d^4 \text{ in.}^4 \qquad (1\text{--}13b)$$

---

* E. J. Routh, *Treatise on the Dynamics of a System of Rigid Bodies* (5th ed.; Part I, Elementary Part; London: Macmillan & Co., Ltd., 1891), p. 6.

Example 3. A circular lamina or solid disk about the polar axis. The two semi-axes perpendicular to this axis are in the plane of the circle and are radii. So

$$I = \frac{W}{g} \cdot \frac{r^2 + r^2}{4} = \frac{1}{2} \frac{W}{g} r^2 \tag{1–14}$$

which is twice the previous case.

Example 4. A cylinder about a transverse central axis. This is a mixed case, for it does not fit properly in Routh's Rule. However, let the length be L, the radius r.

The perpendicular semi-axis in the transverse section is r and the section is circular so that the denominator 4 applies. The perpendicular semi-axis in the axial section is $\frac{1}{2}L$ and the section is rectangular so that the denominator should be 3. Together we get

$$I = \frac{W}{g} \left(\frac{r^2}{4} + \frac{(L/2)^2}{3} \right) = \frac{1}{4} \frac{W}{g} \left(r^2 + \frac{1}{3} L^2 \right) \tag{1–15}$$

e.g., if the cylinder is of steel, with $L = 9$ in., $r = 2$ in., and the weight of steel is taken to be 0.282 lb per in.³, then

$$W = 31.84 \text{ lb}$$
$$I = \frac{1}{4} \cdot \frac{31.84}{386} \left(4 + \frac{81}{3} \right) = 0.64 \text{ lb in. sec}^2$$

Sometimes the moment of inertia of a given body is written

$$I = Mk^2 \tag{1–16}$$

Here the dimension k is called the *radius of gyration* and eq. 1–16 may be used as a shorthand method of writing any of the above solutions. The radius k is the root mean square of the radii of all the particles of which the object consists. It can be regarded as giving the radius of an equivalent ring, around the circumference of which all the mass of the body can be concentrated. Thus in the case of the solid disk considered in Example 3 above, since the radii of the particles vary from 0 to r (the outer radius), the simple mean is $r/2$; but with the radii squared and summed up the outer radii have greater effect, giving the radius of gyration obviously as $r/\sqrt{2}$.

The *engineer's unit* of moment of inertia is a weight instead of a mass unit. It is sometimes called moment of inertia, often just "the WR^2 factor," meaning, of course, Wk^2, and is measured in either lb in.² or lb ft². To use this unit in an equation such as eq. 1–10, it is necessary to divide by g.

Of very great value is the *parallel-axis theorem* for transferring moments of inertia. The theorem states

$$I_0 = I_G + Mr^2 \tag{1-17}$$

or the moment of inertia of any body about an axis through point O is equal to the sum of its moment of inertia about a parallel axis through its center of gravity G, and the product of the total mass of the body and the square of the distance transferred, the distance being $OG = r$.

Example 5. The moment of inertia of a thin rod of length L about one end. By Example 1, $I_G = \frac{1}{12}ML^2$. The end is distant $L/2$ from the center so

$$I_{\text{end}} = \frac{1}{12}ML^2 + M(L/2)^2 = \frac{1}{3}ML^2 \tag{1-18}$$

Example 6. The moment of inertia of a sphere about an axis through its point of contact O with a plane surface.

By Routh's Rule:

$$I_G = M\frac{R^2 + R^2}{5} = \frac{2}{5}MR^2$$

Therefore, by eq. 1-17,

$$I_0 = \frac{2}{5}MR^2 + MR^2 = \frac{7}{5}MR^2 \tag{1-19}$$

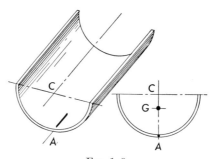

Fig. 1-9.

Example 7. The moment of inertia of a semicylindrical coil of sheet metal about its mid-element A (Fig. 1-9). About C all elements of mass have sensibly the same radius, if the sheet is of small thickness compared to the radius. Hence about C

$$I_C = Mr^2$$

Now C is not the center of gravity, but rather G, and $CG = (2/\pi)r$. The moment of inertia about G is *less* than elsewhere, by eq. 1-17. Thus,

$$I_G = Mr^2 - M\left(\frac{2}{\pi}r\right)^2$$

Transferring again,

$$I_A = \left[Mr^2 - M\left(\frac{2}{\pi}r\right)^2 \right] + M\left(1 - \frac{2}{\pi}\right)^2 r^2$$

$$= 2Mr^2\left(1 - \frac{2}{\pi}\right), \text{ or } 2M \cdot \overline{AC} \cdot \overline{AG}$$

When objects consist of a number of geometrical bodies joined together, the moment of inertia of the whole is the arithmetic sum of the moment of inertia of each of the parts about the same axis. This is merely a consequence of the definition of moment of inertia as a sum of elements.

Example 8. Find the moment of inertia about the pivot axis O of the steel cam follower shown in Fig. 1–10.

a) For the pivot boss, if solid,

$$W_1 = \rho \frac{\pi}{4} D^2 t$$

$$I_1 = \frac{1}{2} \frac{W_1}{g} \cdot \frac{D^2}{4}$$

but the removed axle hole shows W_2 of the same form, with d for D, and similarly an I. Thus for the boss

$$I = \frac{1}{8} \frac{\rho}{g} \frac{\pi}{4} (D^4 - d^4) t = \frac{1}{8} \cdot \frac{0.282}{386} \cdot \frac{\pi}{4} \cdot \left[1 - \left(\frac{1}{2}\right)^4 \right] \frac{3}{8}$$

$$= 0.252 \times 10^{-4} \text{ lb in. sec}^2$$

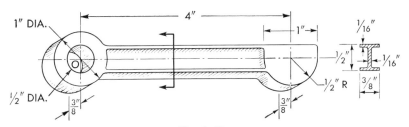

1" DIA.   ½" DIA.   4"   1" $\frac{1}{16}$"   ½" $\frac{1}{16}$"   ½" R $\frac{3}{8}$" $\frac{3}{8}$" $\frac{3}{8}$"

Fig. 1–10.

b) For the center I-section, make the very slight assumption that the ends are square: thus length is 3 in. and center 2 in. from O. Also ignore all fillets.

W of top and bottom flanges $= (0.282)\dfrac{3}{8} \cdot \dfrac{1}{16} \cdot 3 = 0.0198$ lb (each)

I of both flanges about their center of gravity (by transfer)

$$= 2\frac{0.0198}{386}\left\{ \frac{1}{12}\left[\left(\frac{1}{16}\right)^2 + 3^2 \right] + \left(\frac{7}{32}\right)^2 \right\} = 0.819 \times 10^{-4} \text{ lb in. sec}^2$$

W of center web $= (0.282) \dfrac{3}{8} \cdot \dfrac{1}{16} \cdot 3 = 0.0198$ lb

I of web about its center $= \dfrac{0.0198}{386} \cdot \dfrac{1}{12} \left[\left(\dfrac{3}{8} \right)^2 + (3)^2 \right]$
$$= 0.391 \times 10^{-4} \text{ lb in. sec}^2$$

So by transfer, for both flanges and web,

$$I_0 = 1.210 \times 10^{-4} + \frac{3 \times 0.0198}{386} (2.0)^2 = 7.365 \times 10^{-4} \text{ lb in. sec}^2$$

c) Divide the toe into top rectangular part and semicircle.

For the semicircle: $W = (0.282) \dfrac{\pi}{2} \cdot \dfrac{1}{4} \cdot \dfrac{3}{8} = 0.0415$ lb

About its center, $I_C = \dfrac{1}{2} \dfrac{0.0415}{386} \dfrac{1}{4} = 0.1342 \times 10^{-4}$

For the rectangle: $W = (0.282) \, 1 \cdot \dfrac{1}{4} \cdot \dfrac{3}{8} = 0.0264$ lb

About the center of the semicircle (by transfer),

$$I_C = \frac{0.0264}{386} \left[\frac{(1/4)^2 + (1)^2}{12} + (1/8)^2 \right] = 0.0714 \times 10^{-4} \text{ lb in. sec}^2$$

For the whole toe about O (by transfer)

$$I_0 = 0.2056 \times 10^{-4} + \frac{0.0679}{386} (16) = 28.351 \times 10^{-4} \text{ lb in. sec}^2$$

(which for the sake of the decimals must be done other than by slide-rule)

d) For the whole piece

$$I_0 = (0.252 + 7.365 + 28.351) \, 10^{-4} = 35.97 \times 10^{-4} \text{ lb in. sec}^2$$

1–7. Couples, Moments, Torque. Some confusion sometimes exists among these three terms. A couple consists, as its name implies, of a pair of forces, equal in magnitude, opposite and parallel in direction, and a certain distance apart. The effect of a couple is to produce a

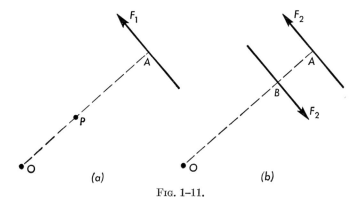

Fig. 1–11.

moment, but a moment can also be produced by one force acting at a distance.

In Fig. 1–11a, a force F_1 is shown acting at a perpendicular distance $\overline{OA}$ from O. The moment of this force around O is $F_1 \times \overline{OA}$. The moment of F_1 about point P is, of course, different, that is, $F_1 \times \overline{PA}$.

Fig. 1–11b shows a pair of equal forces F_2, forming a couple. The moment of the couple about O

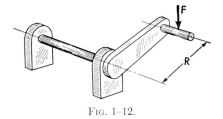

$$M = F_2 \times \overline{OA} - F_2 \times \overline{OB}$$
$$= F_2(\overline{OA} - \overline{OB}) = F_2 \times \overline{AB}$$

This moment is the same as the moment about A, about B, the midpoint of AB, or any other

Fig. 1–12.

point. We may therefore speak of the moment of a couple without mentioning about which point.

A torque is usually a couple in some shaft, and refers to the twisting moment in the shaft. In the case of a crank (Fig. 1–12) it might appear that one force F causes the torque. $F \times R$ is indeed its moment about the shaft, but the other force making the couple is the reaction at the bearing.

A force and a couple may be combined to give a single resultant force. On a certain body there are acting a force F_1 through the point O, and a couple $C = F_2a$, as shown in Fig. 1–13a. The only thing about the couple that concerns us is its moment; Fig. 1–13b therefore shows no change in effect if

$$F_1h = C = F_2a$$

But now the two equal and opposite forces at O have no resultant, thus leaving Fig. 1–13c.

This third figure shows one force which is equivalent to the previous force and couple. The force is of the same magnitude but distant from O by

$$h = \frac{C}{F_1} = \frac{F_2}{F_1} a \qquad (1\text{–}20)$$

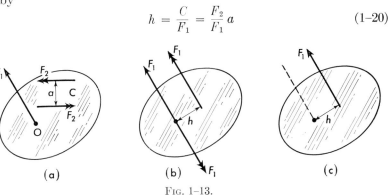

(a)   (b)   (c)

Fig. 1–13.

The opposite thought is also important in dynamics: that a force can be changed into a force and a couple. For instance, a football is kicked below center as in a place kick. What is the effect? From the equation of forces in the direction of the kick (neglecting the weight) we have

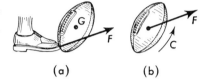

$$F = ma$$

(a)   (b)

Fig. 1–14.

only; and thus it is plain that the initial acceleration of the ball center is *exactly the same* as if the kick were central. But because the kick was below center, there is also a couple effect which spins the ball. In a vacuum the path of the center of the ball would be identical with a kick at any point on the ball. The force F (Fig. 1–14a) is the same as the same force F (Fig. 1–14b) centrally placed, together with a couple.

This is an illustration of what is called the principle of the *independence of the motion of the mass center*.

1–8. Couple Around a Fixed Point and Center of Percussion. Fig. 1–15 shows a compound pendulum, that is, a body of total weight W (which cannot be regarded as concentrated at a point as in the simple pendulum) suspended at O that is distant from G, the center of gravity, by the amount $OG = \bar{r}$.

It was shown in Art. 1–5 that the effect of a tangential acceleration $r\alpha$ is to produce an inertia force ma_G acting at the center of gravity, and an inertia couple $I_G\alpha$. These are shown in Fig. 1–15b; m is the mass of the whole pendulum and a_G the tangential acceleration due to α. I_G is the moment of inertia about G.

Now from the last section we see that this force and couple may be combined either to give one moment, or to give a single force. Take these in order.

(A) *The single inertia moment* is found by taking moments of the two inertia effects about the fixed pivot O. Note that the moment of the couple $I_G\alpha$ is the same about O as about G.

$$\begin{aligned} \Sigma M_0 &= I_G\alpha + (ma_G)\bar{r} \\ &= I_G\alpha + m\bar{r}^2\alpha \qquad \text{since } a_G = \bar{r}\alpha \\ &= I_0\alpha \end{aligned}$$

since by the parallel-axis theorem (eq. 1–17)

$$I_0 = I_G + m\bar{r}^2$$

This one moment presents a new form of eq. 1–10 which is

$$T = I_0\alpha \tag{1–21}$$

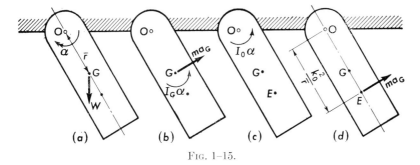

FIG. 1–15.

This form is restricted, for it is applicable only when O is the instant center of rotation. This free-body diagram is shown in Fig. 1–15c.

(B) *The single inertia force* is found by merging the moment into the force, using eq. 1–20. The result is then still the same force ma_G, but its position has been moved outward away from O to a point E given by

$$GE = \frac{I_G\alpha}{ma_G} = \frac{mk_G^2\alpha}{m\bar{r}\alpha}$$

$$= \frac{k_G^2}{\bar{r}} \tag{1–22}$$

This point E, so defined, which lies on the line OG extended, is called the *center of percussion*. The two inertia effects are thus equivalent to a single force ma_G (note it is not ma_E) acting through the center of percussion, Fig. 1–15d.

To correlate with the form $I_0\alpha$, note that the moments in Figs. 1–15 (c) and (d) must be the same so that

$$T_0 = I_0\alpha = mk_0^2\alpha \quad \text{for the one, and}$$

$$T_0 = ma_G(OG + GE) = m\bar{r}\alpha\left(\bar{r} + \frac{k_G^2}{\bar{r}}\right) \text{ for the other.}$$

That these are identical is merely a confirmation of the parallel-axis theorem for moments of inertia:

$$k_0^2 = \bar{r}^2 + k_G^2$$

or
$$OE = k_0^2/\bar{r} \tag{1–23}$$

Suppose now that this pendulum has angular velocity ω as well as angular acceleration α. It is to be noted that whatever the value of the angular velocity ω, the resultant centrifugal force acts along line OG; and whatever the value of α, the tangential force acts through E. Thus we have a theorem: Under all conditions where O is a fixed center of rotation, the resultant of all inertia forces passes through the center of percussion.

As an illustration there is the case of hitting a ball with a bat. In Fig. 1–16 the bat is shown as a compound pendulum in motion with the inertia forces and the reactions R_N and R_T at O, and these together form a system in equilibrium. If some new force F is applied to the body, it will cause a change in the angular acceleration, and thus change the magnitude of $\dfrac{W}{g}\bar{r}\alpha$. If the line of action of F passes through some point K, there will be a change in the equilibrium of moments about E, and so the value of the tangential reaction R_T will change. But if the line of action of the force F passes through E (i.e., let K and E become coincident), then whatever the value of F there will be no change in R_T. If the line of action of F is perpendicular to the centerline OGE, there will be no effect on either component of reaction at the point of support, which is the reason for the name center of percussion. If the bat hits the ball properly, no shock is felt by the hands.

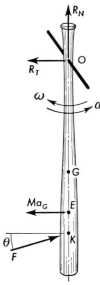

Fig. 1–16.

1–9. Limitations of Equation T = Iα. We summarize Arts. 1–5 and 1–8. The equation $T = I\alpha$ is valid only when I, the moment of inertia of the body, is constant, and, even then, it may be used only in two ways in any problem. One is when the couple is taken around the center of gravity of a rigid body; the other when moments are taken around the fixed or instant center of rotation of the body.

In a body such as the connecting rod of an engine, which undergoes simultaneous translation and rotation so that there is no fixed point, it is safe to use the first; i.e., $T = I_G\alpha$ about the center of gravity (see Chapter 7, page 303).

If you are using $T = I_G\alpha$ about G. This is purely a couple, due to distribution of the mass of a rigid body, and is additional to the inertia forces acting at the center of gravity.

If you are using $T = I_0\alpha$ about a fixed center O. This is both couple and moment of the inertia force acting at the center of gravity. The only inertia force which may then be put at the center of gravity is the centrifugal force. The effect of the inertia force at the center of gravity due to tangential acceleration *is already included* in the moment $I_0\alpha$.

Example 1. A trapdoor (Fig. 1–17) is supported horizontally by the latch P. If the latch is opened, find the initial acceleration of the center of gravity G.

Assume that the door is a uniform thin plate of weight W and length $2l$. Then the moment of inertia about G or O may be found in any handbook, or by Routh's Rule, to be

$$I_G = \frac{W}{g}\frac{l^2}{3} \quad \text{and} \quad I_0 = 4\frac{W}{g}\frac{l^2}{3}$$

if the thickness of the door is negligible when compared with the length. Fig. 1–17 shows the forces involved. If the angular acceleration downward of the trapdoor is α rad/sec², then the acceleration of G is $a_G = l\alpha$. The reversed effective force is shown at G, and also the inertia couple acting around G, opposed in direction to α.

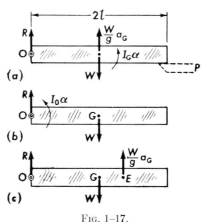

Taking moments about O

$$Wl = \left(\frac{W}{g}l\alpha\right)l + I_G\alpha \quad (1\text{–}24)$$

Note the moment of the couple $I_G\alpha$ is still the same about O as about G.

But now the right-hand side of this equation can be written

$$\left[\frac{W}{g}l^2 + I_G\right]\alpha = I_0\alpha$$

Fig. 1–17.

because of the rule for transfer of center of a moment of inertia. Hence the alternate form is

$$Wl = I_0\alpha \quad (1\text{–}25)$$

Now where eq. 1–24 was derived from Fig. 1–17a, eq. 1–25 is seen in Fig. 1–17b; and these are the same. The inertia force at G must be omitted in Fig. 1–17b. The third method, Fig. 1–17c, shows only a single inertia force at the center of percussion. Taking moments in this case:

$$Wl = \left(\frac{W}{g}l\alpha\right)(k_0^2/l) = \frac{W}{g}k_0^2\alpha$$

which is eq. 1–25 again. Thus any one of these three approaches gives exactly the same thing. Continuing with the problem, from eq. 1–25,

$$\alpha = \frac{Wl}{I_0}$$

so finally,

$$a_G = l\alpha = \frac{Wl^2}{I_0} = \frac{3}{4}g$$

Example 2. Investigate the rolling or slipping of a wheel down a slope, neglecting air resistance. Find the conditions of limiting friction.

Since the wheel is rolling or slipping, the friction force F is up the slope. The slope is at angle θ to the horizontal. Resolving forces along the slope, with a the acceleration of the center along the slope:

$$Mg \sin \theta - F = Ma \quad (a)$$

Perpendicular to the slope, the normal reaction N is given by

$$Mg \cos \theta = N \qquad \text{(b)}$$

By moments about the point of contact

$$Mar + I_G \alpha = Mgr \sin \theta \qquad \text{(c)}$$

Now if the wheel is to roll, the point of contact will be the instantaneous center of rotation, so that $a = r\alpha$. Substituting this in (c) and writing $I_G = Mk^2$,

$$M(ar + k^2 a/r) = Mgr \sin \theta$$

$$a = \frac{r^2}{r^2 + k^2} g \sin \theta \qquad \text{(d)}$$

Thus solving by (a) for the frictional force F necessary for rolling, and by substituting this value of a,

$$F = \frac{k^2}{r^2 + k^2} Mg \sin \theta$$

Now as the coefficient of static friction μ_s must be greater than the ratio F/N, using eq. (b) the *condition for rolling* is

$$\mu_s > \frac{k^2}{r^2 + k^2} \tan \theta \qquad \text{(e)}$$

On the other hand, if the wheel is slipping with rolling, though eqs. (a), (b), and (c) hold, we do not have the geometric relation $a = r\alpha$. Rather, the amount of rolling is determined by the kinetic coefficient of friction μ_k, which must be of its limiting value. Thus

$$F = \mu_k N \qquad \text{(f)}$$

We use this to eliminate F and N between eqs. (a) and (b)

$$Mg \sin \theta - \mu_k Mg \cos \theta = Ma$$

or

$$a = g \sin \theta \left(1 - \frac{\mu_k}{\tan \theta} \right) \qquad \text{(g)}$$

From eqs. (a) and (c) or by taking moments about the center

$$Fr = I_G \alpha$$

Substitute for F from eq. (f) and N from eq. (b):

$$\alpha = (\mu_k r/k^2) g \cos \theta \qquad \text{(h)}$$

Two interesting facts are to be noticed here: first that the radius of gyration is absent from eq. (g) and therefore what is true for one wheel is true for any other wheel or sphere; secondly, that by eqs. (g) and (h) both a and α are constants, and therefore if a body starts slipping it will not recover after the angular velocity has got going, and change over to rolling, or vice versa, unless the friction changes along the slope.

With slipping, $a > r\alpha$; then the *condition for slipping* in terms of μ_k and θ is that eq. (g) be greater than eq. (h) multiplied by r, or

$$\mu_k < \frac{k^2}{r^2 + k^2} \tan \theta$$

Since μ_k is always slightly less than μ_s, there is a narrow range of values of θ where either rolling or slipping might occur.

Example 3. A crane is holding a steel girder by means of two independent wire ropes attached to its hook and the girder ends (Fig. 1–18). The ropes are inclined at an angle of 30° to the vertical and the girder has length L and weight W.

One rope accidentally breaks (or becomes loose). Find the instantaneously changed load in the remaining rope. Assume the ropes of negligible weight in comparison with the girder.

The condition is shown in the figure, with the broken rope shown as a dotted line. Assume an instantaneous angular acceleration α, component accelerations a_H and a_V of G, and a tension F in the rope. In the free-body diagram of the girder, no point is fixed, and therefore we use $I_G\alpha$ as the inertia couple, and $(W/g)a_V$ and $(W/g)a_H$ as the inertia force components at the center.

The three equations of equilibrium (ΣF_V, ΣF_H, and moments about G) are

$$F \cos 30° = W(1 - a_V/g) \quad \text{(a)}$$
$$F \sin 30° = (W/g)a_H \quad \text{(b)}$$
$$F(L/2) \cos 30° = I_G\alpha \quad \text{(c)}$$

As usual, these are not enough, and there is need of geometry. If the rope has a tension F it remains straight, and the acceleration of point A can only be tangential, as a_A in the figure at (b). The acceleration of G must therefore be the vector sum of this a_A and the relative acceleration, or its components are

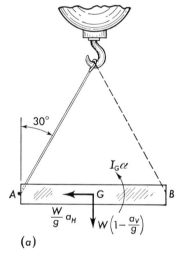

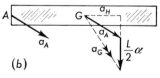

$$a_H = a_A \cos 30° \quad \text{(d)}$$
$$a_V = a_A \sin 30° + (L/2)\alpha \quad \text{(e)}$$

FIG. 1–18.

Now let us obtain F—a matter for manipulation only: for I_G in eq. (c) substitute $(W/g)(L^2/12)$ and see that

$$F \cos 30° = (W/g)(L/6)\alpha \quad \text{(c')}$$

Substitute (d) and (e) to eliminate a_V and a_H in (a) and (b),

$$F \cos 30° = W - (W/g) (a_A \sin 30° + L\alpha/2) \tag{a'}$$
$$= W - (W/g)a_A \sin 30° - 3F \cos 30°$$
$$F \sin 30° = (W/g)a_A \cos 30° \tag{b'}$$

The second line shows α eliminated by using eq. (c'); and thus for F we get

$$F \sin^2 30° = (W - 4F \cos 30°) \cos 30°$$
$$F = W \left(\frac{\cos 30°}{1 + 3 \cos^2 30°} \right) \tag{f}$$
$$= 0.266W$$

Before the break each rope carried half the load W, so that

$$F_0 \cos 30° = W/2$$
$$F_0 = 0.577W$$

For any angle θ of the ropes (in place of the 30° used here) the tension in the remaining rope is instantaneously reduced in the ratio

$$\frac{F}{F_0} = \frac{2 \cos^2 \theta}{1 + 3 \cos^2 \theta} = \frac{2}{3 + \sec^2 \theta} \tag{g}$$

but of course after the girder has swung down to the vertical, that rope will have to carry not only the whole weight W but also centrifugal force due to the angular velocity acquired.

1–10. Three-Dimensional Motion. Most problems in machinery involve only two-dimensional motion, but three dimensions must be considered when unsymmetrical rotors turn, or when rotation or translation of bodies occurs in three geometrical axes or planes. Problems of these types will be considered later in Chapter 6.

1–11. The Method of Work and Energy. A second approach to the solution of problems in dynamics as mentioned in Art. 1–1 is by the analysis of work and energy. Work is defined as

$$W = \int F \, ds \tag{1–26}$$

that is, where a force F applied to a body causes a displacement s in the same direction. If the force is constant through a linear displacement from s_1 to s_2, this then appears as

$$W = F(s_2 - s_1) \tag{1–27}$$

and is measured usually in ft-lb or in.-lb.

When the force F is applied in a direction making an angle θ to the direction of displacement of the body (Fig. 1–19), then the work done by the force on the body is

$$W = (F \cos \theta) (s_2 - s_1) \tag{1–28}$$

as is apparent when the force is resolved into its rectangular components $F \cos \theta$ and $F \sin \theta$, and it is to be noted only the former accomplishes a displacement.

In rotation, a torque T does work when it causes angular displacement

$$W = \int T \, d\theta \tag{1–29}$$

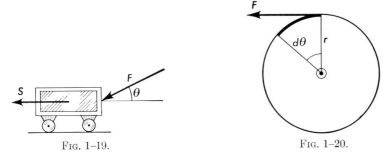

FIG. 1–19.   FIG. 1–20.

for suppose the torque is resolved into a tangential force F at radius r (Fig. 1–20); when the body turns through angle $d\theta$, the force F is displaced a distance $r \, d\theta$, so that the work (for a sequence of such angles $d\theta$) is

$$W = \int F \cdot r \, d\theta = \int T \, d\theta$$

since

$$T = Fr$$

Example 1. A large body is to be lifted off one corner support by pushing under it a slightly higher column. The column is fitted into place at A (Fig. 1–21), and initially is inclined at $15°$ to the vertical. The bottom is then pushed horizontally until it is directly under A. The load P on this corner is 1000 lb; the distance BC is 9 in.; the friction on the floor is 25 per cent. Find the work needed.

The compression in the column at any angle θ of the inclination is $P \sec \theta$. The vertical component of this at the base is P, so that the frictional force is $0.25P$. But the force F must overcome the horizontal component of the compression as well as the friction.

$$F = 0.25P + P \tan \theta$$

Because F is a variable, eq. 1–26 will give the work needed as

$$W = \int F \, dx = P \int_{B}^{C} (0.25 + \tan \theta) dx$$

To integrate this, we need to find the geometrical relation between θ and x. x is the displacement from B to B'; but in triangle $B'CA$, $B'C = AC \tan \theta$ if AC is the depth of the well. The original BC was $AC \tan 15°$, and the data gave this as 9 in. So

$$x = BC - B'C = AC \tan 15° - AC \tan \theta$$
$$\tan \theta = \tan 15° - x/AC = \tan 15° - x \tan 15°/9$$

Hence

$$W = P \int_{x=0}^{x=9} [0.25 + \tan 15° (1 - x/9)]dx$$

$$= 1000 \left[(0.25 + 0.268)x - x^2 \frac{0.268}{18} \right]_0^9$$

$$= 3456 \text{ in.-lb}$$

Note that this does not mean the 1000-lb load is raised 3.456 in., for some of the work is lost to friction. Note also an approximation, for the fact that the column will shorten under stress is not taken into account.

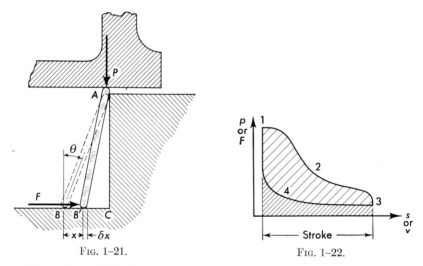

FIG. 1–21.   FIG. 1–22.

Example 2. Find the work done by the steam on the piston of an engine during one revolution when the *P–V* (indicator) diagram is given.

The *P–V* diagram, which will appear as in Fig. 1–22, is in reality a graph of pressure against piston displacement. The pressure *P* acts on the (constant) piston surface area *A*. Thus the ordinate scale may be converted, without changing the graph, to read force, if the pressure scale of the diagram is known. This depends on the spring used within the instrument.

In the working stroke the steam pushes the piston from top *T* to bottom *B*, doing an amount of work given by

$$W = \int_T^B PA \, ds = A \int_T^B P_{1,2,3} \, ds$$

On the exhaust stroke the work is done by the engine on the steam, or the steam does negative work:

$$W = A \int_B^T P_{3,4,1} \, ds$$

The net work done per cycle is the difference, which depends therefore on the area enclosed within the curve.

Suppose the area of a typical diagram is measured by a planimeter as 0.577 sq in. The height of the diagram is 0.82 in., and in the engine this means a pressure difference of 131 psi. The piston area is 80.6 sq in. The length of the diagram is 3.58 in., which corresponds to the engine stroke of 26 in.

Then if the diagram were the rectangle which escribes the actual diagram, it would measure $0.82 \times 3.58 = 2.936$ sq in., and would represent $131 \times 80.6 \times 26$ in.-lb or 22,900 ft-lb of work. The work by the engine per stroke is therefore

$$W = \left(\frac{0.577}{2.936} \right) 22,900 = 4510 \text{ ft-lb}$$

In connection with the idea of negative work an amusing demonstration is recorded[*] as having been made at a meeting of the Royal Society in London in 1951. Two bicycles were fixed up, back to back, with their rear wheels off the ground and connected by a chain. Everything was carefully arranged to minimize any friction loss. Then two men were seated on the bicycles, the one to pedal at a more or less constant speed while the other had to try to resist the motion. After a while the man doing the positive work was far more exhausted than the one whose muscles did negative work, that is, absorbed work! Their work was measured by their oxygen consumption during steady pedaling.

1–12. Potential and Kinetic Energy. Energy, defined as the capacity of any body to do work, is found in two forms that are principally significant in dynamics of machinery: they are potential and kinetic energy. Other forms are found in heat, in electrical, chemical, and atomic energy.

Potential energy has two forms: first there is that due to elevation, which is the product of weight and height; this is the gravitational form. Secondly there is elastic or strain energy of deformable bodies and compressible gases, such as is held by a wound-up spring. Where the elasticity of the body is perfect,[†] this is easily reckoned as the amount of work needed to get it into the strained condition.

Example 1. Find the strain energy in a tie bar of length l and cross-sectional area A, which is stretched a small amount x by the force straining it.

---

[*] "Royal Society's Conversazione," *Engineering*, June 1, 1951, Vol. 171, p. 664.

[†] Most actual materials exhibit some degree of hysteresis: a body stressed and then unloaded remains with a slight strain called "permanent set." In such cases the strain energy potential in a stressed body will obviously be a little less than the work needed to cause the stress.

If the bar is extended by the amount x, then strain $e = x/l$; therefore stress $= Ee = E(x/l)$ where E is the modulus of rigidity (or Young's modulus) of the material.

Then force needed to hold the bar at extended length is

$$F = \frac{AEx}{l} \qquad (1\text{-}30)$$

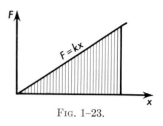

FIG. 1-23.

Note that this force is directly proportional to x, as shown in Fig. 1-23. The work done is shown by the area under the graph, which is *half the final force* multiplied by the extension (i.e., average force multiplied by the extension).

Hence

$$\text{Potential energy} = \frac{1}{2}(Fx) = \frac{1}{2}\frac{AE}{l}x^2 \qquad (1\text{-}31)$$

When applied to coil springs, the factor AE/l is usually called the spring stiffness constant.

Example 2. A block, free to slide without friction in a cross slide, has a spring attached to it. The other end of the spring is fixed at point O (Fig. 1-24). If the block is first at A, find the work needed to move the block from A to B, 6 in., perpendicular to AO. The free length of the spring is 6 in., and the spring stiffness 25 lb/in. extension. The plane ABO is horizontal.

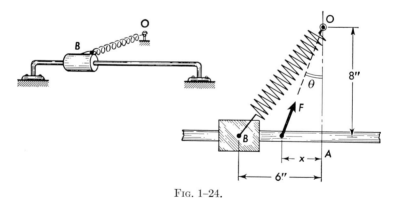

FIG. 1-24.

Method A. By strain energy.

By geometry, $OB = 10$ in.

The only work done is in stretching the spring, not in moving its position around from OA to OB, since there is no friction.

Since initial tension at A is 50 lb and final tension is 100 lb, and since in springs the tension increases linearly with extension, the spring has been extended 2 in. against a mean force of 75 lb. Hence

$$\text{Work required} = \text{Change in potential strain energy}$$
$$= 75 \times 2 = 150 \text{ in.-lb}$$

Method B. By work = force × distance.

Consider an intermediate point a distance x from A. The length of spring is $8 \sec \theta$ or $\sqrt{x^2 + 8^2}$. So in this position the force F of the spring = $25(8 \sec \theta - 6)$.

$$\text{Force against which slide is moving} = F \sin \theta$$
$$= 25(8 \tan \theta - 6 \sin \theta)$$

The slide will move an element of distance dx against this force. Hence

$$\text{Total work} = 25 \int_{x=0}^{x=6} (8 \tan \theta - 6 \sin \theta)dx$$

By geometry, $\tan \theta = \dfrac{x}{8}$ and $\sin \theta = \dfrac{x}{\sqrt{x^2 + 8^2}}$.

Therefore

$$\text{Work} = 25 \int_0^6 \left(x - \frac{6x}{\sqrt{x^2 + 8^2}} \right) dx$$
$$= 25 \left[x^2/2 - 6\sqrt{x^2 + 8^2} \right]_{x=0}^{x=6}$$
$$= 25[18 - 6(10 - 8)] = 25 \times 6$$
$$= 150 \text{ in.-lb}$$

In *this* problem this second method is considerably longer, yet there are many cases in which the first method is not available, as, for instance, when there is friction involved in the motion of the slide.

The kinetic energy of a particle appeared in eq. 1–5 as

$$\text{K.E.} = \tfrac{1}{2}mv^2 \qquad\qquad (1\text{–}32)$$

Because of the squared term, this is not a vector. It is not affected by sense of direction for $(-v)^2 = v^2$. Moreover if the velocity v should be at an inclination θ to some arbitrarily chosen axes (x, y), this velocity may be resolved into components $v_x = v \cos \theta$ and $v_y = v \sin \theta$, and the kinetic energy is the arithmetic sum of the components of energy.

$$\text{K.E.} = \tfrac{1}{2}mv_x^2 + \tfrac{1}{2}mv_y^2 \qquad\qquad (1\text{–}33)$$

since

$$v_x^2 + v_y^2 = v^2(\cos^2 \theta + \sin^2 \theta) = v^2$$

For any system of particles the kinetic energy is the sum of the energies of the elements. Thus for a rigid body in rotation about any axis O

$$K.E. = \tfrac{1}{2}Mv_G^2 + \tfrac{1}{2}I_G\omega^2 \qquad (1\text{-}34)$$

where M is the whole mass, v_G the velocity of the center of gravity G, I_G the moment of inertia about G, and ω the angular velocity.

About the instantaneous center of rotation O of the body, this may be abbreviated, for $v_G = \bar{r}\omega$, and thus

$$K.E. = \tfrac{1}{2}M\bar{r}^2\omega^2 + \tfrac{1}{2}I_G\omega^2$$
$$= \tfrac{1}{2}I_0\omega^2 \qquad (1\text{-}35)$$

Example 3. A sphere, of weight 5 lb and radius 3 in., rolls down a slope with velocity 24 ft/sec. Find its kinetic energy.

Since $I_G = (2/5)Mr^2$, $I_0 = (7/5)Mr^2$ where O is the contact point on the periphery,

$$K.E. = \frac{1}{2}\left(\frac{7}{5}Mr^2\right)\omega^2 = \frac{7}{10}Mv^2$$
$$= \frac{7}{10} \cdot \frac{5}{32.2}(24)^2 = 62.6 \text{ ft-lb}$$

It may be shown that this is the same as the sum of translational and rotational energies as:

$$\text{Translational K.E.} = \tfrac{1}{2}Mv^2 = 44.7 \text{ ft-lb}$$

From geometry the angular velocity $\omega = 24 \times 12 \div 3 = 96$ rad/sec.

$$\text{Rotational K.E.} = \tfrac{1}{2}I_G\omega^2 = \tfrac{1}{2}\left[\frac{2}{5} \cdot \frac{5}{32.2} \cdot \frac{(3)^2}{12}\right](96)^2 = 17.9 \text{ ft-lb}$$

Example 4. A motorcycle weighs 400 lb, which includes the weight of each wheel (50 lb). The diameter of the wheels is 18 in. and the radius of gyration 6 in. about the center. Find the kinetic energy when the cycle travels at 60 mph.

$$\text{Translational K.E.} = \tfrac{1}{2} \cdot \frac{400}{32.2}(88)^2 = 48{,}099 \text{ ft-lb}$$

(since 60 mph = 88 ft/sec.)

Then for the angular velocity of the wheels:

$$\omega = \frac{88 \times 2}{1.5} = 117.3 \text{ rad/sec}$$

$$\text{Rotational K.E. of two wheels} = 2 \cdot \tfrac{1}{2} \cdot \frac{50}{32.2}\left(\frac{6}{12}\right)^2(117.3)^2$$

$$\left(= \frac{1}{9} \text{ of linear K.E.} \right)$$

$$= 5344 \text{ ft-lb}$$
$$\text{Total K.E.} = 53{,}443 \text{ ft-lb}$$

if we ignore the rotational energies of the various parts in the motor. Note that the weight of the wheels is included in the computation of the translational kinetic energy, for the centers of gravity of the wheels travel with the body, and the rotational energy is additional.

1–13. Conservation of Energy. If a body or system of bodies is acted upon by no outside forces, the energy may change form (e.g., from potential to kinetic) but the quantity remains constant. This is the principle of conservation of energy.

A common cause of the loss of energy in a system (i.e., a nonconservative system) is outside friction. For example, a block slides down a slope: due to friction, energy will be lost and the amount lost will be the product of the frictional force and the distance traveled. Thus the gain of kinetic energy as the block reaches the bottom of the slope will not be equal to the potential energy loss. Another common cause of loss in a system is impact. When two bodies collide, the energy of the two after impact is less than before. The lost energy has gone to create heat and sound.

1–14. Linear Momentum and Impulse. The third method of attack on problems in dynamics is that of momentum. In Art. 1–1, by the integration of Newton's second law it appeared that

$$mv_2 - mv_1 = \int_{t_1}^{t_2} F \, dt \qquad (1\text{–}4)$$

The principle is most commonly applied to problems concerning an impact between two bodies. The impact may be of exceedingly short duration, so that the impulse involves forces of great magnitude; yet since it has the same duration for both, and actions and reactions are equal (referring to Fig. 1–25)

$$m_1 u_1 = \int F \, dt + m_1 v_1$$
$$m_2 u_2 + \int F \, dt = m_2 v_2$$

which is stated: the mass m_1 with velocity u_1 approaches mass m_2 with lesser velocity u_2; the momentum $m_1 u_1$ is converted into impulse and remaining momentum $m_1 v_1$; the momentum $m_2 u_2$ picks up the impulse and is thus increased to $m_2 v_2$.

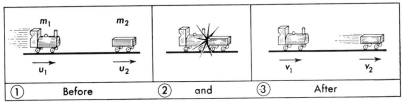

Fig. 1–25.

The usefulness of the method, however, is not limited to cases of impact. There is no limitation in eq. 1–4 as to the length of time $t_2 - t_1$.

Example 1. Find the minimum time required for an automobile to reach 60 mph if the coefficient of friction between tires and road is 2/3. Neglect air resistance.

For minimum time, the maximum force of friction must propel the car continuously. Assuming half the weight W is on the rear wheels, the frictional force $F = (2/3)(W/2) = W/3$. The impulse Ft produces momentum,

$$Ft = \frac{W}{g} v$$

$$t = \frac{Wv}{Fg} = \frac{88}{0.333 \times 32.2} = 8.2 \text{ sec}$$

The time necessary is therefore 8.2 seconds plus the time required to change gears, and this is independent of the size of the automobile. This could also be calculated by $F = ma$, but it would be more round-about. Note also that the final kinetic energy (neglecting rotational) is $mv^2/2$ so that the horsepower needed to produce this in 8.2 seconds is *proportional* to the weight (mass) of the car, and is $(8/300)$ W bhp. Further horsepower is needed to overcome internal friction of the motor and transmission, of course.

The principle of momentum is very useful in cases of flowing mass, as occur in fluid impact. Suppose a fluid impinges on a solid face, and its momentum is destroyed. If mass m arrives per second, there is exerted a force

$$F = mv \text{ lb sec per sec}$$

Per unit area of the face, the mass m arriving is μv where μ is the mass per unit volume of the fluid. Thus

$$\text{Force per unit area} = \text{Pressure} = \mu v^2 \qquad (1\text{–}36)$$

This supposes that the fluid leaves the surface smoothly at right angles to its original direction of flow.

Example 2. Find the pressure due to wind striking normally to a house wall, or the resistance to motion of a body in still air.

The normal weight of air is 0.0765 lb/cu ft. The pressure due to an arrival velocity v ft/sec is

$$p = \frac{0.0765}{32.2} v^2 = 0.00256 v^2 \text{ lb/sq ft}$$

Of course, wind does not lose entirely its original sense of momentum; in fact, some reverse bounce and eddying occur. Experimental records*

* *Trans. A.S.C.E.*, v. 105, p. 1713 (1940).

point to a pressure given by the somewhat larger figure $p = 0.0033v^2$ lb/sq ft, when the partial vacuum on the leeward side is also reckoned.

Where wind passes relative to a streamlined body, the pressure is much less. Against a spherical body, pressure per square foot of frontal projected area is $0.0006v^2$.

Example 3. Sand falls vertically from one belt conveyor to a lower conveyor, as shown in Fig. 1–26. (The vertical fall is, of course, an assumption, for actually there would be parabolic fall.) The speed of both conveyors is 400 ft/min; the lower conveyor is inclined for a 100-ft rise in 300 ft horizontal, and its surface is 2 ft below the other where shown in the figure. Flow of sand is 600 tons per hour. Find the horsepower needed to overcome the impact of the falling sand.

The impact velocity of the falling sand is not more than

$$v = \frac{400}{60} + \sqrt{2gh} = 18.01 \text{ ft/sec}$$

for this assumes the upper conveyor projects the sand downward. This has vector components

$$\text{normal to belt: } (3/\sqrt{10})18.01 \text{ ft/sec}$$
$$\text{down along belt: } (1/\sqrt{10})18.01 \text{ ft/sec}$$

The former produces a pressure by the belt onto the fixed tray beneath the belt, and thus causes a frictional force resisting motion of the belt; the latter involves a momentum to be overcome by the belt. Consider the latter first.

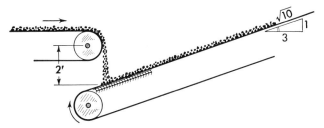

FIG. 1–26.

a) Velocity change needed along belt $= (18.01/\sqrt{10}) + (400/60) = 12.36$ ft/sec. Weight per second flowing $= 333$ lb.

Impulse needed $= (333/32.2) \times 12.36$ lb sec per sec $= 127.8$ lb

This is the force of impact to be overcome.

b) Momentum normal to belt destroyed per second:

$$(333/32.2)(3/\sqrt{10})18.01 = 176.7 \text{ lb}$$

The coefficient of friction between the belt and the steel support tray is taken as 25 per cent.

Frictional force to be overcome $= 0.25 \times 176.7 = 44.2$ lb

Thus horsepower needed to overcome these two resistances at the velocity given is

$$\frac{(127.8 + 44.2)400}{33,000} = 2.08 \text{ hp}$$

And this is additional to the horsepower needed to elevate the sand, and to overcome regular belt frictions. (*Note*: The dimensions used here are based on an assumed belt width of 30 or 36 in.)

And so we see why this calculation is not usually suggested in books on conveyor design. In comparison with the horsepower needed to drive the belt, and the uncertainties of friction, the above is negligible.

1–15. Angular Momentum. Two-Dimensional Moment of Momentum. The simplest use of the principle of conservation of the angular momentum of rigid bodies rotating about fixed axes is very similar to the corresponding principle of linear momentum. The principle is as follows.

A particle of elemental mass m at radius r in a rigid body (or any connected system of bodies) is submitted to a force F. Taking moments of the force about axis O, we apply Newton's law to the action.

$$Fr = \left[\frac{d}{dt}(mv) \right] r$$

Applying this first to a single body in which O is the fixed axis of rotation, we have $v = r\omega$ and the product Fr is a torque. Summing all these elements for the body

$$T = \Sigma Fr = \frac{d}{dt}(\Sigma mr^2\omega) = \frac{d}{dt}(I\omega) \tag{1–37}$$

The derivative of this gives the familiar formula $T = I\alpha$, for I a constant. The integral produces the angular momentum relation

$$\int T \, dt = I_2\omega_2 - I_1\omega_1 \tag{1–38}$$

Angular momentum is thus defined as the product of moment of inertia and angular velocity, or, more importantly (as will be seen), as the sum of the moments of the linear momenta of all particles comprising the body or system. Angular impulse is the sum of the moments of linear impulses, together with the time integrals of any couples.

Equation 1–38 also proves the principle of the conservation of angular momentum about a fixed axis, for in the absence of any angular impulse over that interval of time the angular momentum of a system or rigid body about a fixed axis remains constant.

A well-known demonstration of this exists in the ability of a figure-skater to go into a fast spin: by starting to revolve slowly with her arms extended, and then drawing her arms in close she reduces her moment of inertia and increases her spin.

Example 1. In an automobile synchro-mesh gear box, two gears on the same axis are brought into contact by a cone clutch. Before contact the first with $I_1 = 4$ lb in.^{2} (engineer's units) rotates at 2000 rpm, the second with $I_2 = 16$ lb in.^{2} at 1000 rpm in the same direction. What is the resultant speed, and what constant torque is needed to accomplish the mesh in 1/4 sec?

The retarding impulse on the first is equal to the accelerating impulse on the second. With speeds ω before and Ω after contact,

$$I_1(\omega_1 - \Omega) = \int T \, dt = I_2(\Omega - \omega_2)$$

$$\Omega = \frac{I_1\omega_1 + I_2\omega_2}{I_1 + I_2} = \frac{8000 + 16{,}000}{20} = 1200 \text{ rpm}$$

$$\int T \, dt = Tt = I_1(\omega_1 - \Omega)$$

$$= \frac{4}{386}(2000 - 1200)\frac{2\pi}{60} = 0.868 \text{ lb in. sec}$$

and for $t = 1/4$,
$$T = 3.47 \text{ lb in.}$$

It is very important to remember angular momentum as *moment* of momentum which may be changed by *moment* of impulse. For instance, a common occasion of impact arises in the sudden meshing of gears on neighboring axes, and the angular momentum of the two systems does not then remain unchanged.

The relation of eq. 1–38 applies to one axis only. It is the *force* between the meshing teeth which has an equal and opposite reaction, of equal duration. The *moments* of this impulse on the two gears are thus proportional to their respective radii.

Example 2. In Fig. 1–27, the gear is twice the diameter of the pinion. Initially they are counter-rotating at the same speed ω. Then the gear slides into mesh. Find its subsequent speed Ω.

Assume the moment of inertia of the pinion to be I and that of the gear $4I$. Take the linear impulse at the clashing teeth as $\int F \, dt$. Then by moments about the two axes severally

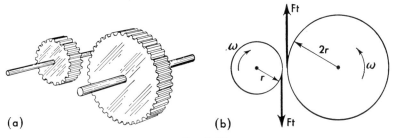

(a)   (b)

Fig. 1–27.

$$4I \cdot \omega - (\int F \, dt)2r = 4I \cdot \Omega \quad \text{for the gear}$$
$$I\omega + (\int F \, dt)r \;\; = I \cdot 2\Omega \quad \text{for the pinion}$$

Adding the first to twice the second:

$$\Omega = \frac{3}{4}\omega$$

Let us compare this with the result of the faulty assumption that the angular momentum remains constant. Taking account of the sense of rotation

$$4I\omega - I\omega = 4I\Omega - I \cdot 2\Omega$$
$$\Omega = \frac{3}{2}\omega$$

which is ludicrous, for obviously the gear does not increase its speed.

1–16. General Case of Two-Dimensional Moment of Momentum. We will now derive the expression for the moment of momentum of any laminar body having any motion in its plane, about any point within it.

The moment of momentum is the sum of the moments of the momenta of all particles P within it. Thus

$$\int T \, dt = \Sigma(mva) \tag{1–39}$$

where m is the mass of an element P, v its instantaneous velocity, and a the perpendicular from the line of action of that velocity to the point A about which these moments are taken (Fig. 1–28). Now break this momentum mv into its two components: $mr\omega$ due to its velocity relative to the mass center G, and mv_G due to the velocity of the center. The right-hand side of the expression 1–39 becomes the sum of the moments of these components. But the sum of the moments of all such momenta as mv_G is the moment of their resultant Mv_G about A. Secondly, the sum of the moments of all the momentum components relative to and *about G*

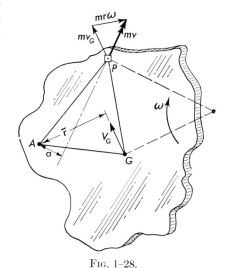

Fig. 1–28.

is $\Sigma(mr\omega \cdot r)$ which is a couple $I_G\omega$, and thus being a couple, its moment about A is the same as about G. Equation 1–39 becomes

$$\int T \, dt = (Mv_G)\bar{r} + I_G\omega \tag{1–40}$$

The derivative of this is seen as the familiar moment of the inertia of a floating link.

The most useful result of this is the principle of the conservation of moment of momentum. Even though a body in plane motion receives an impulse—a linear one—the angular impulse about the point of application of this linear impulse will, of course, be zero, and the moment of momentum of the body is thus unchanged about this point.

Example. A bar of length l oscillates on two supports AB as in Fig. 1–29. The two supports are a distance $2a$ apart, and when the bar is in contact with both, the center of gravity is midway between.

Suppose that the bar pivots about A approaching B, and that just before impact it has angular velocity ω_1. Then the moment of momentum about B' (the point to contact B) is

$$H_{B'} = -Ma^2\omega_1 + \frac{1}{12}Ml^2\omega_1$$

The impulse at B has no moment about B', so that the moment of momentum is unchanged by it. Let the subsequent angular velocity be ω_2:

$$H_{B'} = +Ma^2\omega_2 + \frac{1}{12}Ml^2\omega_2$$

which gives for ω_2

$$\omega_2 = \left[\frac{(l^2/12) - a^2}{(l^2/12) + a^2}\right]\omega_1$$

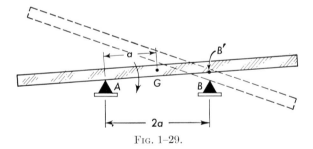

Fig. 1–29.

This assumes inelastic impact, without a bounce off the new support. If $l = 12$ ft and $2a = 4$ ft, this yields $\omega_2 = \omega_1/2$.

As a result of the impact, the loss of energy for each alternation of support is

$$\Delta E = \tfrac{1}{2}I_A\omega_1^2 - \tfrac{1}{2}I_B\omega_2^2$$

or since $I_A = I_B$ with the mass center equidistant

$$\Delta E = \tfrac{1}{2}M(l^2/12 + a^2)(\omega_1^2 - \omega_2^2)$$
$$= 2M\omega_1^2\left(\frac{a^2l^2}{12a^2 + l^2}\right)$$

For the dimensions already used as illustration, the body loses three-quarters of its initial energy on the first bounce; three-quarters of that remaining on the second, etc. Strictly by this theory alone the oscillations never cease, but the further losses due to air friction, etc., soon will quiet them.

1-17. Combined Linear and Angular Momentum. In the case of a system of bodies, some with angular momentum and others with linear momentum, the moment of the linear momentum is included with the angular momentum after the manner of eq. 1-40.

Example 1. A horizontal conveyor track consists of a number of cylindrical rollers which are free to rotate about fixed horizontal and parallel axes. Each roller has radius r, and moment of inertia I about its axis; consecutive rollers are equally spaced.

All rollers are initially at rest when a rectangular crate of mass M is projected with horizontal velocity u onto the first roller of the conveyor. Assuming that all slipping between a roller and the crate ceases before contact is lost, and that the base of the crate is equal in length to three spaces between rollers, find how far the crate travels before stopping.

Observe that this requires investigation of a step-by-step change. Each time a new roller is met the velocity is reduced in a certain proportion.

As the crate meets the first roller, it brings a momentum Mu to bear on the surface of the roller. After slipping ceases, the velocity of the crate will be v_1 where the moments of the momenta show that

$$Mur = Mv_1r + Iv_1/r$$
$$v_1 = \frac{M}{M + I/r^2}u$$

The initial kinetic energy is $E_0 = \frac{1}{2}Mu^2$. The energy remaining is

$$E_1 = \frac{1}{2}Mv_1^2 + \frac{1}{2}Iv_1^2/r^2 = \left(\frac{M}{M + I/r^2}\right)E_0$$

During the second impact we have a reduction to velocity v_2

$$Mv_1r + Iv_1/r = Mv_2r + 2Iv_2/r$$
$$v_2 = \left(\frac{M + I/r^2}{M + 2I/r^2}\right)v_1 = \left(\frac{M}{M + 2I/r^2}\right)u$$

And the remaining kinetic energy E_2 is

$$E_2 = \left(\frac{M}{M + 2I/r^2}\right)E_0$$

Similarly after the third impact

$$v_3 = \left(\frac{M}{M + 3I/r^2}\right)u$$

$$E_3 = \left(\frac{M}{M + 3I/r^2}\right)E_0$$

But on the fourth impact a new item enters: as the crate makes contact with the new roller, it loses contact with the first, which is left spinning with a surface speed v_3.

$$Mv_3r + 2Iv_3/r = Mv_4r + 3Iv_4/r$$

$$v_4 = \left(\frac{M + 2I/r^2}{M + 3I/r^2}\right)v_3$$

And ignoring the roller left uselessly idling, the effective energy remaining is

$$E_4 = \tfrac{1}{2}(Mv_4^2 + 3Iv_4^2/r^2) = \left(\frac{M + 2I/r^2}{M + 3I/r^2}\right)^2 E_3$$

Then

$$E_5 = \left(\frac{M + 2I/r^2}{M + 3I/r^2}\right)^4 E_3$$

$$E_6 = \left(\frac{M + 2I/r^2}{M + 3I/r^2}\right)^6 E_3$$

.   .   .   .   .   .

Thus, theoretically the crate never stops, for succeeding velocities are always a proportion of the preceding. It must be friction loss between the roller and its axle, not friction between roller and crate, which stops the body as observed.

Suppose the rollers are solid and cylindrical, of weight 50 lb each, and the crate weighs 200 lb. Then since

$$I = 1/2 \frac{W}{g}r^2$$

each successive impact (after the fourth) causes a reduction in the velocity in the ratio $250:275$, or a loss of 9.1 per cent, and a loss of 17.4 per cent of the remaining energy.

Example 2. A ball of diameter 1 in., rolling on a horizontal plane, encounters a step of height 2/10 in., normal to its path. Assuming inelastic impact and no slipping, find the minimum velocity of the ball needed to surmount the step, Fig. 1–30.

Let the velocity before impact be v, and ω the angular velocity immediately after impact. There is no change in the moment of momentum about the top edge A of the step. Before impact there is angular momentum $I_G v/r$, and the moment of the horizontal linear momentum of the mass center about A is $Mv(r - h)$. After impact there is angular momentum of rotation about A.

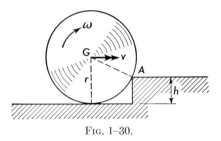

Fɪɢ. 1–30.

$$I_G v/r + Mv(r - h) = I_A \omega \tag{a}$$

$$\left[\frac{2}{5}Mr + M(r - h)\right]v = \frac{7}{5}Mr^2\omega$$

Thus

$$r\omega = \left\{\left[\frac{2}{5}\cdot\frac{1}{2} + \frac{3}{10}\right] \div \frac{7}{5}\left(\frac{1}{2}\right)\right\}v$$

$$= 5/7v \tag{b}$$

Now, to surmount the step, the remaining kinetic energy must be enough for the rise:

$$\tfrac{1}{2}I_A\omega^2 > Mgh \text{ which is } \frac{7}{10}r^2\omega^2 > gh$$

From (b)

$$v^2 > \frac{14}{5}gh$$

which yields a velocity independent of the weight of the ball, given by $v > 1.226$ ft/sec.

PROBLEMS

1–1.* The overhead valve of a Diesel engine is operated by cam, push rod, and overhead horizontal rocker, as in Fig. 1–P–1.† The push rod and valve stem move vertically. The push rod weighs 0.30 lb; the valve, cotter, and spring cap assembly weigh 0.45 lb. The rocker has a weight of 2.75 lb with a radius of gyration 2.8 in.; its center of gravity is in the pivot axis. The spring has a stiffness of 33 lb/in. of compression; the spring weight may be neglected.

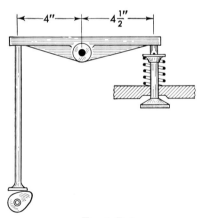

Fɪɢ. 1–P–1.

* Answers to many odd-numbered problems will be found at the end of the book.
† Problem figures are numbered to correspond to the problem number throughout.

At the point where the spring is compressed $1\frac{1}{4}$ in., the upward acceleration of the push rod is 1500 ft/sec². Determine the force between cam and push rod.

(U.L.)

1–2. A four-bar chain has two cranks and a connecting rod, all identical and of uniform weight per unit length: they each weigh 16.1 lb and are 2 ft long between bearing centers. The distance between the fixed crank centers is also 2 ft. The driving crank is accelerating its rotation at 100 rad/sec², and at the instant that it is at right angles to the line of fixed centers it is rotating at 30 rad/sec.

Find the input torque needed for this motion at this instant if the resistance of the driven crank is measured as a constant torque of 25 lb ft.

1–3. A solid spherical ball rolls down a 30° inclined plane. Find its acceleration.

1–4. Find the minimum coefficient of friction needed for pure rolling of a solid spherical ball down a 30° inclined plane.

1–5. A uniform rod AB, 36 in. long and weighing 2 lb, lies on a frictionless horizontal table. A force of 3 lb is applied perpendicularly to its axis and horizontally at the end A of the rod. Prove that the point of rotation is the center of percussion of the rod with respect to point A, and find the acceleration of the end B.

1–6. A speed governor is represented by the figure in simplified form. To the

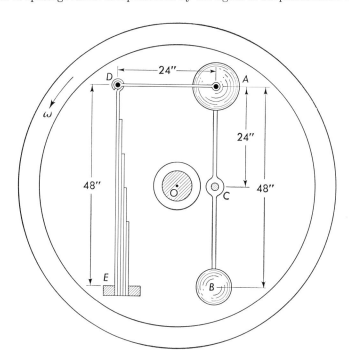

FIG. 1–P–6.

flywheel of a steam engine is attached a bar AB carrying two masses A and B, freely pivoted at C. Mass A weighs 50 lb, mass B weighs 30 lb, and the bar may be regarded as massless. Pivot C is at radius 12 in. from O, the center of rotation

The movement of mass A is restrained by the (weightless) link AD, which carries tension from deflection of the leaf spring DE.

The angles EDA, DAC, and ACO are all right angles, and the fibers of DE straight when the system turns at 300 rpm, constant speed. Find the forces on the pin-bearing surfaces at D, A, and C. (At rest the leaves of the spring curve to the left from E upward.)

1–7. A rope can safely sustain a tension T; show that the shortest time in which it can raise a weight W through a height h, so that W comes to rest at the end of the ascent, is $\sqrt{\dfrac{2h}{g}\left(\dfrac{T}{T-W}\right)}$, provided the mass of the rope itself is ignored. (C.U.)

1–8. A square lamina is suspended by vertical strings tied to two adjacent corners, so that two edges of the square are vertical. If one string is cut, show that the tension in the remaining string is instantaneously reduced to four-fifths of its former value. (C.U.)

1–9. In the figure a box $ABCD$ is hinged along one edge A, and supported by two equal rods DE and EF. The hinge at E is initially held, with DEF straight. All hinges are frictionless and their axes parallel. The box weighs 100 lb and its moment of inertia is 150 lb ft² about an axis parallel to the hinges through its center of gravity G, where G is at the center of the square $ABCD$. Each rod weighs 10 lb and its moment of inertia is 6 lb ft² about a transverse axis through its center of gravity midway between the hinges.

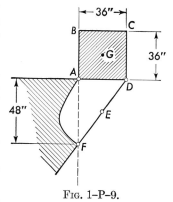

Fig. 1–P–9.

If equilibrium is just disturbed and E is released just below the line DF, show that, when the box has fallen so that D is vertically below A, the angular velocity of the box is about 4.5 rad/sec. (C.U.)

1–10. A crane winch is a hollow steel cylinder, 12-in. outside diam, 9-in. inside diam, and 4 ft long, with horizontal axis. Upon it is wound (without overlapping) 1-in. diam steel and hemp rope, which weighs 1.58 lb per ft. The total length of rope is 35 ft, of which initially 5 ft hang from the winch drum vertically; at the end there hangs stationary an 80-lb weight.

The brake suddenly fails. Find the velocity of the weight after it has fallen 15 ft, neglecting all friction.

1–11. Two spherical weights of 5 lb each and 2-in. diam are set at the same radius R upon a cross bar, as in the figure. The cross bar is attached to a 1-in. diam square-threaded screw, doubly threaded, with pitch $\frac{1}{5}$ in. Screw and cross bar together weigh 20 lb and have a radius of gyration of 1 in. The screw is held within a frame, with axis vertical.

Assuming no friction, find the radius R to which the balls should be adjusted so that after release from rest they will have moved 2 in. downward in the first 10 sec.

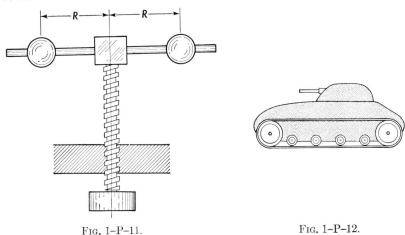

FIG. 1–P–11.   FIG. 1–P–12.

1–12. The figure illustrates a tank moving on a pair of caterpillar tracks. The end wheels are sprocket wheels of radius R; the four wheels shown between are plain wheels with radius r. The combined mass moment of inertia for the four sprockets about their axes is I_S, and for the eight plain wheels is I_P. The total mass of the tracks is M_T, the mass of all wheels (less tracks) is M_W, and the mass of the body is M. Write an expression for the total kinetic energy when the tank moves with velocity V.

If the draw-bar pull required to overcome friction is T, find an expression for the acceleration of the tank under the influence of its own weight when it is descending a slope inclined at an angle θ with the horizontal.   (C.U.)

1–13. A cylinder, 12 in. in diameter and 24 in. long, has plane ends. It floats with axis vertical in water contained by a cylindrical vessel of 18 in. internal diameter. The weight of the cylinder is 60 lb; water weighs 62.5 lb per cu ft. Find the work needed to depress the cylinder until the top is flush with water.
(C.U.)

1–14. Find the work needed to wind up a clock spring, for which the maximum torque is 25 lb in. when wound up 15 turns. The torque is found to vary according to the graph of Fig. 1–P–14.

1–15. The weightless rigid lever OB, 32 in. long, is pivoted freely at O. A tension spring of stiffness 100 lb/in. is attached perpendicularly at A, 12 in. from O, as in Fig. 1-P-15 on the following page. Find the work to be done by the normal force F to move B 2 in.

1–16. The lever and spring of Problem 1–15 are the same. But the lever is to be taken as flexible: it is a steel strip, $\frac{1}{8}$ in. $\times$ 2 in., bent by force F (Fig. 1–P–15) in the more flexible direction. Find the work needed to depress end B by 2 in.

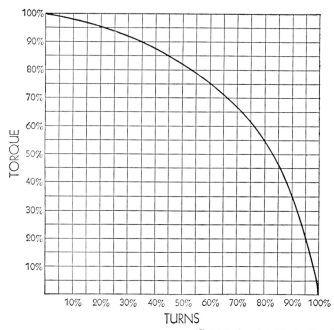

Fig. 1–P–14.

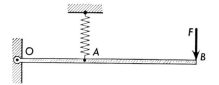

Fig. 1–P–15.

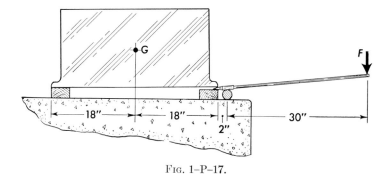

Fig. 1–P–17.

1–17. A crowbar is used to raise a machine on one side, as in the figure. The bar between machine end and fulcrum can be taken as inflexible, being much stiffer than the handle end; but from fulcrum to handle it is a round-section

$\frac{3}{4}$-in. diam steel bar. Find the work expended in raising this edge of a 2000-lb machine a height of 0.03 in. after insertion of the bar.

1-18. A force F constantly tangential is applied to the bob of a simple pendulum. Prove that the work done by this force in moving the pendulum from the vertical to a position making an angle θ with the vertical is equal to the change in potential energy due to the height of the bob.

1-19. The engine mechanism has crank length R and connecting-rod length L. The piston exerts a variable force F to overcome the constant frictional torque T resisting the turning of the crank. Show that the work done by force F, moving through the stroke $2R$ from outer to inner dead center, is equal to πT (the work done by the torque), friction being neglected, even though the force F theoretically reaches an infinite magnitude.

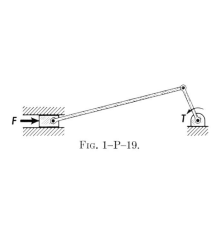

Fig. 1–P–19.

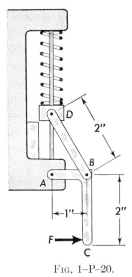

Fig. 1–P–20.

1-20. Find the work needed to raise the toggle in the figure just past top dead center against the spring. The spring has no compression in the position shown. The plane of the figure is vertical; the weight of the angle-piece ABC is 0.3 lb, of link BD 0.2 lb, and of the collar 0.2 lb, while the spring stiffness is 2 lb per in. compression. The links are assumed incompressible and inflexible.

1-21. The lock of an automobile door will engage only if the angular velocity of the closing door exceeds ω. The door swings about vertical hinges; it has a radius of gyration k about the hinges, and its center of gravity is at a distance r from the line of the hinges. Show that, if the door is at rest and at right angles to the side of the car when the car starts with uniform acceleration a, the door will close itself provided $a > \omega^2 k^2/2r$. Neglect air resistance. (C.U.)

1-22. A continuous stream of sand falls vertically through a funnel onto a revolving disk in a device to be attached to trucks for spreading sand on icy roads. The disk turns at 500 rpm and distributes 300 lb of sand per minute. The sand leaves the periphery of the 18-in. diam disk radially, relative to the disk. Find the horsepower required to impart this motion to the sand.

1–23. Show that the least angle at which a drawing board must be tilted in order that a pencil of uniform hexagonal cross section may just be able to roll down it at a constant mean speed, without slipping, is about $6\frac{1}{2}°$.

The radius of gyration of a regular hexagonal area of side a about an axis through its center and normal to its plane is $a\sqrt{5/12}$. The material of the pencil may be treated as homogeneous. Assume that the faces of the pencil are slightly concave so that contact occurs at the edges only. (C.U.)

1–24. It is important that hexagonal bar stock should always roll down an inclined plane, where it is to be transferred from one conveyor to another. It may be presumed that there is no slipping, and that the longitudinal axis of the bars remains horizontal.

Find the minimum slope to ensure that no bar can remain at rest on it.

1–25. A light-railroad truck runs down an inclined track until the front wheels reach a level section, as in the figure. The radius of gyration of the truck about an axis through its center of gravity and parallel to the axles is k; the moment of inertia of the wheels may be neglected. If the velocity of the truck is v just before the front wheels reach the bottom, show that the angular velocity of the truck after this first impact is

$$\frac{2a \cot \alpha - h}{(2a \cot \alpha - h)^2 + a^2 + k^2} v$$

(Clue: Use the instantaneous center of rotation of the truck body.)

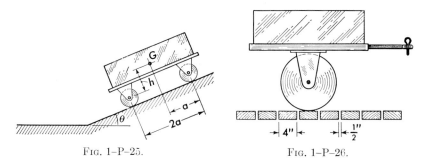

Fig. 1–P–25.   Fig. 1–P–26.

1–26. Find approximately the horsepower needed to pull a light trailer behind a car at 40 mph over the cobblestone road illustrated in the figure. The tires may be assumed rigid and the springs omitted.

The trailer's loaded body weighs 1200 lb; the wheels each weigh 25 lb, are of 30-in. diameter and have a radius of gyration of 12 in.

1–27. A motor A has a 6-in. diam pulley and drives by belt a 12-in. diam pulley keyed to a countershaft. A grind wheel C with fast and loose pulleys of 3-in. diam is driven by another belt from a 24-in. diam pulley on the countershaft. The moments of inertia of the rotating parts are as follows: A, 450 lb in.^{2}; B, 800 lb in.^{2}; C, 16 lb in.^{2}.

When the motor is running at 600 rpm with its power cut off, the belt to the grinder is quickly shifted from the loose to the fast pulley. Show that, by the time all belt slipping ceases, the motor speed will have fallen to about 430 rpm.

Assume that the mass of the belts and the effects of bearing and wind friction during the short time that belt slipping continues may be neglected.   (C.U.)

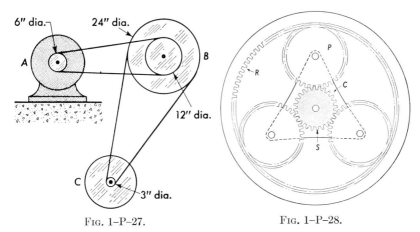

FIG. 1–P–27.   FIG. 1–P–28.

1–28. The figure represents an automobile's overdrive unit. The sun gear S is fixed; the triangular cage C carries three short axles on which three planetary gears P turn freely. As these run around the sun gear, they carry forward the internal-tooth ring gear R on the driven shaft. S has 24 teeth, and R 96 teeth of diametral pitch 8. The moments of inertia of C and R about the center of rotation are 25 lb in.^{2} and 300 lb in.^{2}, and of each gear P about its own center is 10 lb in.^{2}. These gears P weigh 4 lb each.

(a) Find the kinetic energy of the unit when the driving shaft carrying C turns at 3000 rpm.

(b) What angular acceleration will R have, if a torque of 200 lb in. is applied to C in excess of any torque required to overcome friction?

1–29. In the epicyclic gear of Fig. 1-P-29 the shaft A is compound with the arm carrying the pinion D while B is free to rotate on the shaft C. The capital letters A, B, C, and D denote the moments of inertia of these members about their respective axes, A including the mass of the pinion D, while the lower-case letters b, c, and d are the pitch circle radii of the wheels B, C, and D respectively. A band brake operates on the outside of B.

Initially the brake is off and the mechanism revolves freely, the angular velocity of B being ω while that of C has any value. The brake is then applied, bringing B to rest.

Show that the moment of the impulse of the braking force and the energy absorbed by the brake are both independent of the initial angular velocity of C.

If the moment of inertia D is neglected, show that the energy absorbed by the brake is

$$\frac{1}{2} \frac{c^2 AB + b^2 AC + (b+c)^2 BC}{c^2 A + (b+c)^2 C} \omega^2$$

and that (a) if C is initially at rest its final angular velocity is $\dfrac{bcA}{c^2A + (b + c)^2C}\,\omega$, and (b) if the whole mechanism initially has the angular velocity ω the final angular velocity of C is

$$\frac{(b + c)[cA + (b + c)C]}{c^2A + (b + c)^2C}\,\omega$$

Neglect energy losses in the gearing and bearings. (C.U.)

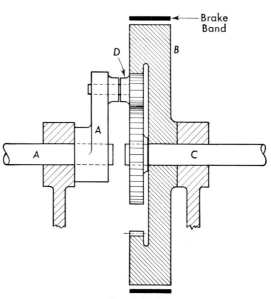

Fɪɢ. 1–P–29.

1–30. A small rectangular block of weight 2 lb is placed on the smooth inclined face of a large wedge of weight **7** lb and slope 30° from the horizontal. The wedge is free to slide on a smooth horizontal plane in a direction perpendicular to its edge. There is no friction anywhere. Show that if the system starts from rest, the block will slide down a distance of 3 ft measured along the face of the inclined plane in 0.558 sec. (C.U.)

1–31. Two spheres have the same appearance, the same diameter, and the same weight. One however is made of a heavier material and is hollow. How will you determine which is the solid one without marring either? No X-ray machine is available.

1–32. Write out the complete Greek alphabet, both capital and lower-case letters, with their names.

Chapter 2

EQUATIONS OF MOTION

2-1. The Concept. The difference between an equation of motion of a body and the type of problems that have illustrated the material of the first chapter is in general merely this, that it will describe displacements, velocities, or accelerations of bodies during a continuous change, at any instant during the change, instead of only before and after.

Consider a particle falling freely in a vacuum. It is well known that after a fall of amount H, it will have gained a velocity given (by energy exchange) as

$$v = \sqrt{2gH}$$

This is a "before-and-after" energy analysis. But is not this equally true for any drop h? Suppose the particle has dropped only h, any fraction of H, we have

$$v = \sqrt{2gh} \tag{2-1}$$

and this equation gives the velocity at *any* point on the way down. It is therefore an equation of motion in terms of velocity and displacement.

Now the calculus can enter the picture: since velocities, accelerations, and displacements are all related by derivatives and integrals, then if by any means we have come upon an equation of motion concerning one of these, we may obtain an equation in the others (provided we can integrate).

The eq. 2-1 gives the velocity after any drop h. When $h = x$, the velocity is $\sqrt{2gx}$. Moreover the velocity at that instant is the rate of change of that x, or dx/dt. So it may be written

$$\frac{dx}{dt} = \sqrt{2gx} \tag{2-2}$$

We may either differentiate this to find the acceleration

$$\frac{d^2x}{dt^2} = \sqrt{\frac{g}{2x}} \cdot \frac{dx}{dt} = g \tag{2-3}$$

or integrate for the displacement x in terms of t, that is, after any time t from the start,

$$\int \frac{dx}{\sqrt{2gx}} = \int dt$$

$$\frac{2\sqrt{x}}{\sqrt{2g}} = t + c \tag{2-4}$$

Integration entails the determination of a constant c which appears necessarily. Here we note that eq. 2–1 states tacitly that the velocity was zero at the top, so we will assume also $t = 0$ when $x = 0$; and when this is substituted in eq. 2–4 it yields $c = 0$. Thus

$$\sqrt{2x} = \sqrt{g} \cdot t + 0$$

$$x = \tfrac{1}{2}gt^2 \tag{2-5}$$

This, then, is the basic "equation of motion" (i.e., equation of displacement), and the other two (eqs. 2–2 and 2–3) are called "differential equations of motion" since they involve derivatives. Some differential equations are hard to integrate, some are even impossible to integrate exactly. But by good fortune those that arise under the usual simplifying assumptions in dynamics of machinery are generally of a few simple types. The mathematical problems of their solution are set out briefly in the Appendix to this chapter (page 74).

Equations of motion for various problems are derived by analyzing the situation by inertia, energy, or momentum methods, but the analysis is made for some intermediate station during the motion, as for example h in eq. 2–1 was part way down the fall.

2–2. Inertia Method. Body falling through a resistant medium.

a) *Example.* A body is falling through air, which has a resistance proportional to the square of the velocity. Find the velocity after time t from the start.

The force downward is W and the upward resistance is kv^2. The net force produces the acceleration down.

$$\frac{W}{g}a = W - kv^2$$

Write $a = \dfrac{dv}{dt}$ not $\dfrac{d^2x}{dt^2}$ because of v on the right-hand side.

$$\frac{dv}{dt} = g\left(1 - \frac{k}{W}v^2\right)$$

$$\int_0^v \frac{dv}{1 - \dfrac{k}{W}v^2} = g\int_0^t dt$$

At this point limits have been inserted on the integral, to show the initial velocity is zero when $t = 0$ and at any other particular time t the velocity is v; this is the alternative to introducing, and then solving for, the arbitrary constant of integration. Integration gives

$$\frac{1}{2}\sqrt{\frac{W}{k}} \log_e \left(\frac{1 + \sqrt{\frac{k}{W}}v}{1 - \sqrt{\frac{k}{W}}v} \right) = gt$$

$$\frac{1 + \sqrt{\frac{k}{W}} \cdot v}{1 - \sqrt{\frac{k}{W}} \cdot v} = e^{2g\sqrt{k/W} \cdot t}$$

To simplify the appearance of this, write $v_0 = \sqrt{W/k}$; for dimensions show it is a velocity; whence,

$$v = v_0 \left(\frac{e^{2gt/v_0} - 1}{e^{2gt/v_0} + 1} \right)$$

Obviously, as t gets large, that is, after a long time, v approaches v_0 in value, for the term in parenthesis tends to the value unity.

b) As an alternate problem we desire to find the velocity in terms of the distance fallen. This involves the important substitution given by eq. 2-6.

The preceding problem showed that

$$\frac{dv}{dt} = g\left(1 - \frac{k}{W}v^2\right)$$

The substitution to get in terms of s (distance) instead of t (time) is

$$\text{Acceleration} = \frac{dv}{dt} = \frac{dv}{ds} \times \frac{ds}{dt} = v\frac{dv}{ds} \qquad (2\text{-}6)$$

Hence

$$v\frac{dv}{ds} = g\left(1 - \frac{k}{W}v^2\right)$$

Now it is possible to integrate with respect to s, by separating the variables:

$$\int_0^v \frac{v\,dv}{1 - \frac{k}{W}v^2} = g\int_0^s ds$$

$$-\frac{W}{2k} \log_e \left(1 - \frac{k}{W}v^2\right) = gs$$

$$1 - \frac{k}{W}v^2 = e^{-2kgs/W}$$

$$v = \sqrt{\frac{W}{k}(1 - e^{-2kgs/W})}$$

Note that as $s \to \infty$, the velocity approaches asymptotically its limiting value $v_0 = \sqrt{\frac{W}{k}}$, which is referred to as the terminal velocity.

2–3. Change of Energy Method. This method is only slightly different from the above. It consists of writing the change of energy between one intermediate point of the travel and another point an infinitesimal distance further along.

For example, consider again the same problem of the weight falling in the resisting medium.

Let the weight drop a distance s from the starting point to the intermediate point, and $(s + ds)$ to the next point. The intermediate point is not specific but is *any* distance s. Between these points,

$$\text{P.E. lost} = W\,ds \tag{2–7}$$

$$\text{K.E. gained} = \frac{1}{2}\frac{W}{g}(v + dv)^2 - \frac{1}{2}\frac{W}{g}v^2$$

$$= \frac{1}{2}\frac{W}{g} \cdot 2v\,dv$$

where the velocity of the weight is v when it is at position s, and $(v + dv)$ when at $(s + ds)$. Small quantities of higher than first order are always negligible when multiplying out such expressions. Then we may write

$$\text{Work done against resistance} = kv^2 \cdot ds$$

since over so small a change, we may regard the velocity as constant, so that kv^2 is the resistance force. If with more precise care we assume the mean velocity over the interval is better given by the arithmetic mean velocity

$$\frac{v + (v + dv)}{2} = v + \frac{1}{2}\,dv$$

the work done against resistance is

$$k\left(v + \frac{dv}{2}\right)^2 ds = kv^2\,ds + kv \cdot dv \cdot ds + \frac{1}{4}k(dv)^2\,ds$$

and thus the improvement is only in higher orders of diminutives, which is negligible. The greater precision does not help.

So putting into an equation the conversion of potential energy into work and kinetic energy:

$$W\,ds = kv^2\,ds + \frac{W}{g}v\,dv \tag{2–8}$$

$$(W - kv^2) = \frac{W}{g}\frac{v \cdot dv}{ds}$$

This is the same as the equation obtained by the method in Art. 2–2.

2–4. Examples with Changing Mass. Newton's law, that we have used so continuously, states that force is proportional to rate of change of momentum. When the mass of the body or particle subjected to this force is constant, the law becomes

$$F = \frac{d}{dt}(mv) = ma$$

But when the mass is variable, the derivative has two terms

$$F = \frac{d}{dt}(mv) = m\frac{dv}{dt} + v\frac{dm}{dt} \qquad (2\text{-}9)$$

Again, in the case of angular motion, the law derived from the moments of the above is that the torque is proportional to the rate of change of the moment of momentum. In the case of plane rotation about a fixed axis this becomes

$$T = \frac{d}{dt}(I\omega) = I\alpha + \omega\frac{dI}{dt} \qquad (2\text{-}10)$$

Example 1. Rocket Propulsion. A rocket, when full, has a mass M, but is ejecting mass μ per sec with jet velocity v_j relative to the nozzle. After any time t, the instantaneous mass of the rocket is $(M - \mu t)$, and if the velocity is then v, the force upward, by eq. 2–9, is

$$F = (M - \mu t)\frac{dv}{dt} - \mu v \qquad (i)$$

This is obtained from the impulse of the departing mass μ.

$$F = \mu(v_j - v) \qquad (ii)$$

If the weight and air resistance are ignored and we assume no friction loss in the jet, these F's are equal, so that the equation of motion is

$$(M - \mu t)\frac{dv}{dt} = \mu v_j \qquad (2\text{-}11)$$

In integrating this, suppose that the final velocity v_{max} is reached when the fraction k of the original mass M is burned and that this takes T sec. The mass of fuel carried at the start is kM, and $\mu T = kM$.

$$\int_0^{v_{max}} dv = \mu v_j \int_0^T \frac{dt}{M - \mu t}$$

$$v_{max} = v_j\left[- \log_e(M - \mu t)\right]_0^T$$

$$= v_j \log_e\left(\frac{M}{M - \mu T}\right)$$

$$v_{max} = v_j \log_e\left(\frac{1}{1 - k}\right)$$

Now the weight and air resistance cv^2 should be included, for without them the eq. 2–11 above is not a valid one physically; it was only solved here because it concentrates on the momentum aspect of the problem. The net force of eq. (ii) causing the acceleration in eq. (i) is really only

$$\mu(v_j - v) - W - cv^2$$

and with $W = (M - \mu t)g$ we have

$$\mu(v_j - v) - (M - \mu t)g - cv^2 = (M - \mu t)\frac{dv}{dt} - \mu v$$

or

$$\mu v_j = (M - \mu t)\left(g + \frac{dv}{dt}\right) + cv^2 \tag{2-12}$$

But it so happens that this is a case of one of those equations that cannot be integrated by ordinary mathematical methods, for the variables v and t cannot be separated to give two integrals. The method of solution is graphical and approximate.

First we need to put in the numbers M, μ, v_j, and c that apply, and solve eq. 2–12 for the initial acceleration when $v = 0$. We start to draw a graph (Fig. 2–1) of velocity against time, by assuming that this initial acceleration is constant for a very short time δt, say one-tenth of a second. At the end of this interval we have a close value for the velocity $v_1 = (dv/dt)_0 \times (\delta t)$, shown at point A. So put this in eq. 2–12 and find a new acceleration $(dv/dt)_1$ which is assumed to last for the next tenth of a second, and which gives us velocity v_2 at B. Continuing in this way, we get a graph which is a series of short straight lines, and it is then smoothed to a curve.

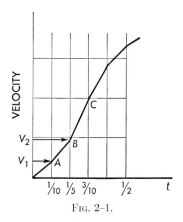

FIG. 2–1.

By finding the area under this curve by a planimeter, we effect an approximate integration which can give us the distance covered in any time.

Example 2. A chain, initially vertical and dropping, meets a horizontal table with velocity v_0 and subsides upon it without rebound. Find the load on the table as a function of time.

Suppose the first contact is made when $t = 0$. After a further time t, the velocity of the moving chain will be

$$v = v_0 + gt$$

In the next very short interval dt, the length of chain that stops is

$$dl = (v_0 + gt)dt$$

and if the chain has a mass m per unit length, the rate of destruction of momentum is

$$\frac{d}{dt}\Big[(m \cdot dl)v \Big] = \frac{d}{dt}\Big[m(v_0 + gt)^2 \cdot dt \Big] = m(v_0 + gt)^2$$

which is the force from the continuous impulse. But there is also the weight lying on the table at time t, which is

$$W = mg\!\int dl = mg \int_0^t (v_0 + gt)dt$$

$$= mg(v_0 t + \tfrac{1}{2}gt^2)$$

So the load on the table is the sum of these two forces. It happens therefore to be a quadratic function of time.

$$P = m(v_0 + gt)^2 + mg(v_0 t + \tfrac{1}{2}gt^2)$$
$$= m(v_0^2 + 3v_0 gt + \tfrac{3}{2}g^2 t^2)$$

Example 3. A machine consists of a wheel rotating about a vertical axis, and holding a number of bottles or cups at radius r ft. Initially the wheel with empty bottles has moment of inertia I lb ft sec^2 and rotates at angular velocity ω_1 rad/sec. As the wheel rotates freely, the bottles are filled at the steady rate of w lb of liquid per sec. Find the angular velocity after t sec and the angle turned through, assuming the diameter of the bottles is small compared to the radius of the wheel.   (C.U.)

Initially the angular momentum $= I\omega_1$.

As the liquid falls vertically, it has no moment of impulse about the axis of the wheel; torque T in eq. 2–10 is zero. Thus the angular momentum will be constant. After t sec the weight of liquid in the bottles is wt, and the new moment of inertia of the wheel is $I + \dfrac{wt}{g}r^2$.

Therefore

$$I\omega_1 = \left(I + \frac{wt}{g}r^2\right)\omega_2$$

Now ω_2 is the angular velocity after any time t. Treating t as a variable, and writing $\omega_2 = d\theta/dt$

$$\frac{I\omega_1}{I + \dfrac{wt}{g}r^2} = \frac{d\theta}{dt}$$

$$\theta = \int_0^t \frac{I\omega_1}{I + \dfrac{wr^2}{g}\cdot t}\,dt$$

$$= \frac{I\omega_1 g}{wr^2}\log_e\!\left(1 + \frac{wr^2 t}{gI}\right)$$

If the instantaneous value of $\left(I + \dfrac{wt}{g}r^2\right)$ at any time t is written simply as I', this expression appears as

$$\theta = \left(\frac{I}{I' - I}\right)\omega_1 t \,\log_e\!\frac{I'}{I}$$

2–5. The Equations of Forces and the Equations of Geometry. In problems of particle dynamics, a single equation of motion may be deduced by the methods of inertia, of energy, or of momentum. But with rigid body problems, or problems about a group of particles, two or three such equations may be written, and then there is need of equations of geometry connecting the linear and rotational motions of the various parts. One example follows, and another is found in the next Article.

Example. In the letter press shown in Fig. 1–P–11, the screw has 1-in. diameter square threads, of pitch 8 to the inch, and doubly threaded. The weight of the screw and wrench bar is 30 lb, with moment of inertia (WR^2) 1100 lb in.². The coefficient of sliding friction between screw and frame, while running, is 0.10. The air resistance to the spin amounts to a torque of 0.5ω lb in. for angular velocity ω rad/sec.

Find the equation of motion of spin, if it is started spinning (downward) at 20 rad/sec.

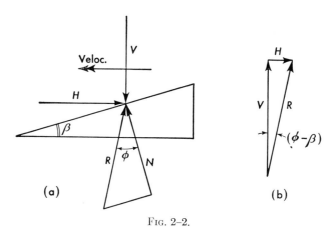

Fig. 2–2.

We use the inertia force method: for convenience, gather up all the downward load on the screw thread to show it as in Fig. 2–2a, as if it acted at a point, and is represented by the vertical force V.

The slope of the thread is such as to drop 1/4 in. in one circumference of the pitch diameter (15/16 in.) so

$$\beta = \tan^{-1}\frac{1/4}{15\pi/16} = \tan^{-1}\frac{4}{15\pi} = 4°51'$$

The normal reaction N from the thread is combined with the friction to give resistance R making angle ϕ with the normal, where

Friction angle $\phi = \tan^{-1}0.10 = 5°43'$

Now ϕ is greater than β, so that the spin velocity ω must be slowing up. Assume then linear acceleration a upward and angular acceleration α opposing the rotation. From the vector force diagram (Fig. 2–2b)

$$V = R \cos (\phi - \beta) = W + \frac{W}{g}a$$

and by moments of horizontal forces, with $r = 15/32$ in.,

$$Hr = Rr \sin (\phi - \beta) = I\alpha - 0.5\omega$$

Eliminate R:

$$\left(W + \frac{W}{g}a\right)r \sin (\phi - \beta) = (I\alpha - 0.5\omega) \cos (\phi - \beta) \qquad \text{(i)}$$

We need to transform the acceleration a into angular acceleration, and here is need of the equation of geometry: observe a turn of 2π radians will drop the screw vertically $1/4$ in.; thus

$$\frac{a}{1/4} = \frac{\alpha}{2\pi} \qquad \text{(ii)}$$

Combining (i) and (ii):

$$\left(\frac{W}{g}\frac{r \tan (\phi - \beta)}{8\pi} - I\right)\alpha + 0.5\omega + Wr \tan (\phi - \beta) = 0$$

Now turning to the numerical side of the problem: of the two terms within parentheses the first with W is found to be negligibly small; substituting $W = 30$, $g = 386$, $\tan (\phi - \beta) = \tan 52' = 0.015$, $I = 1100/386$. and $\alpha = -d\omega/dt$ (since it was a deceleration) we obtain

$$2.85\frac{d\omega}{dt} + 0.5\omega + 0.211 = 0$$

Mathematically this is solved either as a simple separable type, or as a linear differential of the first order (see the Appendix to this chapter); the solution is an exponential of the form

$$\omega = A + Be^{\lambda t}$$

After substitution of this solution to check, the initial condition that at $t = 0$, $\omega = 20$ gives values to the arbitrary constants; the required equation appears as

$$\omega = 0.42 + 19.58e^{-0.175t}$$

2–6. Choice of Variable. In many problems of rigid body motion, it is convenient, as in the example just given, to use two or more variables, such as linear and angular dimensions, to set up the kinetic equations. Equations of geometry are then needed to relate these dimensions; but it does not matter which dimension is chosen — in general any one will

do to proceed with the mathematical part of the problem, though one
is usually more appropriate to the solution sought.

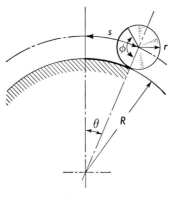

FIG. 2–3.

Example. A cylindrical wheel of weight W, radius r, and mass moment
of inertia I about its center rolls upon a large fixed cylinder of radius R,
Fig. 2–3. Friction is sufficient to prevent slip.

We choose the energy method: suppose the wheel has reached the
position defined either by arc s or angle θ. Then, since leaving the top,

$$\text{P.E.} = W(R + r)(1 - \cos\theta)$$

Kinetic energy is both linear and rotational:

$$\text{Lin. K.E.} = \frac{1}{2}\frac{W}{g}\left(\frac{ds}{dt}\right)^2 \quad \text{or} \quad \frac{1}{2}\frac{W}{g}\left[(R + r)\frac{d\theta}{dt}\right]^2$$

$$\text{Rot. K.E.} = \frac{1}{2}I\left[\frac{(ds/dt)}{r}\right]^2 \quad \text{or} \quad \frac{1}{2}I\left[\frac{d}{dt}(\theta + \phi)\right]^2$$

Here are three variables; the equations of geometry that relate them
are

$$s = (R + r)\theta$$
$$R\theta = r\phi$$

They may be differentiated. So the conservation of energy is expressed as

$$\frac{1}{2}\left(\frac{W}{g} + \frac{I}{r^2}\right)\left(\frac{ds}{dt}\right)^2 + W(R + r)\left[1 - \cos\left(\frac{s}{R + r}\right)\right] = \text{const}$$

or

$$\frac{1}{2}\left[\frac{W}{g}(R + r)^2 + \frac{I(R + r)^2}{r^2}\right]\left(\frac{d\theta}{dt}\right)^2 + W(R + r)(1 - \cos\theta) = \text{const}$$

The second is better because of the simpler cosine term. If we then set
$I = 1/2\ (W/g)r^2$, it reduces to

$$\frac{3(R+r)}{4g}\dot{\theta}^2 + (1 - \cos\theta) = \text{const}$$

where $\dot{\theta}$ is a short way to write $d\theta/dt$.*

2-7. Resistance Varying with Displacement.

Example. A cylindrical log of length l floats vertically in water. The specific gravity of the log is $\rho(<1)$. The log is depressed a distance s and released. Find the position of the log after time t.

The equilibrium depth of the log is ρl (Fig. 2–4) and from the surface to the lowest point when fully depressed is $(\rho l + s)$. Consider the equilibrium at any point when the log has risen a distance x above this

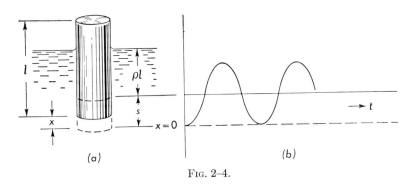

(a)   (b)

Fig. 2–4.

low point. The buoyant force due to the weight of water displaced is $62.4A(\rho l + s - x)$ where 62.4 lb/cu ft is the weight of water and A is the cross-sectional area of the log, and the weight of the log is $(62.4\rho)Al$. Hence net upward force $= 62.4A(s - x)$. This produces in the log an acceleration $\ddot{x}$ upward,* so that

$$62.4A(s - x) = \frac{62.4\,\rho Al}{g}\ddot{x}$$

$$\ddot{x} + \frac{g}{\rho l}(x - s) = 0$$

This is the simple harmonic type of differential equation, explained on pages 76 and 77 in the Appendix to this chapter.

The constant in the equation must be eliminated by the substitution

$$x - s = y$$

giving

$$\ddot{y} + \frac{g}{\rho l}y = 0$$

By comparison with the solution of the general type, it is seen that if

* Dots (and occasionally primes) are a recognized device to indicate derivatives with respect to time. Thus $\dot{x} = dx/dt$ and $\ddot{x} = d^2x/dt^2$, etc.

$$\omega^2 = \frac{g}{\rho l}$$

$$y = A \sin \omega t + B \cos \omega t$$

Substituting back again into x:

$$x = s + A \sin \sqrt{\frac{g}{\rho l}}t + B \cos \sqrt{\frac{g}{\rho l}}t \qquad (2\text{–}13)$$

Now we may obtain values for A and B particular to this problem by observing the initial conditions,

$$x = 0 \quad \text{and} \quad \frac{dx}{dt} = 0 \quad \text{when } t = 0$$

Differentiating the eq. 2–13 above to obtain an equation in $\dfrac{dx}{dt}$ for this substitution:

$$\frac{dx}{dt} = A\sqrt{\frac{g}{\rho l}} \cos \sqrt{\frac{g}{\rho l}}t - B\sqrt{\frac{g}{\rho l}} \sin \sqrt{\frac{g}{\rho l}}t \qquad (2\text{–}14)$$

Now for $\dfrac{dx}{dt}$ to be zero at $t = 0$, we have $A = 0$. Hence in eq. 2–13 since $x = 0$ when $t = 0$, $B = -s$.

So the solution of the problem is

$$x = s\left(1 - \cos \sqrt{\frac{g}{\rho l}}t\right) \qquad (2\text{–}15)$$

which means that the bottom point of the log must move as shown in Fig. 2–4b.

Let us find also the time it takes for the log to return first to its central position. (Of course it will overshoot the mark.)

The log is in its initial position again when $x = s$. Suppose this takes time t_1. From eq. 2–15

$$s = s - s \cos \sqrt{\frac{g}{\rho l}}t_1$$

This means that $\cos \sqrt{\dfrac{g}{\rho l}}t_1 = 0$, or $\sqrt{\dfrac{g}{\rho l}}t_1 = \pi/2$ since $\cos \pi/2 = 0$.

Hence $t_1 = \dfrac{\pi}{2}\sqrt{\dfrac{\rho l}{g}}$ sec.

There are other solutions for $\cos \sqrt{g/\rho l}\, t_1 = 0$ because $\cos 3\pi/2$, $\cos 5\pi/2$, etc., are zero. All these are valid solutions, and give the time elapsed until the log returns to $x = s$ for the second, third, fourth time, etc.

2–8. Hyperbolic Motion. Another equation of motion often occurs which appears very similar to the foregoing equation, but is a very different motion.

Example. A uniform chain of length L and weight w per unit length lies on a table which has a coefficient of friction μ. If a length a of the chain is pulled over the edge, prove that there will be motion only if a is greater than a measure a_1 given by

$$a_1 = \frac{\mu}{1 + \mu}L$$

Then assuming this is so, find the displacement after time t. Consider that there is a small wheel (of negligible inertia) let into the edge of the table, so that the corner is turned smoothly.

Let a be the length of chain hanging over the edge (Fig. 2–5) at the beginning. Then the length on the table is $(L - a)$ and the normal reaction with the table is

$$N = w(L - a)$$

The weight of chain hanging over, less the tension due to friction, is the accelerating force, or

$$F = wa - \mu w(L - a)$$

if friction has reached its maximum. Thus there will be no motion unless

$$wa > \mu w(L - a)$$
$$a > \mu L - \mu a$$
$$a > \left(\frac{\mu}{1 + \mu}\right)L$$

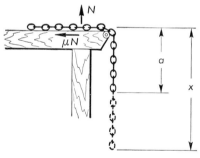

Fig. 2–5.

Thus a must be greater than a_1. Suppose then that motion has started and that the length of chain hanging is x. The accelerating force at this moment is

$$F = wx - \mu w(L - x)$$

From the value of a_1, this reduces to the net force

$$F = w(1 + \mu)(x - a_1)$$

which must accelerate the whole chain.

$$\frac{wL}{g}\frac{d^2x}{dt^2} = w(1 + \mu)(x - a_1)$$

This is a standard form of a differential equation of the hyperbolic type. Reference to the Appendix of this chapter (page 78) will show that if we first put $(x - a_1) = y$, we obtain

$$\frac{d^2y}{dt^2} - (1 + \mu)\frac{g}{L}y = 0 \tag{2-16}$$

which may be recognized as eq. 2–49. If then

$$(1 + \mu)\frac{g}{L} = p^2$$

the solution has the form

$$y = A \sinh pt + B \cosh pt$$

or

$$x = A \sinh pt + B \cosh pt + a_1 \tag{2-17}$$

The constants A and B are arbitrary, but to find the values that are peculiar to this problem, suppose that initially

$$x = a_2 > a_1 \quad \text{and} \quad \dot{x} = 0 \quad \text{when } t = 0$$

Differentiating* the equation above

$$\frac{dx}{dt} = Ap \cosh pt + Bp \sinh pt$$

The constants of integration appear to be $A = 0$ and $B = a_2 - a_1$. So the displacement of the bottom of the chain is

$$x = a_1 + (a_2 - a_1) \cosh pt$$

where $p = \sqrt{(1 + \mu)\frac{g}{L}}$.

It is worth noting that this problem can be solved also by energy relationships, but, on the other hand, another similar problem such as is shown in Fig. 2–6, where the chain on the table lies coiled up in such a manner that every link will not move until pulled by its neighbor over the edge, cannot be solved by energy equations; for in this latter problem motion involves a continual series of impulses, jerking successive links into motion. This problem is therefore solved by momentum equations, and is similar to Example 2 of Art. 2–4.

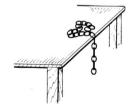

FIG. 2–6.

2–9. Stable and Unstable Equilibrium. The contrast between the simple harmonic and the hyperbolic motions is interesting. The former,

---

* In differentiating, sinh becomes cosh, and cosh becomes sinh, *without* any negative signs entering as with sines and cosines. Also the values of sinh $0 = 0$ and cosh $0 = 1$ are exactly as in the case of sin $0°$ and cos $0°$.

being defined by a solution in sines and cosines, is a motion which keeps reversing and repeating itself. The latter, being defined in terms of hyperbolic sines and cosines (sinh and cosh), or real exponentials, is a motion in which the velocity continually increases as the object progresses away from the starting point.

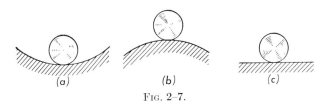

(a)   (b)   (c)

Fig. 2–7.

The simple harmonic motion is typical of an object displaced from a position of *stable equilibrium*, as the ball in the bottom of a bowl in Fig. 2–7a. The ball, if moved, will immediately on release try to regain its former position. This is the motion of the simplest type of vibration and is dealt with in much greater detail in the next two chapters.

The hyperbolic motion is typical of the motion of a body displaced from a position of *unstable equilibrium*, Fig. 2–7b. Here there is equilibrium only as long as the ball is *exactly* on top of the hill. As soon as displaced, the ball has no tendency to return but quickly runs away.

A third sort of equilibrium is shown in Fig. 2–7c. This is *neutral* or indifferent equilibrium: a ball on a flat surface. When displaced, it is perfectly happy in its new position.

We will now develop a more general definition of equilibrium for any system of bodies. Suppose the system is in equilibrium in some configuration signified by P. There are presumed to be a number of forces, torques, and moments acting on the system, and then the system is moved a very small distance dx or around a very small angle $d\theta$, or both. Consequently some small amount of work will be done:

$$dW = (\Sigma F_x)dx + (\Sigma T)d\theta \qquad (2\text{--}18)$$

If dx or $d\theta$ were sizable, this might be positive or negative work according to the direction of the net force or torque. But since dx and $d\theta$ are minute, the net force and torque are those active at the position P; by taking equilibrium as a position where the system remains static, we know that the net forces and torques in any sense are zero (by Newton's law). Thus if s is a displacement either linear or angular (either x or θ), we have deduced that at P

$$\frac{dW}{ds} = 0 \qquad (2\text{--}19)$$

As a consequence, *if the potential energy of a system is a maximum or minimum in any position P, that position is one of equilibrium.* And moreover, if the potential energy is plotted against any displacement s, points of inflection in the curve, and any horizontal lines in it, also show points of equilibrium.

Let us consider a minimum energy position, such as in Fig. 2–7a. Let the body be moved by an amount sizable enough so that work is done. Since at P the energy was a minimum, at any other place Q the potential energy is greater, provided the work is against conservative forces, and not against such things as friction. Since the potential of the body increased, the motion was accomplished by an outside agency which had to work against net forces (or torques) directed toward P. Thus released at Q, these net forces will start the body back toward P. We therefore conclude that *a position of minimum potential energy is one of stable equilibrium.*

A similar reasoning can be applied to a position of maximum potential. Since movement (against conservative forces) in any manner reduces the potential, the work done is negative and the net forces at Q must be directed away from P. Released at Q, the body will be repelled by P. *A position of maximum potential energy is one of unstable equilibrium.*

As to the neutral equilibrium, as in Fig. 2–7c, note that when displaced to any Q, we still have $dW/ds = 0$; there is therefore no rate of change of dW/ds with s. The three types of equilibrium are therefore distinguishable (by either condition in each case) by

Stable: $\dfrac{d^2W}{ds^2}$ positive at P; or net force at Q toward P.

Unstable: $\dfrac{d^2W}{ds^2}$ negative at P; or net force at Q away from P.

Neutral: $\dfrac{d^2W}{ds^2} = 0$; or net force at Q and P both zero.

When the motion of the body under consideration involves overcoming friction, equilibrium is maintained over a range of positions instead of at a point, as is common observation. This will not be investigated here; however, it is plain that beyond the range the above force definitions hold true.

Before proceeding, note that the work expressed in eq. 2–18 is called "virtual work," for, since dx and $d\theta$ are infinitesimally small, the work done is a hypothetical amount, whatever the values of ΣF or ΣT.

Example. A column of length l is raised to a vertical position on a rough floor by means of a rope passed over a pulley vertically above it and at height h. When in position, the rope is tied with tension T to an anchoring ring as shown (Fig. 2–8). With the rope of length a and elastic constant k lb per in., and the column of weight w, determine whether this equilibrium is stable or not.

Suppose the column is by chance displaced an angle θ from the vertical, will it return? The potential energy lost by the column is

$$wl/2 - (wl/2)\cos\theta$$

For a small angle θ this may be written $wl\theta^2/4$, which we obtain by using the first two terms of the series which expresses $\cos\theta$, since the usual assumption $\cos\theta = 1$ when θ is small does not help. Thus

$$\cos\theta = 1 - \tfrac{1}{2}\theta^2 + \cdot \cdot \cdot \quad (2\text{--}20)$$

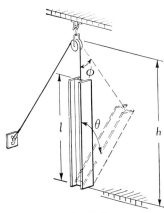

Now with the column at this inclination, the distance between the column top and the pulley is x, given by

$$x^2 = h^2 + l^2 - 2hl\cos\theta$$

so that the extension of the rope is

$$e = x - (h - l)$$

Again we cannot put $\cos\theta = 1$ or e vanishes, instead by eq. 2–20

$$x^2 = (h - l)^2 + hl\theta^2$$

$$e = (h - l)\left[\sqrt{1 + \frac{hl\theta^2}{(h - l)^2}} - 1\right]$$

And by means of a binomial series this time:

$$e = \frac{1}{2}\frac{hl}{h - l}\theta^2 + \cdot \cdot \cdot$$

The tension in the rope is T, and since θ is very small and the length $(h - l)$ is only a small part of the rope, we may presume it does not change; thus the work done by the displaced column in stretching the rope is Te. (More accurately, tension varies with θ^2, so that the next term would involve θ^4.)

The condition for stability is that the strain energy gain be greater than the potential energy loss of the column, or

$$\frac{1}{2}T\left(\frac{hl}{h - l}\right)\theta^2 > \frac{wl}{4}\theta^2$$

$$T > \frac{h - l}{2h}w$$

This is, of course, the same minimum tension as was necessary to raise the column earlier. A conclusion is then that the rope must be tied to the ring with the same full tension; the rope must not be even partially slackened, or the column is unstable.

2–10. Two or More Degrees of Freedom. When a body is able to move in two ways, two equations of motion are required to describe it. An example that is well known is the case of the trajectory of a projectile, and this may be found in many books on elementary mechanics. One equation describes the horizontal motion x of the body, another, incorporating a different system of forces, describes the height y at any time t. Another example may be found in Chapter 1 (page 24) in the analysis of the ball that both rolls and slips down a slope. One equation describes the linear motion of the center of gravity, the other the angular motion.

For complete representation in space, six equations are needed to describe any motion of any one rigid body. Three are normally of the form $\Sigma F = ma$ for the motion of the center of mass in the x, y, and z directions respectively, and the other three are concerned with torque about the three axes and the resulting rate of change of moment of momentum. As an alternative to the principle of momentum, the principle of energy is often used.

The number of degrees of freedom of any body is defined by the number of independent equations or independent variables that are needed to specify its motion.

Motion from Geometry

2–11. Motion in Linkages and Other Mechanisms. In order to find an equation of motion in many cases, the emphasis is found to bear upon the geometry of the case rather than upon the balance of real and inertia forces, of energy, or of momentum. This is particularly true when several members are joined to form a mechanism.

In most mechanisms, such as the cam and follower, the simple engine or slider-crank, and the four-bar chain, which will be taken up here, the

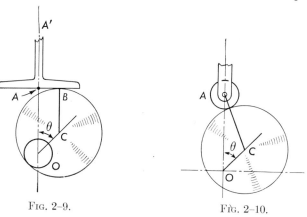

FIG. 2–9.   FIG. 2–10.

assumption is usually made that the driving shaft (it is generally a shaft) turns at a constant speed. On this basis, the acceleration of the various members may be ascertained; then the inertia effects may be found, and we can determine, for instance, the varying torque necessary to drive the mechanism by overcoming the reflected effects of this inertia.

The geometry of the figure and the desired acceleration may be found both by graphical means and by algebraic analysis. However, unfortunately, in all but the simplest mechanisms the algebra becomes very unwieldy; and for this reason the graphical method is usually adopted. This method is to be found well explained in many texts on the kinematics of mechanisms, and so it will be omitted here. Rather, it will be presumed that the reader has knowledge of this approach and has access to such books—further use of it will be made in Chapter 7.

We turn instead to probe the algebraic method although we have admitted it gets involved. But to what purpose? The great disadvantage of the geometrical as compared to the algebraic method lies in the assumptions necessary, such as the assumption already suggested that the driver runs at constant speed. If the inertia of the driven members is to reflect upon the driver, requiring of it a rapidly varying torque as it continues to drive, how can that driver maintain that constant speed, unless it has infinite mass? And if it fails to maintain the constant speed, the graphical analysis of accelerations, giving the reflected inertia effect, is wrong!

In most cases of machines, of course, the driver does maintain so nearly a constant speed that the graphical analysis is completely satisfactory. There are approximations to every analysis—for instance, it is generally overlooked that the members of a linkage are elastic.

But there are also an increasing number of applications where the driving mass is small, and the reflected inertia effects of great concern; analog computing mechanisms and automatic controls are two cases in point. For these either the algebraic method or a tedious series of trial-and-error graphical solutions is needed.

2–12. Circular Cam Motion. A cam of radius R is rotating about a point O (Fig. 2–9) which is eccentric from the geometrical center C of the cam by an amount e. The cam drives a flat-faced (mushroom) follower, with its face perpendicular to the line of its motion A–A'.

The point of contact B is always a point of tangency, and thus BC is parallel to AA'. Let the inclination of the line OC at the instant considered be θ. The height of A, the center of the follower's face, is always the same as B, and measured as h from the fixed point O it is

$$h = OC \cdot \cos \theta + BC = e \cdot \cos \theta + R$$

From its highest position the follower has thus moved downward:

$$x = (OC + CB) - h = e - e \cos \theta \qquad (2\text{--}21)$$

This is the geometrical relationship between the displacement of the follower and the angular displacement of the cam. If the angular velocity $d\theta/dt$ of the cam is constant and of value ω, the velocity of the follower is

$$\frac{dx}{dt} = e \sin \theta \left(\frac{d\theta}{dt}\right) = e\omega \sin \theta \qquad (2\text{--}22)$$

and its acceleration

$$\frac{d^2x}{dt^2} = e\omega \cos \theta \left(\frac{d\theta}{dt}\right) = e\omega^2 \cos \theta \qquad (2\text{--}23)$$

It therefore moves with simple harmonic motion, provided that neither the fluctuating reaction torques from the follower affect the constant speed drive, nor the circular shape of the cam bend the follower.

As a second problem, let us consider the same cam driving a roller follower of radius r (Fig. 2–10). The center of the roller A moves in a path in line with the center O of rotation of the cam.

The three points A, C, and the point of contact of the two circles are always collinear so that $AC = R + r$. Thus OCA is a triangle with angle $AOC = \theta$. The motion of A with respect to the fixed point O is therefore exactly the same as that of the slider crank mechanism, to be taken up in the next article, with $OC = e$ equivalent to the radius R of the crank throw and $AC = R + r$ equivalent to the length L of the connecting rod.

Other cams encountered in machines are of two classes. Either they are of a special shape designed to produce specific motion chosen by the designer, or else they are formed by "four arcs" of circles. The latter, which occur on automobile camshafts, may be analyzed by four successive equations* of the above type. Certain characteristics of the former type will be taken up in Chapter 9.

Example. Find the torque needed to drive the cam in Fig. 2–9 at constant speed. It is assumed that the follower weighs W lb; that contact is maintained by a compression spring of stiffness constant k, which at maximum rise of the follower exerts a force S; and that the coefficient of friction between cam and follower is f.

Suppose the normal contact force between the follower and the cam is F (which will be determined later). In Fig. 2–11a the angle θ is in the first quadrant, and the friction force fF on the cam is in the direction shown, so that the torque needed to turn the crankshaft is

$$T = fF(R + e \cos \theta) - Fe \sin \theta \qquad (2\text{--}24)$$

* See G. L. Guillet, *Kinematics of Machines* (New York: John Wiley & Sons, Inc.) in the 3rd or earlier editions (1st ed. 1928, pp. 94–103).

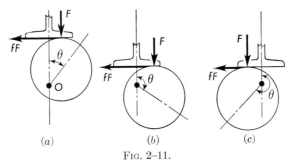

(a)   (b)   (c)

FIG. 2–11.

Friction opposes, and the normal force helps, the motion. We had better check this equation for later quadrants in case the signs change when the cam is raising the follower. In the second quadrant (Fig. 2–11b), as in all quadrants, friction opposes the rotation. The moment arm is still the height h, for cos θ is negative. Thus eq. 2–24 is valid for the second quadrant. In the third (Fig. 2–11c) both forces have a moment opposing rotation, but that of F is still $-Fe \sin \theta$, for sin θ is itself negative. Similarly in the fourth quadrant, and so the eq. 2–24 above is valid without change for the whole cycle.

Now the downward force F is the sum of the spring and inertia forces. The displacement x (eq. 2–21) is measured downward from the top: thus x is positive downward and when d^2x/dt^2 by eq. 2–23 is positive it also means it is downward. Remembering inertia is a reversed effective force, we have

$$F = (\text{Spring force}) + (\text{Weight}) - (\text{Inertia force})$$
$$= (S - kx) + W - (W/g)(d^2x/dt^2)$$
$$= S - k(e - e \cos \theta) + W - (W/g)e\omega^2 \cos \theta$$
$$= (S + W - ke) + (k - W\omega^2/g)e \cos \theta \qquad (2\text{--}25)$$

Substituting this value of F into eq. 2–24, the torque needed to drive the cam through any cycle is obtained.

2–13. The Slider-Crank or Simple Engine. The crank OB of radius R rotates about the fixed main bearing O (Fig. 2–12) with an angular velocity generally assumed constant. The connecting rod AB, of length L, joins the crank pin B to the wrist pin (piston pin) A in the piston. The line of motion of this point A, extended, passes through O.

Let the angle BOA through which the crank has turned since the piston was in its extended dead-center position be called θ, and the contemporary displacement of the point A be s. Then

$$s = (R + L) - \overline{AO}$$

If the angle of obliquity of the connecting rod be ϕ then

$$AO = R \cos \theta + L \cos \phi$$

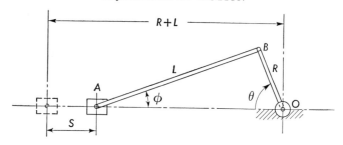

FIG. 2–12.

where ϕ is always related to θ by

$$L \sin \phi = R \sin \theta \tag{2-26}$$

Thus the equation of motion of the piston in terms of θ alone is

$$s = R + L - R \cos \theta - L \sqrt{1 - (R/L)^2 \sin^2 \theta} \tag{2-27}$$

The velocity and acceleration of the piston may be found by differentiating this, with $d\theta/dt = \omega$, a constant:

$$\frac{ds}{dt} = R\omega \left[\sin \theta + \tfrac{1}{2}(R/L)\frac{\sin 2\theta}{\sqrt{1 - (R/L)^2 \sin^2 \theta}} \right] \tag{2-28}$$

$$\frac{d^2 s}{dt^2} = R\omega^2 \left[\cos \theta + (R/L)\frac{\cos 2\theta}{(1 - (R/L)^2 \sin^2 \theta)^{1/2}} + \right.$$
$$\left. \tfrac{1}{4}(R/L)^3 \frac{\sin^2 2\theta}{(1 - (R/L)^2 \sin^2 \theta)^{3/2}} \right] \tag{2-29}$$

This applies to any such linkage, and to the cam follower mentioned in the preceding section. But it is an unpleasantly complicated equation, so we look for a way to simplify it, if possible. In most engines the ratio L/R is somewhat greater than 3, sometimes as high as 6. Thus even with the value 3, the terms with factor $(R/L)^2$ can amount to no more than 11 per cent of those without any such factor, those with $(R/L)^3$ cannot amount to quite 4 per cent, and this suggests expanding the radical in eq. 2–27 into polynomial series:

$$s = R(1 - \cos \theta) + L \left[1 - 1 + \frac{1}{2}\left(\frac{R}{L}\right)^2 \sin^2 \theta - \frac{1}{2 \cdot 4}\left(\frac{R}{L}\right)^4 \sin^4 \theta + \right.$$
$$\left. \frac{1 \cdot 3}{2 \cdot 4 \cdot 6}\left(\frac{R}{L}\right)^6 \sin^6 \theta - \cdots \right]$$

$$= R \left[1 - \cos \theta + \frac{1}{2}\frac{R}{L} \sin^2 \theta - \frac{1}{8}\left(\frac{R}{L}\right)^3 \sin^4 \theta + \cdots \right] \tag{2-30}$$

$$\frac{ds}{dt} = R\omega \left[\sin \theta + \frac{1}{2}\frac{R}{L} \sin 2\theta - \frac{1}{4}\left(\frac{R}{L}\right)^3 \sin^2 \theta \sin 2\theta + \cdots \right] \tag{2-31}$$

$$\frac{d^2s}{dt^2} = R\omega^2 \left[\cos \theta + \frac{R}{L} \cos 2\theta - \cdots \right] \tag{2-32}$$

Only two terms are generally significant in velocity and acceleration, and these are much more manageable equations.

Now whereas we shall have occasion to use these formulae again in Chapters 7 and 8, if it is desired to find the acceleration of any point other than A and B in this mechanism, recourse is generally made to the graphical methods available.

One other item may be mentioned concerning the slider-crank, that the angular velocity of the connecting rod at any time is found in the derivative of eq. 2–26 or

$$\frac{d\phi}{dt} = \frac{R \cos \theta}{L \cos \phi} \left(\frac{d\theta}{dt} \right) = \left(\frac{R}{L} \right) \omega \cos \theta \left[1 - \left(\frac{R}{L} \right)^2 \sin^2 \theta \right]^{-1/2} \tag{2-33}$$

2–14. The Four-Bar Linkage (Quadric Chain). We will determine an equation for the angular velocity of the driven crank BP for any angular velocity of the driving crank AO of the four-bar linkage shown in Fig. 2–13. The driving crank is taken to be of unit length, and the lengths of the other members are referred to that unit length.

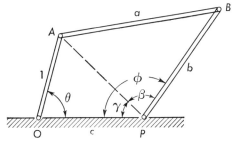

FIG. 2–13.

Let $AB = a$, $BP = b$, OP (fixed) $= c$. Let the angle AOP be θ, and the angular velocity of this driver is then $d\theta/dt$, which may be written θ'.

The variable distance AP is taken as x, which by the geometry is governed by

$$x^2 = 1 + c^2 - 2c \cos \theta \tag{2-34}$$

The interior angle ϕ of the driven crank is divided by this line into β and γ where

$$x \sin \gamma = \sin \theta$$
$$x \cos \gamma = c - \cos \theta \tag{2-35}$$

and

$$a^2 = b^2 + x^2 - 2bx \cos \beta \tag{2-36}$$

Thus the position of the driven crank is

$$\phi = \beta + \gamma$$

$$\phi = \sin^{-1}\left(\frac{\sin \theta}{x}\right) + \cos^{-1}\left(\frac{b^2 + x^2 - a^2}{2bx}\right)$$

and its angular velocity is found by differentiation

$$\frac{d\phi}{dt} = \phi' = \frac{\cos \theta \cdot \theta' - (\sin \theta/x)x'}{c - \cos \theta} - \frac{(a^2 - b^2 + x^2)x'}{x \sqrt{4b^2x^2 - (a^2 - b^2 - x^2)^2}}$$

Substitution of $x' = dx/dt$ follows, for by differentiating eq. 2–34

$$xx' = c \sin \theta \cdot \theta' \qquad (2\text{–}37)$$

$$\phi' = -\theta'\left\{\frac{1 - c \cos \theta}{x^2} + \frac{[1 + (a^2 - b^2)/x^2]c \sin \theta}{\sqrt{4b^2x^2 - (a^2 - b^2 - x^2)^2}}\right\} \qquad (2\text{–}38)$$

And substitution for x^2 from eq. 2–34 for those remaining terms completes the task.

APPENDIX

The Solution of Certain Differential Equations

Separable Type. If

$$F(y)\frac{dy}{dx} = f(x)$$

where $F(y)$ represents any function of y (which may include y^2, y^n, $\sin y$, e^y, etc.) and $f(x)$ represents any function of x, then

$$\int F \cdot dy = \int f \cdot dx \qquad (2\text{–}39)$$

which may be integrated.

Example. Suppose

$$I\frac{d\omega}{dt} = Wr + at + bt^2$$

The variable ω corresponds to y, and t to x; $F(y)$ is merely the constant I; W, r, a, b are other constants. Then

$$\int I \, d\omega = \int (Wr + at + bt^2)dt$$
$$I\omega = Wrt + \tfrac{1}{2}at^2 + \tfrac{1}{3}bt^3 + (\text{const})$$

Separable Type Involving Reciprocals. If

$$F(x)\frac{dy}{dx} = f(y)$$

then

$$\int \frac{dy}{f(y)} = \int \frac{dx}{F(x)} \qquad (2\text{–}40)$$

Example. Suppose

$$(a + bs)v\frac{dv}{ds} = k(1 + cv^2)$$

then

$$\int \frac{v\,dv}{1 + cv^2} = k\int \frac{ds}{a + bs}$$

$$\frac{1}{2c}\log_e (1 + cv^2) = \frac{k}{b}\log_e (a + bs) + (\text{const})$$

With the constant as $\log_e d$, this becomes

$$(1 + cv^2)^{\frac{1}{2c}} = d(a + bs)^{k/b}$$

Containing Squares of First-Order Derivative. The square root of such an equation can sometimes be taken, or it may be treated as a quadratic in dy/dx, and the resulting simpler equations may be soluble by simple methods. See also eq. 2–45.

Example. Suppose

$$(a + bt)\left(\frac{ds}{dt}\right)^2 = f + ks^2$$

then

$$\int \frac{ds}{\sqrt{f + ks^2}} = \int \frac{dt}{\sqrt{a + bt}}$$

by taking the square root.

Second-Order Differential Equation (i.e., containing second derivatives as highest) Containing No Function of the Dependent Variable. If

$$\frac{d^2y}{dx^2} + f(x)\left(\frac{dy}{dx}\right)^n + F(x) = 0 \qquad (2\text{--}41)$$

substitution of the derivative $dy/dx = u$, in which case $d^2y/dx^2 = du/dx$, will reduce the order of the equation. But there must be no term in y.

Example. Suppose

$$\frac{d^2y/dx^2}{1 + (dy/dx)^2} = a + bx$$

Let $dy/dx = \theta$ then

$$\frac{d\theta}{dx} = (a + bx)(1 + \theta^2)$$

which is of the separable type, soluble for θ. This type also arises where relations of velocity and acceleration, deduced from a problem, are written in terms of ds/dt and d^2s/dt^2 when they are more easily written as v and dv/dt, provided no terms in displacement are present.

The Simple Harmonic Equation. If

$$a\frac{d^2x}{dt^2} + bx = 0$$

where a and b are both positive constants. Divide by a, and set $b/a = \omega^2$, to obtain

$$\frac{d^2x}{dt^2} + \omega^2 x = 0 \qquad (2\text{–}42)$$

Multiply both sides by $2\frac{dx}{dt}$, for it is observed that

$$\frac{d}{dt}(x^2) = 2x\frac{dx}{dt} \qquad (2\text{–}43)$$

and

$$\frac{d}{dt}\left[\left(\frac{dx}{dt}\right)^2\right] = 2\frac{dx}{dt}\cdot\frac{d^2x}{dt^2} \qquad (2\text{–}44)$$

and so integrate

$$2\frac{dx}{dt}\frac{d^2x}{dt^2} = -2\omega^2 x\frac{dx}{dt}$$

$$\left(\frac{dx}{dt}\right)^2 = (\text{const}) - \omega^2 x^2 \qquad (2\text{–}45)$$

Let the constant be a^2; it must be positive if dx/dt is to be real, and therefore we may write it as a square. Then

$$\frac{dx}{dt} = \sqrt{a^2 - \omega^2 x^2}$$

This is now separable:

$$\int dt = \int \frac{dx}{\sqrt{a^2 - \omega^2 x^2}}$$

And this may be solved by reference to some tables, or by the trigonometric substitution

$$\omega x = a \sin\theta$$

whence

$$\omega\cdot dx = a\cos\theta\,d\theta$$

$$t = \int \frac{(a/\omega)\cos\theta\,d\theta}{\sqrt{a^2 - a^2\sin^2\theta}} = \frac{1}{\omega}\int d\theta$$

$$\omega t + \phi = \theta$$

where ϕ is the new (second) arbitrary constant. Transposing to x

$$x = A\sin(\omega t + \phi) \qquad (2\text{–}46)$$

$$x = A_1 \sin\omega t + A_2 \cos\omega t \qquad (2\text{–}47)$$

where A is arbitrary, replacing and equal to a/ω, and A_1 and A_2 may be found from the expansion of eq. 2–46 by the formula $\sin(\alpha + \beta) = \sin\alpha\cos\beta + \cos\alpha\sin\beta$.

Simple Harmonic Equation with a Constant. The simple harmonic equation sometimes has a constant instead of zero on the right-hand side. This can be reduced to the standard form by a simple substitution, which is effectively a change in one coordinate.

$$a \frac{d^2x}{dt^2} + bx = c \tag{2-48}$$

$$\frac{d^2x}{dt^2} + \frac{b}{a}\left(x - \frac{c}{b}\right) = 0$$

Let

$$x - \frac{c}{b} = y$$

then

$$\frac{dx}{dt} = \frac{dy}{dt}, \text{ and also } \frac{d^2x}{dt^2} = \frac{d^2y}{dt^2}$$

Substitute:

$$\frac{d^2y}{dt^2} + \frac{b}{a} y = 0$$

This is now in the standard form of eq. 2–42 and may be solved for y by the previous method.

Hyperbolic Type. This is

$$a \frac{d^2x}{dt^2} - bx = 0 \tag{2-49}$$

where again a and b are both positive constants. Note that we have exactly the same as the simple harmonic type (eq. 2–42) except for the negative sign. Comparing the solution of this type, however, let us write

$$p^2 = -\frac{b}{a} = -\omega^2$$

and obtain

$$\frac{d^2x}{dt^2} + p^2x = 0$$

This is the simple harmonic type, although it includes a factor p which is an imaginary quantity involving $\sqrt{-1} = i$.

The solution must follow the preceding, so that

$$x = A_1 \sin pt + A_2 \cos pt$$

$$x = A_1 \sin i \sqrt{\frac{b}{a}}t + A_2 \cos i \sqrt{\frac{b}{a}}t$$

The meaning of trigonometric functions with imaginary arguments is seen by the identities

$$\sin iy = i \sinh y$$
$$\cos iy = \cosh y$$

where sinh and cosh are the hyperbolic sine and cosine functions. So

$$x = A \sinh \sqrt{\frac{b}{a}}t + B \cosh \sqrt{\frac{b}{a}}t \tag{2-50}$$

These hyperbolic functions have their values tabulated in some reference manuals* and are used just like trigonometric functions.

The hyperbolic type equation, as eq. 2–49, sometimes has a constant on the right-hand side. The procedure is exactly the same as for the simple harmonic type; the equation is reduced to standard form by a linear substitution of the form

$$y = x - x_0$$

Linear Differential Equation, Second Order, with Constant Coefficients. This is the broad type:

$$A \frac{d^2y}{dx^2} + B \frac{dy}{dx} + Cy = 0 \tag{2–51}$$

when A, B, C are any constants, positive or negative.

There is a standard substitution which solves all of this type. We assume the solution to be of the general form:

$$y = ce^{\lambda x}$$

where λ is to be found, and c is the constant of integration. Then if the above is true

$$\frac{dy}{dx} = c\lambda e^{\lambda x}$$

$$\frac{d^2y}{dx^2} = c\lambda^2 e^{\lambda x}$$

Substitute:

$$[A\lambda^2 + B\lambda + C]ce^{\lambda x} = 0$$

Now since neither c nor $e^{\lambda x}$ can be zero, we obtain what is called the "characteristic equation" or the "auxiliary equation"

$$A\lambda^2 + B\lambda + C = 0$$

and this may be solved to obtain λ.

$$\lambda = -\frac{B}{2A} \pm \sqrt{\frac{B^2}{4A^2} - \frac{C}{A}}$$

These are therefore two values of λ which will satisfy; suppose they are λ_1, λ_2. Both of the following are then solutions:

$$y = c_1 e^{\lambda_1 x}$$
$$y = c_2 e^{\lambda_2 x}$$

But since the original equation was of second order, which requires two integrations, two arbitrary constants of integration must arise in obtaining an equation in x. The general solution then must be

$$y = c_1 e^{\lambda_1 x} + c_2 e^{\lambda_2 x} \tag{2–52}$$

* L. S. Marks (ed.), *Mechanical Engineers' Handbook* (New York: McGraw-Hill Book Co., Inc.); B. O. Peirce, *Short Table of Integrals* (Boston: Ginn & Co.); R. S. Burington, *Handbook of Math. Tables and Formulas* (Sandusky, Ohio: Handbook Publishers, Inc.).

This may be checked by substitution, if desired. *Note*: The equations which we have called the simple harmonic and the hyperbolic types of course belong to this general family, and they may be solved by this method as well as by that already shown.

To convert the exponential form of solution into the trigonometric or hyperbolic forms, the following relations should be remembered, which are known as Euler's formulas:

$$\left.\begin{aligned}
e^{ix} &= \cos x + i \sin x \\
e^{-ix} &= \cos x - i \sin x \\
e^{x} &= \cosh x + \sinh x \\
e^{-x} &= \cosh x - \sinh x
\end{aligned}\right\} \qquad (2\text{-}53)$$

For examples of this type, turn to Chapter 5.

General Linear Differential Equation of Second Order, with Constant Coefficients. This type

$$A \frac{d^2y}{dx^2} + B \frac{dy}{dx} + Cy = f(x) \qquad (2\text{-}54)$$

where A, B, C are constants and $f(x)$ is any function of x, is solved in two stages.

First we take the left-hand side and set it equal to zero. We then have what is called the "homogeneous" equation, and its solution is of course eq. 2–52 as just found.

In this connection it is important to observe that if we substitute this solution (eq. 2–52), which is named the "complementary function," into eq. 2–54, from

$$y = c_1 e^{\lambda_1 x} + c_2 e^{\lambda_2 x} \qquad (2\text{-}52)$$

of course we get only

$$A \frac{d^2y}{dx^2} + B \frac{dy}{dx} + Cy = 0$$

but eq. 2–52 does contain two arbitrary constants, and since eq. 2–54 needs only two integrations, two such constants are sufficient.

But eq. 2–52 is not enough. Suppose we add some other function of x, say $g(x)$ (which we will have to try to find later), and presume that the proper solution is

$$y = c_1 e^{\lambda_1 x} + c_2 e^{\lambda_2 x} + g \qquad (2\text{-}55)$$

and substitute this in eq. 2-54. We get from the first two items only zero on each side, or for the three items

$$0 + A \frac{d^2g}{dx^2} + B \frac{dg}{dx} + Cg = 0 + f(x)$$

Perhaps it does not appear that this equation is any better than the first, for it merely has g where y was before. Yet it is better, for it will show an equality for any function g at all that can satisfy eq. 2–54, and arbitrary constants of integration are not involved.

The search for this function $g(x)$, which is called the "particular integral," comprises the second part of the solution. It is usually found more or less by guessing, using such guide posts as are available (from those who have searched the country before). The complete solution will be eq. 2–55, which can be expressed as

$$y = [\text{Complementary function (eq. 2–52)}] + [\text{Particular integral}]$$

Particular Integrals. Certain types of the function $f(x)$ in eq. 2–54 occur with greater frequency.

(i) If $f(x)$ is a constant d, the particular integral is obviously $y = d/C$, for all the derivatives vanish.

(ii) If $f(x)$ is a polynomial, say $p + qx + rx^2 + sx^3$, then the particular integral must also be a polynomial of the same degree. For the derivatives will all be polynomials, each of one less degree, and thus whatever is the highest degree in $f(x)$ must also occur in the term y.

Example.

$$m\,\frac{d^2y}{dx^2} + 5n\,\frac{dy}{dx} + 6y = 1 + 3px + qx^3$$

Suppose

$$y = g(x) = a + bx + cx^2 + dx^3$$

is a particular integral. Then

$$dy/dx = b + 2cx + 3dx^2$$
$$d^2y/dx^2 = 2c + 6dx$$

Substitute:

$$2m(c + 3dx) + 5n(b + 2cx + 3dx^2) + 6(a + bx + cx^2 + dx^3) =$$
$$1 + 3px + qx^3$$

This must be true for all values of x, and thus the coefficients in each degree must be equal

(for x^3)	$6d = q$	or	$d = q/6$
(for x^2)	$15nd + 6c = 0$	or	$c = -(5/2)nd$
(for x^1)	$6md + 10nc + 6b = 3p$		whence b
(for x^0)	$2mc + 5nb + 6a = 1$		whence a

(iii) If $f(x)$ is of the form $k_1 e^{mx}$, the particular integral must be of the form $k_2 e^{mx}$, where k_2 is some constant determinable by substitution. Since all the differential coefficients will be multiples of e^{mx}, it is obvious that this will satisfy.

(iv) If $f(x)$ is of the form

$$P \sin nx + Q \cos nx$$

where the two n's are the same constant, and P and Q are any constants (including either as zero), the particular integral is of the form

$$y = g(x) = R \sin nx + S \cos nx$$

All the derivatives of this expression are multiples of either sin nx or cos nx, and therefore substitution of this into eq. 2–54 can only give two independent algebraic equations in the coefficients of the sine terms and of the cosine terms.

For an example of this, see page 201.

BIBLIOGRAPHY

On setting up equations:

OLDENBURGER, R. *Mathematical Engineering Analysis*. New York: The Macmillan Co., 1950, Chaps. 1 and 2.

On the algebraic analysis of linkages:

TALBOURDET, G. "Mathematical Solution of 4-Bar Linkages," *Machine Design*, May, 1941, p. 65; June, 1941, p. 81; July, 1941, p. 73.

SVOBODA, A. *Computing Mechanisms and Linkages*. ("MIT Radiation Laboratory Series," Vol. 27.) New York: McGraw-Hill Book Co., Inc., 1948.

PROBLEMS

2–1. A stone falls in the still water of a deep lake. The water friction is proportional to both pressure and velocity. Write the differential equation for its motion (acceleration).

2–2. A bob on the end of a string swings as a pendulum in a vacuum (i.e., no friction, so constant energy).

    a) Write the equation for the angular acceleration of the string in terms of θ, its angle with the vertical.

    b) Write the condition for conservation of energy in terms of θ and angular velocity.

    c) Differentiate (b) to get (a).

2–3. Fig. 1–24 shows a mass M guided to slide without friction on a fixed horizontal guide rod AB and acted upon by a spring stretched between M and a fixed pin O. The perpendicular distance AO is P, and this is also the free (unstretched) length of the spring. The spring constant is k. Write the differential equation for the sliding motion of M (a) in terms of the displacement x from the normal point A, (b) in terms of the angle θ between the spring and the normal.

2–4. Write the differential equation of motion of a snowball which rolls up a constant thickness of snow as it rolls down a hill of slope θ. Assume the "ball" to be a spirally wound cylinder, like a rolled carpet.

2–5. A cylinder of radius ρ forms a drum upon which is wound a length of (massless) inextensible rope. From the free end of the rope hangs a weight W. The cylindrical drum is integral with a gear A, radius R, which is in mesh with pinion B, radius r. Both A and B rotate on horizontal fixed axes. The moment of inertia of pinion B is I_B, and of gear A and drum together is I_A. Find the velocity of weight W after it has been released from rest for t seconds.

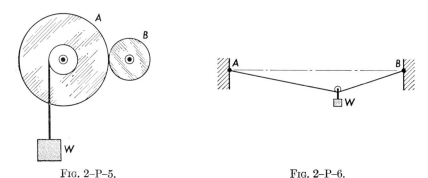

Fig. 2–P–5.   Fig. 2–P–6.

2-6. A weight W hangs from a pulley of negligible diameter which is free to run upon, and hangs upon, a rope held by two pins A and B, as in the figure. The pins are at the same height from the ground and 6 ft apart. The rope is of 78 in. length, and weightless.

If the pulley is released when 19.5 in. horizontally from the center, find its absolute velocity in terms of its position.

2-7. A particle of weight w is projected vertically upward with initial velocity u. The air resistance is given by kwv/u where k is a constant and v the instantaneous velocity. Show that the highest point of the trajectory is

$$H = \frac{u^2}{kg}\left[1 - \frac{\log(1 + k)}{k}\right]$$

And further show that, if T is the time required to reach this highest point, at time $2T$ after the time of projection, the height of the particle is $(2/3)kH$ approximately, provided k is very small.

2-8. A wire rope supported by its ends hangs in the usual catenary shape, which may be represented by the equation

$$y = c \cosh (x/c)$$

A small pulley, to be treated as a cylindrical roller of mass m and radius r, hangs on the rope. Its weight is small enough so that it does not affect the catenary. If the roller is initially stationary at $x = 2c$, find its velocity in terms of any subsequent x.

2-9. The force propelling a particle away from a fixed point P is given by $F_0 - kt$ where F_0 and k are constants, and t is the time that has elapsed since the particle of mass m was stationary at P. Write the equation for the distance of the particle from P at any time t, and find when it returns to P, and with what velocity.

2-10. A straight tube of uniform bore is rotating in a horizontal plane about a vertical axis through its center O with uniform angular velocity Ω. A small particle of mass m is free to slide in the tube, the coefficient of friction between it and the tube being μ.

If at a time t the particle is at a radius r from the center of the tube, show that, neglecting gravity forces, its motion is given by the equation

$$\frac{d^2r}{dt^2} + 2\mu\Omega\frac{dr}{dt} - \Omega^2 r = 0$$

Hence show that, if the length of the tube is $2a$, μ is 0.75, and the particle is projected into the end of the tube with a relative velocity v, the particle will reach the center only if v is greater than $2a\Omega$. (C.U.)

2–11. Draw some of the following curves, and describe their meaning in physical terms if x and y are displacement, v velocity, and t time.

a) $v = v_0(1 - e^{-kx})$ for v vs. x
b) $x = Ae^{-kt}$ for x vs. t with $A = 2$ in., $k = 3$ rad/sec
c) $y = 4\cos\omega t + 3\sin\omega t$ for y vs. ωt
d) $x = 5e^{-3t}\cos 10t$ for x vs. t
e) $y = 5\cos\omega t \cos 10\,\omega t$ for y vs. ωt

2–12. If $x = Ae^{-kt}$, write the acceleration $\ddot{x}$ $(= d^2x/dt^2)$ in terms of x.

2–13. If $y = A\sin(6t + \phi)$ gives the displacement of a body of mass m after any time elapse t, write the equation for its kinetic energy in terms of y, eliminating t and ϕ.

2–14. Solve the following equations mathematically:

a) $y\dfrac{dy}{dt} = (y^2 - 25)^2$ c) $\dfrac{dz}{dt} = 100 - 4z$

b) $\left(\dfrac{dx}{dt}\right)^2 + 16x^2 = 64$ d) $\dfrac{d^2x}{dt^2} = 25x - 3$

2–15. A solid disk wheel of radius r and weight W carries a small weight w attached to it eccentrically at radius a. The wheel is set upon a plane inclined at angle ϕ to the horizontal, and rolls directly down this hill along the line of greatest slope. The plane is perfectly rough, so that only rolling can occur.

a) Show that rolling will start down the slope from any position of rest, provided that $a < \left(\dfrac{W + w}{w}\right)r\sin\phi$.

b) Derive the differential equation of the motion of the center of the wheel, if the wheel starts to roll from rest on the slope with the weight w vertically below the center. Assume that the requirement (a) is fulfilled. Sketch a curve showing the displacement as a function of time.

2–16. An attraction at a carnival consists of a "light-house" tower with a spiral chute down which a boy may slide sitting on a mat. The chute has a uniform slope and drops 45 ft in three complete turns at a constant radius of 20 ft from the vertical centerline of the tower. If the chute is waxed sufficiently on its bottom surface so that friction there is negligible, but the side wall has a coefficient of friction of 0.20 with the boy's hips and shoulder, (a) find the equation of motion in terms of the velocity v at an angle θ from the top, if the initial velocity was zero; (b) find the velocity of the boy emerging at the bottom.

2-17. A particle moves in a horizontal straight line under a retardation (deceleration) kv^{m+1} where v is the speed at time t; k and m are constants. Show that if u is the velocity at time $t = 0$

$$kt = \frac{1}{m}\left[\frac{1}{v^m} - \frac{1}{u^m}\right]$$

and obtain an expression for the distance moved in terms of velocity v.

A bullet fired horizontally with a velocity of 2400 ft/sec is traveling with a velocity of 1500 ft/sec at the end of one second. Assuming that $m = 0.5$, calculate k and find the distance traversed in the first second, if the effect of gravity is ignored.   (U.L.)

2-18. Obtain the expression

$$\rho = \frac{\left[1 + \left(\frac{dy}{dx}\right)^2\right]^{3/2}}{\dfrac{d^2y}{dx^2}}$$

for the radius of curvature at a point of the curve $y = f(x)$.

2-19. A uniform rod of length L and weight W has a hole transversely through it at one end, by which it is supported when hanging from a horizontal shaft. The fit of the hole upon the shaft is such that when the shaft rotates a constant torque T is applied to the rod.

The rod initially hangs vertically, the shaft being stationary. Then the shaft is suddenly given a fast angular velocity which continues indefinitely. Find the minimum value of T necessary if the rod rotates in a vertical plane about the shaft axis.

2-20. Four equal uniform rods, each of mass m and length a, are freely hinged together at their ends to form a lozenge as shown in the figure. The hinge A is suspended from a fixed point, and a weight of mass $2m$ is attached to the hinge C. The weight is raised vertically until the hinges A and C are in contact, the rods being then horizontal; then it is released. Obtain an expression for the velocity of the weight in terms of the angle θ which each rod makes with the horizontal at any instant, and show that it reaches a maximum when $\cos \theta = 1/\sqrt{3}$.   (C.U.)

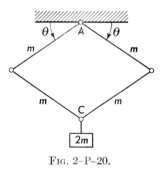

Fig. 2–P–20.

2-21. A golf ball rolls across a green with a velocity v straight toward the hole. If the velocity is great, of course the ball will hit the opposite edge and continue beyond the hole. If the ball has mass m and radius a, while the hole has radius c, show that in order to score, the velocity of arrival at the near edge is given by v in

$$\left[v\left(\frac{5}{7} + \sin\theta\right) - \frac{2gc}{v}\cos\theta\right]^2 < \frac{24}{7}\,ag\,(1 - \sin\theta)$$

where θ is given by arc $\sin\left(1 - \dfrac{2gc^2}{av^2}\right)$. Assume that the edge of the hole and the ball are inelastic, and that there is no slipping upon impact.   (C.U.)

2–22. A simple pendulum has a bob of mass m supported by a light string of length L. A horizontal impulse H is applied to the bob. If the tension in the string is not to exceed twice the weight of the bob, find the greatest allowable value of H, and find the maximum angular deflection in the ensuing motion when H has this value. (U.L.)

2–23. Two gear wheels, one having 20 teeth and a moment of inertia of 20 lb ft², and the other 60 teeth and a moment of inertia of 48 lb ft², are in mesh. The larger gear is driven by a light spiral spring which exerts a torque of 0.2θ lb ft when twisted through an angle of θ rad. If the spring is wound up through 12 complete turns and then released, find:

   a) the maximum angular velocity of the smaller wheel;
   b) the time taken for the spring to unwind its 12 turns;
   c) the time taken for the spring to unwind the first two turns;
   d) the number of turns the spring unwinds in half the time for part (b).

2–24. A rope of weight w lb per foot length, and of a length $(L + l)$ ft, but of negligible thickness, is wound upon a cylindrical drum that is free to rotate about a horizontal axis. The drum has a moment of inertia I about its axis and is of radius r. There is no overlapping of the coiled rope. If initially a short length l of the rope hangs stationary from the drum, which is then released so that the rope starts to unwind, find the time for the whole length of rope to unwind. (Assume that the tail end of the rope remains in contact with the drum until the last moment without flipping out).

Then if $L = 9.068$ ft, $l = 1$ ft, $w = 2$ lb/ft, $r = 1.5$ ft, and $I = 3$ lb ft sec², find the time in seconds.

2–25. A light plane sheet of metal AB is pivoted along the horizontal edge A and supported vertically at its edge B by a spring of stiffness $k = 2$ lb/in., $AB = 6$ ft. A weight W of 10 lb is then placed gently upon the sheet at distance $x = 1$ ft from A, until equilibrium is established, and then W is released. Find its velocity as it passes the edge B, all friction being neglected.

Explain whether this result is high or low since the mass of the sheet AB is not considered.

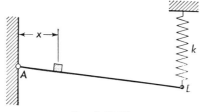

Fig. 2–P–25.

2–26. A wheel of radius R, weight W, and moment of inertia $WR^2/2$ carries an eccentric weight w at radius a inside the rim. The wheel is set upon a horizontal plane with w vertically above the center, which is then given a velocity v horizontally.

a) Write the equation of motion of the center; sketch graphs of both the velocity and displacement of the center against time, neglecting friction.

b) Sketch the velocity curve of the wheel on the horizontal path if friction is active. Identify any marked changes in form with physical facts.

2–27. A platform is supported by a pair of crossed bars AB and CD hinged together at their middle points, as in the figure. It is raised by a horizontal force applied at C, with the point A fixed. The mass of the platform is M. Each bar has a mass m, an effective length $2a$, and a moment of inertia $ma^2/3$ about its center of gravity, which coincides with the center of the hinge. The travel of the platform is limited by stops (not shown) at the positions in which the bars make angles of 30° and 60° with the horizontal. Friction can be neglected.

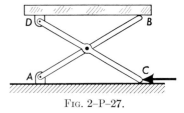

Fig. 2–P–27.

When the platform is in its lowest position, a steady force is applied which is just sufficient to set it in motion. Show that the platform will reach the highest position with a velocity

$$\sqrt{\frac{(2 - \sqrt{3})(M + m)ga}{\dfrac{M}{4} + \dfrac{2m}{3}}}$$

(C.U.)

2–28. The linkage shown in the figure consists of $2n$ equal, uniform bars of length a, pin-jointed at their ends and middle points in the manner shown. The joint A is fixed, and B slides along the vertical through A. Neglecting all friction, show that, if initially at rest in the position $\theta = \alpha$ and allowed to fall freely under the action of gravity, the nth middle joint will acquire a horizontal component of velocity u_n given by

$$u_n = \frac{2n - 1}{2} \sqrt{\frac{3ga(\cos \alpha - \cos \theta)}{n^2 + \tan^2 \theta}}$$

Given that

$$\sum_{r = 1}^{r = n}(2r - 1)^2 = \frac{1}{3} n(4n^2 - 1)$$

(C.U.)

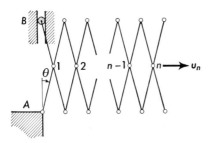

Fig. 2–P–28.

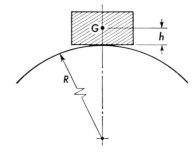

Fig. 2–P–29.

2-29. A rectangular box is balanced upon the top of a fixed cylinder of radius R. The center of gravity G of the box is of height h above the contact point (see the figure). Show that the box is in stable equilibrium in this position provided that h is less than R.

2-30. Find the required value of k for any position of stability to exist in the system shown in the figure. The spring, of stiffness k and under tension W when $\theta = 0$, is attached at radius a to the cylindrical drum. The drum, which has a radius r and is free to rotate about the fixed horizontal axis A, carries wound around it a light string by which hangs weight W. Distance AB can be taken to be very long compared with radius a.

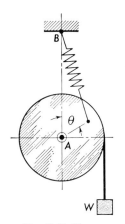

FIG. 2-P-30.

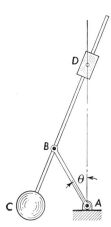

FIG. 2-P-31.

2-31. A Schlick pendulum consists of a light rod AB which supports a rod CD by the pin at B. The rod carries at C a ball of mass m and is free to slide through a pivoted sleeve at D, shown in the figure. D is vertically above the fixed pin A, and AB makes an angle θ with the vertical.

If $AB = r$, $AD = h$, and $BC = l$, show that the linkage is in stable equilibrium in the position $\theta = 0$ provided

$$rl > (h - r)^2$$

2-32. Four balls are arranged in a pyramid, three touching each other and the ground, the fourth on top. Find the minimum coefficient of friction for which they remain still.

2-33. An electric switch is simplified to show a light rod AB of length 4 in. carrying a mass B of weight 3 lb, and freely pivoted at A. At the mid-point C($AC = 2$ in.) is attached a spring CD of

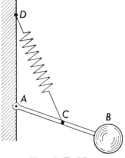

FIG. 2-P-33.

stiffness k. $AD = 2$ in. When the angle DAC is 90°, the spring exerts no force. Find the value of k for a position of stable equilibrium with angle $DAC = 135$°, if D is vertically above A.

If AB is held horizontally and released, will it then pass the lowest position and reach the other side under the influence of gravity?

2–34. A moving-picture projection screen is 0.05 in. thick and is rolled up upon a cylindrical spool of diameter 1 in. The screen is 12 ft long, and is of such width that it weighs 1 lb per foot of length. As it is unrolled from the spool, a torsion spring increases the retracting torque from its minimum of 4 lb in. by $\frac{1}{8}$ lb in. per turn of the spool. It may be assumed that the screen rolls upon the spool spirally (not stepwise) so that when N turns are upon the spool the radius is $0.5 + 0.05N$ in.

a) Investigate the equilibrium of the partially unwound screen hanging from the spool.

b) If, when fully pulled down, the screen is released, will it roll up completely?

c) Redesign the spring.

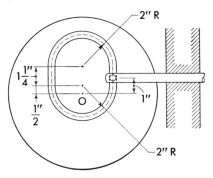

FIG. 2–P–35.

2–35. A face cam consists of a circular plate in which a groove has been cut to the dimensions shown in the figure. The center of rotation of the plate is at O. The slide follower is operated by a roller which fits closely in the groove. If the cam rotates at the constant speed of 250 rpm, find the velocity of the follower when the cam has turned 45° clockwise from the position illustrated. Thence, with the moment of inertia of the cam as 35 lb in.² and the weight of the follower assembly as 2 lb, write the total kinetic energy of the mechanism.

2–36. Solve the above for some position other than 45°.

2–37. A cam consisting of a circular disk of radius r in. is mounted eccentrically on a horizontal shaft, the distance between the axis of the shaft and the center of the disk being a in. The cam rotates at a uniform speed and actuates a follower which has a horizontal flat face so guided that its movement is vertical. The follower is kept in contact with the cam by a spring which exerts a force of k lb per in. movement of the follower and is unstrained when the follower is in its lowest position. If the moving parts of the follower have a mass of M lb, show that the greatest angular velocity ω of the cam consistent with the follower always remaining in contact with the cam is given by

$$\omega^2 = \frac{(M + 2ak)g}{Ma}$$

Also show that if the cam is rotated at this velocity, then the work done against friction per revolution of the cam is $\pi \mu g[M + ka][2r - a]$, where μ is the coefficient of friction between the cam and the follower, and friction elsewhere is neglected.

(C.U.)

2–38. A lever, shown diagrammatically in the figure, swings in a vertical plane through 5° above and 5° below the horizontal. It is actuated by a cam with a circular profile which slides on the flat palm of the lever. The radius of gyration of the lever about its mass center is 2 in.

Find (a) the maximum normal reaction between the lever and the cam when the latter rotates at 100 rpm; and (b) the greatest possible speed of the cam shaft for contact between cam and lever to be unbroken. (U.L.)

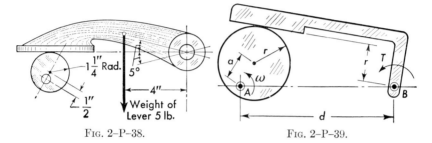

FIG. 2–P–38.   FIG. 2–P–39.

2–39. The figure shows a rocker which is caused to oscillate about the axis B by an eccentric cam, with radius r and eccentricity a, rotating about A with constant angular velocity ω. The moment of inertia about B of the rocker and parts attached to it is I, and it is kept in contact with the cam by a constant torque T applied as shown. The coefficient of friction between cam and rocker is μ.

Find the greatest angular velocity of the rocker and, neglecting its weight, show that when it is in its upper extreme position the normal pressure between the cam and the rocker is

$$\frac{T\sqrt{d^2 - a^2} - Ia\omega^2}{d^2 - a^2 - \mu r\sqrt{d^2 - a^2}}$$

(C.U.)

2–40. The Oldham coupling can be converted to give a two-to-one velocity ratio if it is designed as in the figure. The driving crank ABC rotates about center B with $AB = BC = r$. The driven member is a disk with two rectangular grooves cut in the face, crossing at the center D, about which it may rotate. Two slides in these grooves are held by pins to points A and C. Distance BD between the parallel axes of rotation equals r.

Prove whether the driven shaft through D turns at a constant speed, or only averages half the speed of rotation of the driving crank. Assume a constant speed of the driver.

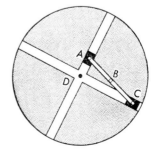

FIG. 2–P–40.

2–41. The figure shows the mechanism of part of a mechanical computer. The driving shaft A rotates at constant speed ω_A in the direction shown. Two balls B are contained, but perfectly free to turn, within a cylindrical case, the position of which is governed by the arm C. The two balls maintain a good friction contact with the shaft D, of diameter d. Turning of disk A therefore necessitates the shaft being driven (if $r \neq 0$). The centerlines of A and D intersect.

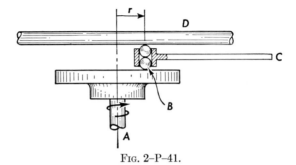

Fig. 2–P–41.

The radius r at which C holds the balls is also governed (through a mechanism not shown) by the angle θ turned by shaft A. Suppose the radius instantaneously is given by

$$r = A \sin \theta$$

Write an equation for the angle ϕ turned by shaft D in terms of θ, and in terms of t, assuming $t = 0$ when $\theta = 0$.

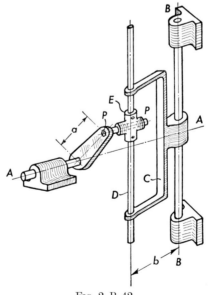

Fig. 2–P–42.

2–42. A crank of radius a rotates with constant angular velocity ω about an axis AA, which intersects a second axis BB at right angles (see the figure). On the axis BB is mounted a forked arm C carrying a rod D, free to slide parallel to BB at a distance b from it. Fixed to D is a block E, in a hole of which the crankpin PP fits.

Write an expression for the kinetic energy of the linkage.   (C.U.)

Chapter 3

SIMPLE HARMONIC MOTION

3–1. Definitions. Simple harmonic motion is the basic motion of most vibrations. By the word "basic" we mean it is largely a theoretical motion which does not often occur in pure form, but that the motions which do occur are only slight variations from simple harmonic motion. The variations are caused by such effects as friction which are always present to a greater or less degree.

Simple harmonic motion is the most important form of a class of motions called *periodic*. If any body moves in such a way that at regular intervals it returns to its starting point and repeats exactly in each interval the motion undertaken in the previous interval, then the motion is periodic, and the constant interval of time between any one point in the motion and the same point in the next cycle is called the *period*.

The equations of simple harmonic motion have been introduced already. The motion may be represented graphically by a sinusoidal wave, and the equation

$$x = A \sin (\omega t + \phi) \tag{3-1}$$

where A, ϕ are two constants depending, in any particular case, on the starting conditions (i.e., when $t = 0$).

The differential equation of the motion is generally encountered first and is

$$\frac{d^2x}{dt^2} + \omega^2 x = 0 \tag{3-2}$$

The differential equation shows another definition of simple harmonic motion: it is the linear motion of a particle such that its acceleration is always directed toward a certain fixed point (which is the center of the motion) and moreover is proportional to the displacement from that point.

Let us look again at eq. 3–1 and change it as follows:

$$x = A \sin (\omega t + \phi) \tag{3-1}$$
$$= A \sin \omega t \cos \phi + A \sin \phi \cos \omega t$$

$$x = A' \sin \omega t + B' \cos \omega t \tag{3-3}$$

92

Now a single sine wave is seen to be the same as the sum of a sine and a cosine wave. In a regular sine wave, the curve starts at the origin. But in eq. 3–1 the time axis is displaced, as seen in Fig. 3–1, for when $t = 0$, x has the value $A \sin \phi$. The angle ϕ is therefore responsible for the displacement of the time axis, and it is called a *phase angle*. It does not affect the motion at all.

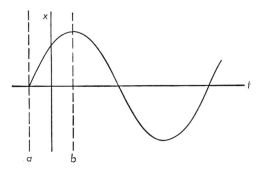

Fɪɢ. 3–1.

In eq. 3–3 there are two arbitrary constants, which are fixed by the starting conditions of a particular problem. For instance, let us choose to measure time from the instant that the particle is in the middle of its swing. Then $x = 0$ when $t = 0$ and in eq. 3–3 $B' = 0$, giving

$$x = A' \sin \omega t \qquad\qquad (3\text{–}4\mathrm{a})$$

As an alternative, time might be measured from the instant that the displacement is a maximum, say C, and the velocity is zero. Differentiate eq. 3–3 for the velocity

$$\frac{dx}{dt} = A'\omega \cos \omega t - B'\omega \sin \omega t$$

Then $A' = 0$ and $B' = C$, so

$$x = C \cos \omega t \qquad\qquad (3\text{–}4\mathrm{b})$$

Note that the only thing we have changed is the instant for $t = 0$. The motion is the same, but the time origins differ as shown at (a) and (b) in Fig. 3–1.

Thus in solving eq. 3–2 we may freely write the solution as either (3–4a) or (3–4b) if we remember that we are then fixing the initial conditions of time.

Now the maximum value of any sine or cosine is unity. Hence in eq. 3–4 the maximum displacement from the center of the motion is A' or C. This is called the *amplitude* of the motion, shown as A in Fig. 3–2.

Consider the sine motion of eq. 3–4a. A sine function repeats itself after the angle 2π. At $t = 0$, since $\sin 0° = 0$, the particle is in its central position $x = 0$. A period will have elapsed when the angle of the sine, that is ωt, has reached the value 2π. In other words, if τ is the length of the period in seconds,

$$\omega \tau = 2\pi$$

$$\tau = \frac{2\pi}{\omega} \; \text{sec} \tag{3–5}$$

(Note that this is not the same as saying that the period is the lapse of time until the particle returns to the original position $x = 0$.)

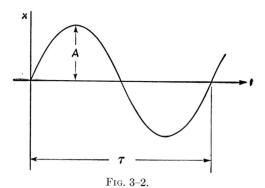

Fig. 3–2.

The reciprocal of the period is the *frequency*, or number of cycles per second

$$f = \frac{\omega}{2\pi} \; \sim/\text{sec or cps} \tag{3–6}$$

A quick method of drawing an approximate cosine curve (Fig. 3–3) is worth noting. The method is used by navigators in reckoning the

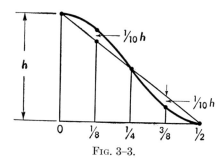

Fig. 3–3.

height of water in a harbor at times between high and low tide. If h is the total change in height, i.e., the double amplitude, or difference between high and low tides, then

at time zero (high tide)	height $= h$
at one-eighth period	height $= \frac{3}{4}h + \frac{1}{10}h$ approx.
at one-quarter period	height $= \frac{1}{2}h$
at three-eighths period	height $= \frac{1}{4}h - \frac{1}{10}h$ approx.
at half period (low tide)	height $= 0$

3-2. Circular Frequency. Vector Representation. The symbol ω has appeared so far squared as the ratio of magnitude of acceleration to displacement, as in eq. 3-2, and it has been seen to be proportional to the period of the motion. Its physical meaning can be shown by means of the hypothetical *auxiliary circle.*

In Fig. 3-4 is shown a vector OP which rotates around the fixed point O with constant angular velocity ω rad/sec. After time t the angle $POQ = \omega t$, if the time is measured from the instant when OP lies on OQ.

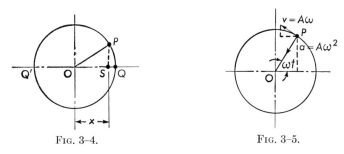

FIG. 3-4.   FIG. 3-5.

The projection of the vector on the diameter $Q'OQ$ is

$$OS = x = OP \cos \omega t$$

The maximum value of x will be OQ which equals OP; thus if A is the amplitude of the motion, $A = OP$ and

$$x = A \cos \omega t$$

This is the same as eq. 3-4b, and so leads to an alternative definition of simple harmonic motion:

Simple harmonic motion is the motion of a point which is the projection on the diameter of a circle of another point moving with constant speed around the circumference of the circle.

Obviously, when P has traveled a full circumference, a cycle has been completed: that is, when $\omega t = 2\pi$, then t will have the particular value τ, a period.

$$\tau = 2\pi/\omega \qquad \text{or} \qquad f = \omega/2\pi$$

This is as shown in eqs. 3-5 and 3-6. Because the frequency and angular velocity of the vector are thus related by a constant, ω is often called the *circular frequency*.

There are further comparisons available in this auxiliary circle. If the vector OP rotates at angular velocity ω, the tangential velocity of P (Fig. 3–5) is $A\omega$ where A is the length OP. The projection of this gives the simple harmonic velocity*

$$\dot{x} = -A\omega \sin \omega t$$

The acceleration* is normal toward the center and of amount $A\omega^2$. The projection of this on the same diameter gives

$$\ddot{x} = -A\omega^2 \cos \omega t$$

3–3. The Case of the Weighted Spring. The simplest example of simple harmonic motion occurs in the motion of a mass attached to the end of a coil spring, when the other end of the spring is rigidly attached to a foundation. Fig. 3–6 shows such an arrangement, with the mass of weight W free to move horizontally; the "wheels" under W are merely to represent frictionless motion and are not to be considered as wheels with weight, moment of inertia, etc., or any motion. For simplicity, the mass of the spring will also be ignored.

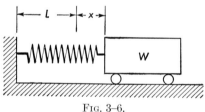

FIG. 3–6.

Suppose the spring has free length L, but has been stretched by moving the weight a distance x to the right. The spring is able to take tension and compression, and has a *stiffness* constant of k—that is, for a stretch $+ x$ (to the right), it has a restoring force kx to the left.

The signs involved must be observed carefully for it will depend upon them whether the equation we derive will be of the harmonic type or the hyperbolic type (ref. Chap. 2, Arts. 2–7 and 2–8).

The force kx is unopposed; therefore it will accelerate the mass to the left. This acceleration has the direction to *reduce* x, hence it is $-d^2x/dt^2$

$$kx = \frac{W}{g}a = -\frac{W}{g}\ddot{x} \tag{3–7}$$

Now divide by W/g, and we have the standard form of the equation (eq. 3–2)

* $\dot{x}$ means dx/dt, $\ddot{x} = d^2x/dt^2$. See footnote on page 61.

$$\ddot{x} + \left(\frac{kg}{W}\right)x = 0$$

This standard form has a known solution (eq. 3–1 or 3–3)

$$x = A \sin \omega t + B \cos \omega t$$

where

$$\omega = \sqrt{kg/W}$$

To determine the values of A and B, some knowledge or assumption of the manner in which the oscillation was started is necessary, as was explained earlier.

Example. A weight of 5 lb is attached to a spring of stiffness 8 lb per inch. This spring is stretched 2 in. and released. Find the equation of motion, maximum acceleration, maximum velocity, amplitude of the motion, and the frequency of the oscillation. Neglect all damping, and neglect the mass of the spring.

The differential equation of motion will be

$$kx = -\frac{W}{g}\ddot{x} \tag{3–7}$$

So $\omega^2 = \dfrac{kg}{W} = \dfrac{8 \times 386}{5} = 617.6$

$$\omega = 24.85 \text{ rad/sec}$$

The double integration of eq. 3–7 will give

$$x = A \sin 24.85t + B \cos 24.85t \tag{3–8}$$

And by differentiation

$$\dot{x} = 24.85A \cos 24.85t - 24.85B \sin 24.85t \tag{3–9}$$

Initial conditions are $x = 2$, $\dot{x} = 0$, when $t = 0$; these conditions will yield the correct values of A and B that apply in this problem. At $t = 0$, the sine is zero, the cosine unity; hence

From eq. 3–8 $2 = 0 + B$
From eq. 3–9 $0 = 24.85A - 0$

Thus $A = 0$, $B = 2$ and the equation of motion (eq. 3–8) is corrected to

$$x = 2 \cos 24.85t \tag{3–8a}$$

From this, the amplitude is 2 in., and from the value of ω the frequency is given by

$$f = \frac{\omega}{2\pi} = \frac{24.85}{2\pi} = 3.96 \text{ cycles per sec}$$

From eq. 3–9

$$\dot{x} = (24.85 \times 2) \cos 24.85t$$

Thus the maximum velocity is

$$\dot{x}_{\max} = (\text{Amplitude})\omega = 49.7 \text{ in./sec} = 4.14 \text{ ft/sec}$$

From eq. 3–7 (or by differentiating eq. 3–8a) the maximum acceleration occurs when x is a maximum:

$$\ddot{x}_{\max} = (\text{Amplitude})\omega^2 = 1235 \text{ in./sec}^2 = 103 \text{ ft/sec}^2$$

3–4. Vertical Motion of Spring and Mass. Suppose now as an alternative that the weight W is hanging vertically from the same spring. We will show that the characteristics of the motion are unchanged, except that the center of any oscillation will now be lowered by the amount Δ which is the static extension of the spring due to the weight W.

For in Fig. 3–7 let the free length of spring be L, the stiffness k; then the static extension will be given by the equation of static equilibrium

$$W = k\Delta \qquad\qquad (3\text{--}10)$$

Now if at any instant the spring is extended an amount y, the equation of dynamic equilibrium will be

$$ky - W = -\frac{W}{g}\ddot{y}$$

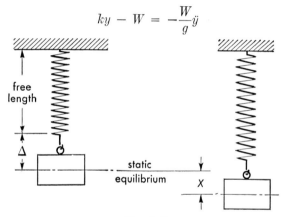

Fig. 3–7.

This is an equation of the harmonic type with a constant term, discussed in the last chapter (page 76). Note that

$$ky - W = k\left(y - \frac{W}{k}\right) = k(y - \Delta)$$

Then if we substitute $y - \Delta = x$, from which $\ddot{y} = \ddot{x}$, we obtain the equation

$$kx = -\frac{W}{g}\ddot{x}$$

in which x is the dimension shown in Fig. 3–7, and

$$x = A \sin \omega t + B \cos \omega t \qquad \text{with } \omega = \sqrt{\frac{kg}{W}}$$

This is the same result as for the horizontal case except that for the whole extension y of the spring we had to substitute $x = y - \Delta$.

Example. Centrally loaded beam or shaft. A shaft of uniform section, simply supported at the ends of a span of length *l*, carries a body of weight *W* at mid-span (Fig. 3–8). In comparison with this weight, the weight of the shaft itself is negligible.

Find the frequency of its natural vibration if once started.

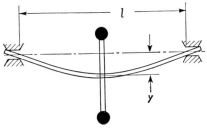

FIG. 3-8.

We find from structural handbooks that the central static deflection under a concentrated load *W* is

$$\Delta = \frac{Wl^3}{48EI} \text{ in.}$$

where *l* is the length of shaft in inches, *E* its modulus of elasticity, and *I* its moment of inertia of cross-sectional area about the neutral axis in in.⁴ units.

At any other deflection *y* there will be a spring force tending to restore equilibrium, which will have the magnitude

$$F = \left(\frac{48EI}{l^3}\right)y = ky$$

where *k* represents this spring constant.

Writing the inertia equation for lateral vibration

$$-\frac{W}{g}\ddot{y} = ky - W$$

$$\omega = \sqrt{\frac{kg}{W}} = \sqrt{\frac{48EIg}{Wl^3}}$$

$$f = \frac{1}{2\pi}\sqrt{\frac{48EIg}{Wl^3}}$$

Take a numerical case:

A 2-in. diam shaft carries a 120-lb turbine wheel which is mounted symmetrically between bearings 14 in. apart. With the running-fit clearance the bearings may be regarded as simply supporting for small deflections. The frequency of transverse (lateral) vibration is wanted.

$W = 120$ lb; $l = 14$ in.; E for steel $= 30 \times 10^6$ lb/in.²; $I = \pi d^4/64 = 0.785$ in.⁴; $g = 386$ in./sec².

$$f = \frac{1}{2\pi}\sqrt{\frac{48 \times 30 \times 10^6 \times 0.785 \times 386}{120 \times 14^3}} = 183 \text{ cps}$$

3–5. Frequency in Terms of Static Deflection. We have found that the natural frequency of vibration of a sprung weight is given by

$$f = \frac{\omega}{2\pi} = \frac{1}{2\pi}\sqrt{\frac{kg}{W}} \text{ cps}$$

If we use eq. 3–10 we get an alternative and useful expression:

$$f = \frac{1}{2\pi}\sqrt{\frac{g}{\Delta}} \text{ cps} \qquad (3\text{–}11)$$

If Δ is expressed in inches, then $g = 386$ in./sec^2 and eq. 3–11 becomes

$$f = \frac{3.127}{\sqrt{\Delta}} \text{ cps}$$

But be sure that there is no confusion of mind: Δ is the static deflection due to the one weight under gravity. It is not the amplitude.

The amplitude of a free harmonic oscillation depends only on the starting conditions. The frequency depends on springs and masses. There is no relation between the two.

Example 1. In the last article, the problem of the centrally loaded shaft gave the result

$$f = \frac{1}{2\pi}\sqrt{\frac{48\,EIg}{Wl^3}}$$

but

$$\Delta = \frac{Wl^3}{48EI}$$

hence

$$f = \frac{1}{2\pi}\sqrt{\frac{g}{\Delta}}$$

Example 2. A cantilever with end load. Suppose in Fig. 3–9 the load W is large compared with the weight of the cantilever itself.

The static deflection due to such end load is

$$\Delta = \frac{Wl^3}{3EI}$$

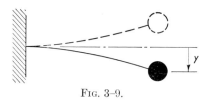

Fig. 3–9.

By repeating the computations as in the previous example it can quickly be seen that

$$f = \frac{1}{2\pi}\sqrt{\frac{3\,EIg}{Wl^3}} = \frac{1}{2\pi}\sqrt{\frac{g}{\Delta}}$$

Numerically, suppose the end of the cantilever is depressed below its static position by 0.2025 in. when a 2-ton load W is added.

$$\Delta = 0.2025$$

The natural frequency of this loaded cantilever is

$$f = \frac{3.127}{\sqrt{0.2025}} = \frac{3.127}{0.45} = \text{approx. 7 cps}$$

If a different load W were attached to the same cantilever, the frequency would be different, because Δ would be different.

3–6. Two Bodies Kinematically Connected. When two bodies are so arranged that their motions are directly related by kinematic considerations, their oscillations will occur together with the same frequency.

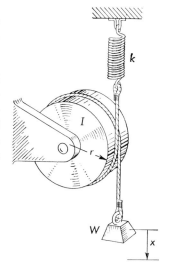

Example. Figure 3–10 shows a string from the lower end of a spring which passes around a drum before reaching a weight, to which it is tied. The drum is free to rotate about a fixed horizontal axis. Find the frequency of the motion, with the following data:

Suspended weight   5 lb
Weight of drum   27 lb
Drum diameter 12 in.; radius of gyration
    4 in.
Spring stiffness 20 lb/in.

Fig. 3–10.

Assume the weight is displaced a distance x below equilibrium, and thus has acceleration $\ddot{x}$ which is positive downward.

Force upward of spring $= kx + W$
Inertia force upward of $W = (W/g)\,\ddot{x} - W$

Note the static loads W now disappear and could have been ignored. Now taking moments about the center of rotation of the drum,

$$\left(kx + \frac{W}{g}\,\ddot{x}\right) r = I\alpha \text{ counterclockwise}$$

The angular acceleration α is related kinematically to the linear acceleration $\ddot{x}$ of the string, but, since $\ddot{x}$ is positive downward,

$$r\alpha = -\ddot{x}$$

The equation in x is then

$$\left(kx + \frac{W}{g}\,\ddot{x}\right) r^2 = -I\ddot{x}$$

or

$$\left(\frac{W}{g} + \frac{I}{r^2}\right)\ddot{x} + kx = 0$$

Numerically: $\left(\dfrac{5}{386} + \dfrac{27 \times 4^2}{386 \times 6^2}\right)\ddot{x} + 20x = 0 \text{ lb}$

$$\ddot{x} + \left(\frac{20 \times 386}{5 + 12}\right)x = 0$$

Thus the circular frequency $\omega = \sqrt{\dfrac{20 \times 386}{17}} = 21.3 \text{ rad/sec}$

And frequency $= \dfrac{\omega}{2\pi} = 3.39 \text{ cps}$

Note that it is not permissible here to use eq. 3–11, for the moment of inertia of the drum does not affect the static deflection but affects the frequency considerably.

3–7. Compounded Springs. Sometimes two or more springs act on a single mass. There are several possible arrangements as shown in Fig. 3–11. The problem is to find the equivalent spring constant, that is, to find the constant for a single spring which could replace the several springs without changing the frequency or deflection.

a) SPRINGS IN SERIES (Fig. 3–11a). In this case the tension in the two springs is the same. Suppose F lb pull is applied. Spring (1) extends F/k_1 in. and spring (2) extends F/k_2 in. The total extension is $F/k_1 + F/k_2$, due to F lb.

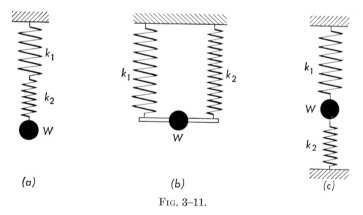

(a)   (b)   (c)

FIG. 3–11.

A single spring of spring constant k_e will be equivalent to the two springs if

$$\frac{1}{k_e} = \frac{1}{k_1} + \frac{1}{k_2} \tag{3–12}$$

b) SPRINGS IN PARALLEL. (Fig. 3–11b). Suppose the weight is half way between the two springs on a light bar which can rotate. Suppose a force of F lb is applied at W, then half the force acts on each spring. Spring (1) extends $F/2k_1$, and spring (2) extends $F/2k_2$, while the bar turns. If the bar has no appreciable moment of inertia, the turning torque is neglected, and the vertical movement of the weight W is the mean of the extensions of the springs or

$$\frac{1}{2}\left(\frac{F}{2k_1} + \frac{F}{2k_2}\right) = \frac{F}{k_e} \qquad (3\text{–}13)$$

The spring constant is four times that of case (a).

c) SPRING EITHER SIDE OF WEIGHT (Fig. 3–11c). If both springs are in initial tension, and the weight is moved down, the top spring increases its tension, and the bottom spring decreases its pull down. A decrease in the pull down is exactly the same as an increase in push up. Thus the system is the same as one in which the springs have the same stiffness in tension and compression, and have no initial tension in the center position. The weight in moving has thus to work against both springs and

$$k_e = k_1 + k_2 \qquad (3\text{–}14)$$

d) If in Fig. 3–11b the bar joining the springs is by some means kept from rotating, then the system is the same as that in part (c). The mass must move against the arithmetic sum effect of the two springs, and eq. 3–14 applies again.

Finally with any of these systems, when the equivalent spring constant is obtained, the natural frequency of a weight W suspended for vertical oscillation is

$$f = \frac{1}{2\pi}\sqrt{\frac{k_e g}{W}}$$

just as in Art. 3–4.

3–8. The Energy Approach. If a free vibration is not damped, then while the motion is in progress no external work is being done, and thus we have a system of constant energy. Consider again the spring of Fig. 3–7. At any intermediate position, with extension x from the static equilibrium position the total energy is the sum of potential energy in the spring and kinetic energy of the weight (if again for simplicity the weight of the spring is ignored). The potential energy is reckoned in two parts: (a) that lost in lowering of the weight, and (b) that gained by stretching the spring. It has already been explained that the latter, called strain energy, is equal to the amount of work needed to get the spring into its strained condition; it is the product of the mean tension of the spring and the distance stretched.

Now if we stretch the spring an amount x measured from the static equilibrium position, the spring being vertical, the increase in potential energy from strain is *not* $\frac{1}{2}kx^2$ because

Strain energy at static equilibrium position $= \frac{1}{2}k\Delta^2$
Strain energy at extension x beyond static $= \frac{1}{2}k(\Delta + x)^2$
Increase in potential energy from strain $= \frac{1}{2}kx^2 + k\Delta x$

Now by definition of Δ, the static equilibrium extension from free length,

$$k\Delta = W$$

Considering the potential energy of height also,

Total change in potential energy $= \frac{1}{2}kx^2 + k\Delta x - Wx = \frac{1}{2}kx^2$

Thus the potential energy change is the same as if the motion were horizontal and the potential energy due to change in height can, it seems, be ignored in this manner.

The kinetic energy depends on the velocity at displacement x, where $v = \dot{x}$, so

$$\text{Kinetic energy} = \frac{1}{2}\frac{W}{g}\dot{x}^2$$

Hence the energy equation is

$$\frac{1}{2}\frac{W}{g}\dot{x}^2 + \frac{1}{2}kx^2 = \text{constant} \tag{3-15}$$

Differentiating: $\qquad \dfrac{W}{g}\dot{x}\ddot{x} + kx\dot{x} = 0$

Dividing by $\dot{x}$, which cannot be zero for all values of x,

$$\frac{W}{g}\ddot{x} + kx = 0$$

Thus we have exactly the same equation as by the inertia method. The only immediate advantage in this attack is that we avoid having to consider the signs ($\pm$) of x and $\ddot{x}$, for both x and $\dot{x}$ appeared as squared terms.

This method of obtaining the equation of motion must be carefully distinguished from the following.

3-9. The Maximum Energy Method. Another most useful adaptation of the energy approach is due to Lord Rayleigh and leads very quickly to a solution for the frequency. Note that there have been only potential and kinetic energies involved in Art. 3-8. But at the full amplitude of the vibration there is an instant when the velocity is zero, just as a ball thrown in the air is stationary for an instant at the top of its rise. Then at this position there is only potential energy, which will be the maximum value for potential energy. Again at the center, where $x = 0$, there is no potential energy, so velocity and kinetic energy must be a maximum. Since the total energy is constant throughout, then

Maximum Potential Energy (at maximum displacement)

$$= \text{Maximum Kinetic Energy (at } x = 0) \qquad (3\text{--}16)$$

If we now *assume* that the motion under consideration is simple harmonic, or

$$x = A \sin \omega t$$

Then differentiating,

$$\dot{x} = A\omega \cos \omega t$$

So

$$\text{maximum displacement} = A, \text{ and P.E.}_{\text{max}} = \tfrac{1}{2}kA^2$$

and

$$\text{maximum velocity} = A\omega, \text{ so K.E.}_{\text{max}} = \frac{1}{2}\frac{W}{g}(A\omega)^2$$

Equating

$$\frac{1}{2}\frac{W}{g}A^2\omega^2 = \frac{1}{2}kA^2$$

or

$$\omega^2 = \frac{kg}{W}$$

and frequency,

$$f = \frac{\omega}{2\pi} = \frac{1}{2\pi}\sqrt{\frac{kg}{W}}$$

Example. Two springs, as in Fig. 3–11a, support a weight of 2 lb. If $k_1 = 4$, $k_2 = 5$ lb per in., find the frequency.

Assume a motion $x = A \sin \omega t$ in inches.

$$\text{P.E.}_{\text{max}} = \frac{1}{2}k_e A^2 = \frac{1}{2}\cdot\frac{A^2}{\dfrac{1}{k_1}+\dfrac{1}{k_2}}$$

$$= \frac{1}{2}\cdot\frac{20}{9}\cdot A^2 \text{ in.-lb}$$

$$\text{K.E.}_{\text{max}} = \frac{1}{2}\frac{W}{g}(A\omega)^2 = \frac{1}{2}\cdot\frac{2}{386}\cdot A^2\omega^2 \text{ in.-lb}$$

Equating, and cancelling A^2: $\quad \omega^2 = \dfrac{20}{9}\cdot\dfrac{386}{2} = 429$

$$f = \frac{1}{2\pi}\sqrt{429} = 3.3 \text{ cps}$$

3–10. Motions Simple Harmonic for Small Amplitude Only. The Pendulum.

At this stage we should take careful note that certain simplifications have been made for a purpose, but also certain assumptions. The simplifications have been noted: no damping and no mass to the spring. These will be taken into account later. The assumptions are, first, that Newton's law (force = mass × acceleration) holds, and second, that there is a linear relationship between stress and strain in the spring. We have stated that force is proportional to displacement, or

$$F = kx$$

and that k is the same constant both above and below the static equilibrium position. If the stress–strain relation is different in compression

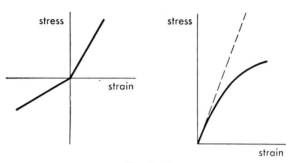

Fig. 3-12.

from that in tension, or, if k is not a constant but a function of x (see
Fig. 3–12), then the motion has a different equation and is a variation
from simple harmonic. An example of a motion not properly simple
harmonic is the pendulum.

A weight W, which is assumed to have
its mass concentrated at a point, is suspended at the end of a long slender rod of
length l whose upper end is free to rotate
about a horizontal axis (Fig. 3–13). The
motion can only be along the arc. When
the angle of the rod from the vertical is θ
radians, the arc length s is given by

$$s = l\theta$$

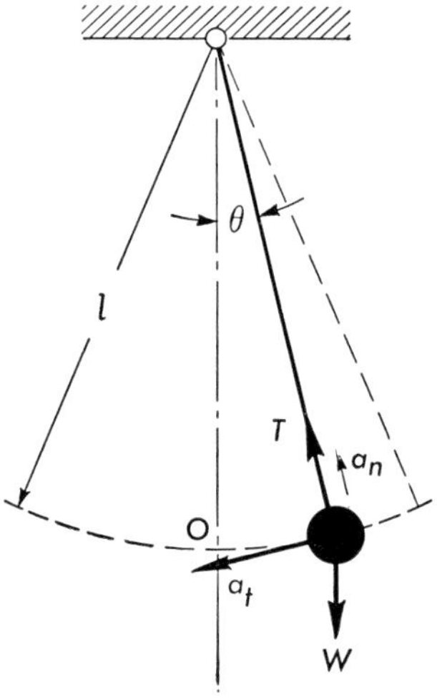

The acceleration of the bob will be normal (along the rod) due to angular velocity, and tangential due to angular acceleration. The tangential acceleration, since
it is directed toward O, will be $-\dfrac{d^2s}{dt^2} =$
$-l\dfrac{d^2\theta}{dt^2}$. The tangential resultant of forces
will produce this acceleration, so

Fig. 3-13.

$$W \sin \theta = -\frac{Wl}{g}\frac{d^2\theta}{dt^2} \tag{3-17}$$

a) First assume that the angle of swing is small; this allows the approximation $\sin \theta = \theta$. The eq. 3–17 then becomes

$$\frac{d^2\theta}{dt^2} = -\frac{g}{l}\theta$$

This is an equation of simple harmonic motion (see eq. 3–2) so that the solution is

$$\theta = \theta_{max} \sin (\omega t + \phi) \text{ rad} \tag{3-18}$$

where $\omega^2 = \dfrac{g}{l}$ and the period $\tau = 2\pi\sqrt{\dfrac{l}{g}}$ sec.

b) Allowing the swing to be great, the solution is more difficult,* and the motion is *not* simple harmonic.

Multiply both sides of eq. 3–17 by $2\dot\theta$ after dividing by $-\dfrac{Wl}{g}$

$$\frac{d^2\theta}{dt^2} = -\frac{g}{l}\sin\theta$$

$$2\dot\theta\ddot\theta = -\frac{2g}{l}\sin\theta\cdot\dot\theta$$

Then integrate with respect to the time t

$$(\dot\theta)^2 = +\frac{2g}{l}\cos\theta + c_1$$

If we take the initial conditions for measuring time to be $t = 0$ when $\theta = \alpha$ and $\dot\theta = 0$ (that is, α is the maximum swing), then

$$c_1 = -\frac{2g}{l}\cos\alpha$$

Substituting:

$$\dot\theta = \frac{d\theta}{dt} = \sqrt{\frac{2g}{l}}\sqrt{\cos\theta - \cos\alpha}$$

Separating the variables in order to integrate:

$$t = \sqrt{\frac{l}{2g}}\int^\theta \frac{d\theta}{\sqrt{\cos\theta - \cos\alpha}}$$

This integral cannot be evaluated in any simple way. It is necessary first to convert cosines into half-angle functions by

$$\cos\theta = 1 - 2\sin^2\theta/2$$
$$\cos\alpha = 1 - 2\sin^2\alpha/2$$

and then express the whole integrand in terms of the ratio $(\sin\theta/2) \div (\sin\alpha/2)$ which is always equal to or less than unity. Then the integrand may be expanded by the binomial theorem to a series and integrated

---

* I. S. and E. S. Sokolnikoff, *Higher Mathematics for Engineers and Physicists* (New York: McGraw-Hill Book Co., Inc., 1941), pp. 236–38; T. von Karman and M. A. Biot, *Mathematical Methods in Engineering* (New York: McGraw-Hill Book Co., Inc., 1940), pp. 115–18.

term by term. The actual work is not given here, but may be found through the references given. The result, however, is that the period of the motion will appear in series form as follows:

$$\tau = 2\pi \sqrt{\frac{l}{g}} \Bigg\{ 1 + \left(\frac{1}{2}\sin\frac{\alpha}{2}\right)^2 + \left(\frac{1 \cdot 3}{2 \cdot 4}\sin^2\frac{\alpha}{2}\right)^2 +$$
$$\left(\frac{1 \cdot 3 \cdot 5}{2 \cdot 4 \cdot 6}\sin^4\frac{\alpha}{2}\right)^2 + \cdots \Bigg\} \quad (3\text{-}19)$$

The period is seen to be a function of the amplitude, which was not the case in simple harmonic motion. A pendulum swings more slowly through wider angles.

c) To obtain the same small-angle motion by use of the maximum energy method, note there is no strain energy, thus

$$\text{Potential energy at angle } \theta = W\,(l - l\cos\theta)$$
$$= Wl(1 - \cos\theta)$$
$$\text{Kinetic energy} \qquad = \frac{1}{2}\frac{W}{g}(l\dot\theta)^2$$

Now if we assume simple harmonic motion, which in fact means assuming small-angle motion, we have

$$\theta = \theta_{\max}\sin\omega t$$
$$\frac{1}{2}\frac{W}{g}(l\theta_{\max}\omega)^2 = Wl(1 - \cos\theta_{\max})$$

The usual approximation for small angles that $\cos\theta = 1$ is of no use here, so we use also the second term of the series expansion*

$$\cos\theta = 1 - \tfrac{1}{2}\theta^2 + \cdots \qquad (3\text{-}20)$$

and this gives

$$\frac{1}{2}\frac{W}{g}l^2\theta^2_{\max}\omega^2 = Wl\left(\frac{1}{2}\theta^2_{\max}\right)$$
$$\omega^2 = \frac{g}{l}$$
$$\text{Period } \tau = \frac{2\pi}{\omega} = 2\pi\sqrt{\frac{l}{g}} \text{ sec}$$

Example 1. The pendulum of a grandfather clock is usually made so that a second will elapse during the swing each way. Find the length in inches.

$$\text{Period} = 2 \text{ sec} = 2\pi\sqrt{\frac{l}{g}}$$
$$l = \frac{g}{\pi^2} = \frac{385.9}{9.870} = 39.1 \text{ in.}$$

* B. O. Peirce, *Short Table of Integrals*, No. 773 (3d ed.; Boston: Ginn & Co., 1929).

Example 2. A pendulum 39.1 in. in length swings with an amplitude of 60° either side. Compare the period with that for small angles.

In eq. 3–19, the term $2\pi\sqrt{\dfrac{l}{g}} = 2$ sec, by the previous example. Then the series factor will be

$$1 + \frac{1}{4}\sin^2 30° + \frac{9}{64}\sin^4 30° + \frac{225}{2304}\sin^8 30° = 1.0717$$

The sum of the complete series is actually 1.0732, as can be found from tables of elliptic functions.

Hence the period is 2.146 sec, which is an increase of over 7 per cent over the period for small-angle swing.

It should be observed that swinging pendulum motion is not by any means the only type that is simple harmonic for small amplitude of motion only. Almost every problem that includes an oscillating lever incurs this limitation.

Example 3. Find the position of the sliding weight W of 3 lb upon the light bar, pivoted as shown in Fig. 3–14, and restrained by the springs shown, so that the frequency of small vibrations shall be one cycle per second. $k_1 = 5$ lb/in., $k_2 = 4$ lb/in., $r = 1.5$ in.

Assume the bar is horizontal in statical equilibrium, or that the whole plane of the figure is horizontal: neither of these will affect frequency.

Assume either that both springs can take both compression and extension, or that they have an initial tension sufficiently great that when deflected they never reach zero tension. A reduced tension (pull) is the same as an increased push. These are normal assumptions.

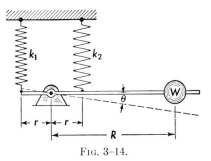

Fig. 3–14.

Take as the variable an angle θ of the bar from horizontal, depressing W. Displacement of W is then $R\theta$, and tangential acceleration $R\ddot{\theta}$. Displacement of k_2 is $r\theta$ down, and of k_1 is $r\theta$ up. Note, since θ is small, we do not consider displacement as $r \sin \theta$, nor do we reckon the slight variation from a right angle between spring and bar. Rather, moments about the pivot give

Spring torque $= (k_1 r\theta)r + (k_2 r\theta)r$ counterclockwise

Thus the equation of motion is

$$(k_1 + k_2)r^2\theta = -\frac{W}{g}R^2\ddot{\theta}$$

This yields

$$\text{frequency} = \frac{1}{2\pi}\sqrt{\frac{(k_1 + k_2)gr^2}{WR^2}} = 1 \text{ (by data)}$$

Solving for R:

$$\sqrt{\frac{(5 + 4)386}{3}} = 2\pi \cdot \frac{R}{1.5}$$

$$R = 8.13 \text{ in.}$$

3–11. Compound Pendulum. The compound pendulum is the general case of the simple pendulum, being a solid body with mass distributed instead of concentrated. It therefore has moment of inertia about its center of mass as well as mass.

In Fig. 3–15 the rigid body with center of gravity G rotates freely about a horizontal axis at O. Let the line OG make an angle θ with the vertical at time t. Then the moment of the weight will produce an angular acceleration α about O, tending to reduce the angle θ. Hence

$$Wr \sin\theta = -I_0\alpha$$

$$Wr \sin\theta = -\frac{W}{g}(k^2 + r^2)\ddot{\theta}$$

where k is the radius of gyration about the center of gravity, and r is the radius from the pivot to the center of gravity.

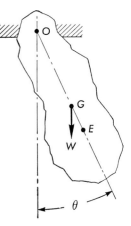

Fig. 3–15.

$$\ddot{\theta} = -g\frac{r}{k^2 + r^2}\sin\theta \qquad (3-21)$$

Comparing this with the eq. 3–17 of the simple pendulum, we see that the motion is the same as that of an equivalent simple pendulum of length

$$l_e = \frac{k^2 + r^2}{r} = \frac{k^2}{r} + r = \overline{OE} \qquad (3-22)$$

Thus l_e, the equivalent length, is the length $\overline{OE}$ where E is the center of percussion. The period of small oscillations is given by

$$\tau = 2\pi\sqrt{\frac{\overline{OE}}{g}}$$

Example. A solid hemisphere lies with its rounded surface on a plane, as in Fig. 3–16. Find the frequency of small oscillations by the maximum energy method.

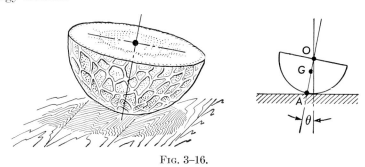

FIG. 3–16.

Let the sphere have radius r, and the distance of the center of gravity G from the center O be denoted by l. Then

$$l = OG = \tfrac{3}{8}r$$

Let the centerline OG be at an angle θ from the vertical, and the weight of the solid be w. Then

$$\text{Potential energy} = wl(1 - \cos\theta)$$

For small angle

$$\text{Maximum P.E.} = \tfrac{1}{2}wl\theta^2_{\text{max}}$$

The kinetic energy consists of the linear K.E. of the center and the angular K.E. of the moment of inertia about the center of gravity. The maximum velocity of the point G is $(r - l)\dot\theta_{\text{max}}$ because the point A will be the instantaneous center of rotation. Thus

$$\text{K.E.}_{\text{max}} = \frac{1}{2}\frac{w}{g}(r - l)^2\dot\theta^2_{\text{max}} + \frac{1}{2}I_G\dot\theta^2_{\text{max}}$$

In the maximum energy method we assume simple harmonic motion of small oscillations

$$\theta = \theta_{\text{max}} \sin \omega t$$

$$\text{K.E.}_{\text{max}} = \frac{1}{2}\frac{w}{g}[(r - l)^2 + k_g^2]\,(\theta_{\text{max}}\omega)^2 = \frac{1}{2}I_A\,\theta^2_{\text{max}}\omega^2$$

Then the circular frequency is found by equating maximum potential and kinetic energies:

$$\omega^2 = \frac{wl}{I_A}$$

The moment of inertia I_A can be found as

$$I_A = I_G + \frac{w}{g}(AG)^2 = \frac{13}{20}\frac{w}{g}r^2$$

since

$$I_G = \frac{2}{5}\frac{w}{g}r^2 - \frac{w}{g}\left(\frac{3}{8}r\right)^2$$

So that

$$\omega^2 = \frac{wl}{I_A} = \frac{20}{13} \cdot \frac{g}{r^2} \cdot \frac{3}{8}r = \frac{15}{26}\frac{g}{r}$$

and frequency

$$f = \frac{1}{2\pi}\sqrt{\frac{15g}{26r}}$$

3–12. Two Special Pendulums. a) KATER'S REVERSIBLE PENDULUM.* We have just found in the last article that if a compound pendulum is suspended from point O, its period is the same as that of a simple pendulum of the same mass, with the mass concentrated at the center of percussion E (Fig. 3–15).

$$\tau_1 = 2\pi\sqrt{\frac{\overline{OE}}{g}} = 2\pi\sqrt{\frac{k^2 + \bar{r}^2}{g\bar{r}}}$$

where $OG = \bar{r}$ and k is the radius of gyration about G.

Now suppose that the compound pendulum is turned upside down and suspended from some point H, distant from G by length L. Then the equation of motion about this new pivot will be

$$WL \sin\theta = -I_H\ddot{\theta}$$

$$\tau_2 = 2\pi\sqrt{\frac{I_H}{WL}} = 2\pi\sqrt{\frac{k^2 + L^2}{gL}}$$

These two can be the same if we make

$$\frac{k^2 + \bar{r}^2}{\bar{r}} = \frac{k^2 + L^2}{L}$$

One solution is obviously if $L = \bar{r}$, but this is not of great interest. There is another possibility:

$$(k^2 + \bar{r}^2)L = (k^2 + L^2)\bar{r}$$
$$k^2L - L^2\bar{r} = k^2\bar{r} - \bar{r}^2L$$
$$(k^2 - \bar{r}L)(L - \bar{r}) = 0$$

So the other solution is

$$L = k^2/\bar{r} \qquad\qquad (3\text{–}23)$$

But this places the point H at E (Fig. 3–15). Thus we deduce that in a compound pendulum, the center of percussion is an alternative center of suspension for a motion with given period. For this reason, the center of percussion is also called the *center* of *oscillation*.

---

* E. J. Routh, *Elementary Rigid Dynamics*, Vol. I of "Dynamics of a System of Rigid Bodies" (5th ed.; London: Macmillan & Co., Ltd., 1891), pp. 73, 81; L. Page, *Introduction to Theoretical Physics* (New York: D. Van Nostrand Co., 1935), p. 131.

b) THE CYCLOIDAL PENDULUM.   It can be shown* that if the bob of
a simple pendulum can be made to travel in a cycloidal path, its motion
is purely simple harmonic for any amplitude up to 90°. This follows
directly from the geometric properties of the cycloid.

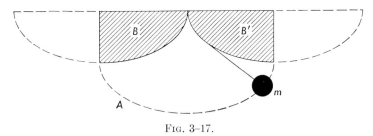

FIG. 3–17.

Furthermore, a simple pendulum bob can be made to move on a
cycloid such as A (Fig. 3–17), if the string is made to wrap itself against
two cheeks B, B', which are two half-cycloids of identical shape to the
cycloid A. Such cheeks, though not as big as those shown, are sometimes used in clocks.

3–13. Amplitude of Oscillations. It may have been noted that in
this chapter the emphasis is mostly on the calculation of the natural
frequencies and periods of various systems. The amplitude of any
oscillation is generally of interest only when the vibration is caused by
some external excitation, such as in problems of forced vibration.
Certain types of this will be considered later, in Chapter 5.

However, when an oscillation cannot be represented by either sine
or cosine wave, but needs the full equation (eq. 3–3), the evaluation of
the amplitude may require some thought.

Reference to the first article of this chapter (page 92) will show that

$$x = A' \sin \omega t + B' \cos \omega t \tag{3–3}$$

may be written

$$x = A \sin (\omega t + \phi) \tag{3–1}$$

where

$$\left.\begin{array}{l} A' = A \cos \phi \\ B' = A \sin \phi \end{array}\right\} \tag{3–24}$$

Angle ϕ is called the phase angle. From eq. 3–1, it is apparent that the
amplitude is A, and the equations 3–24 may be squared and added to
give

$$A = \sqrt{A'^2 + B'^2} \tag{3–25}$$

This may also be shown vectorially, using the auxiliary circle. x is
composed (eq. 3–3) of the sum of the projections onto the horizontal

* J. H. Jeans, *Theoretical Mechanics* (Boston: Ginn & Co., 1907), pp. 265–68;
A. S. Ramsey, *Dynamics* (London: Cambridge University Press, 1929), Vol. I, pp.
108–10.

of a vector OA' and a vector OB' (Fig. 3–18). Since in eq. 3–3 the sine component of A' appears, the vector OA' must lag 90° on the vector OB'.

But now the sum of these two projections is the projection of the one vector OA when $OA^2 = OA'^2 + OB'^2$. The phase angle ϕ appears in the figure as the angle by which OA leads OA', and this is confirmed by dividing eqs. 3–24, giving

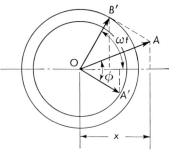

$$\tan \phi = B'/A' \qquad (3\text{–}26)$$

Another point of interest is the relation between the components A' and B' of eq. 3–3 and the initial velocity and displacement of a motion. Differentiate eq. 3–3:

FIG. 3–18.

$$\dot{x} = A'\omega \cos \omega t - B'\omega \sin \omega t \qquad (3\text{–}27)$$

At the start suppose the velocity is V_0 and the displacement is x_0 from equilibrium. Put $t = 0$ in eqs. 3–3 and 3–27, and we obtain

$$x_0 = B'$$
$$V_0 = A'\omega$$

Thus from eq. 3–25 we have that the amplitude of the subsequent oscillation is

$$A = \sqrt{x_0{}^2 + (V_0/\omega)^2} \qquad (3\text{–}28)$$

Note V_0 is squared, so that the sense of V_0 does not matter with respect to x_0. A child is on a swing; you pull the swing out a bit and give a push. Assuming simple harmonic motion, it does not matter whether you push further out or back toward the center; so long as the initial velocity is the same, the amplitude of swing will be the same.

Often a vibration is started by an impact. Consider the following.

Example. A scale pan of weight 1 lb when attached to a spring stretches it 2 in. A weight of 2 lb is then dropped from a height of 3 in. onto the pan without rebound. Find the extension of the spring and the period of vibration resulting.   (C.U.)

The problem may be viewed and solved as follows:

(a) The pan has a certain equilibrium position, but when the weight is on it there will be a new, lower equilibrium. (b) The weight acquires a velocity in dropping and then there will be an impact, so that there will be a loss of energy, although the momentum remains constant. (c) Directly after impact there will be a condition where the combined mass has a velocity and also a displacement above its (new) equilibrium position.

One lb stretches the spring 2 in.; therefore $k = 1/2$ lb/in.

Equilibrium position with pan $\Delta_1 = 2$ in. of stretch

Equilibrium position with pan and weight $\Delta_2 = 6$ in. of stretch

Velocity of weight before impact, $V_1 = \sqrt{2gh}$ (by energy)

Velocity of system after impact, V_2 given by momentum relation

$$MV_1 = (M + m)V_2$$

or

$$V_2 = \frac{W}{W + w}\sqrt{2gh} = \frac{2}{3}\sqrt{2 \times 3 \times g} \text{ in./sec}$$

where $W = 2$ and $w = 1$.

First Method: Straight energy considerations allow that at the lowest position (where the combined mass is stationary) the initial K.E. with the loss in P.E. of height is converted into P.E. of strain in the spring.

$$\text{Initial K.E.} = \left(\frac{W + w}{2g}\right)V_2^2 = \left(\frac{W}{W + w}\right)Wh$$

Let extension be x; then

$$\text{Increase in P.E. of strain} = \tfrac{1}{2}k(x + \Delta_1)^2 - \tfrac{1}{2}k\Delta_1^2$$

where Δ_1 is the original 2-in. stretch

$$= \tfrac{1}{2}kx^2 + k\Delta_1 x = \tfrac{1}{2}kx^2 + wx$$

$$\text{Loss in P.E. of height} = (W + w)x$$

So:

$$\left(\frac{W + w}{2g}\right)V_2^2 + Wx = \frac{1}{2}kx^2$$

Note that the wx terms drop out (because the strain energy is measured from the point of equilibrium of the weight w) but not the Wx term. This is a quadratic in x soluble as follows:

$$\tfrac{1}{4}x^2 - 2x - \tfrac{2}{3}(2 \times 3) = 0$$

$$x = 4 \pm \sqrt{16 + 16} = 9.656 \text{ or } -1.656 \text{ in.}$$

Note that this shows the new equilibrium position 4 in. below Δ_1 and the amplitude of the induced oscillation $\sqrt{32}$ in., which is both below and above the new equilibrium. The maximum extension of the spring is then 11.656 in.

Finally the circular frequency of the oscillation is given quite simply by

$$\omega = \sqrt{\frac{kg}{W + w}}$$

so that the period is

$$\tau = 2\pi\sqrt{\frac{W + w}{kg}} = 0.783 \text{ sec}$$

Second Method: By consideration of the equation of motion we have both initial velocity V_2 and initial displacement $\Delta_1 - \Delta_2 = -4$ in. The equation must be of the form

$$x = A' \sin \omega t + B' \cos \omega t$$

where x is measured from the new equilibrium position. By using eq. 3–28, we know that at $t = 0$, that is, at the instant of the impact,

$$x = B' = -4$$
$$\dot{x} = A'\omega = +V_2$$

But

$$\omega = \sqrt{\frac{kg}{W_1 + W_2}} \text{ so } A' = \frac{W_1}{W_1 + W_2}\sqrt{\frac{2gh(W_1 + W_2)}{kg}} = 4$$

and the total amplitude of the motion is

$$\text{Amplitude} = \sqrt{A'^2 + B'^2}$$
$$= \sqrt{16 + 16} = 5.656$$

This is the same as in the first analysis, giving the maximum stretch of the spring as the original 2 in. plus the 4 in. to the new equilibrium plus 5.656 in. amplitude downward.

3–14. Torsional Vibration. Consider a shaft of uniform section, anchored at one end, and carrying at the other end a disk of mass moment of inertia I (in lb in. sec^2 or similar units) as in Fig. 3–19. To start the motion a torque is applied to the disk that moves a line OA on the disk through an angle θ, and the torque is proportional to the angle. If the outside influence is removed there is restoring torque from the shaft

$$\text{T} = -c\theta$$

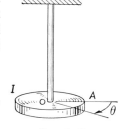

FIG. 3–19.

where c will be in lb in. per radian or similar units. But the relation

$$\text{T} = I\alpha$$

shows the effect of this torque on the disk. Thus the equation of motion becomes—if the moment of inertia of the shaft is ignored

$$I\frac{d^2\theta}{dt^2} = -c\theta$$

The solution of this is (cf. Art. 3–1)

$$\omega = \sqrt{\frac{c}{I}}$$

or

$$f = \frac{1}{2\pi}\sqrt{\frac{c}{I}} \tag{3–29}$$

In this type of motion then, mass moment of inertia has taken the place of the mass, and the torsional spring constant c takes the place of the linear spring constant k. The torsional spring constant of a shaft may be found by

$$c = \frac{GJ_s}{L} \tag{3–30}$$

where G is the shear modulus of the material of the shaft (e.g., 12×10^6 lb/in.² for steel),

J_s is the polar area moment of the section of the shaft (e.g., for a circular shaft $J_s = \frac{\pi d^4}{32}$ in.⁴ if d is diameter in inches),

L is the length of shaft that is twisted; that is, from the anchor to the disk.

When this is substituted, the frequency becomes

$$f = \frac{1}{2\pi}\sqrt{\frac{GJ_s}{IL}} \tag{3–31}$$

While this is just as simple as the case of linear oscillation, yet there are two points where errors are likely to arise. First, there are two moments of inertia: one is the mass moment of the disk, arising from the $T = I\alpha$ law; and the other, the area moment of the shaft section, over which the shear forces due to the torsion act.

The second confusion lies in the fact that there are two angular velocities. One is the actual motion of the disk or rate of change of θ, and the other is the hypothetical angular velocity of the vector ω, representing the circular frequency (of which $\dot\theta$ is the projection when multiplied by the amplitude). The distinction made here is particularly important when the maximum energy method is used.

3–15. Rotating Shaft with Flywheel on Each End. A shaft as in Fig. 3–20, having two flywheels of mass moment of inertia I_A and I_B respectively is rotating at constant speed. Some torsional impulse is applied, causing one to advance with respect to the other. This will cause a torque in the shaft tending to retard the fast one and to advance the other. An oscillation will result, which will be superimposed on the constant speed of both. The constant speed, which will cause only steady conditions, may then be ignored.

In advancing one flywheel and retarding the other, there will be a torque of $+T$ acting, say, on I_A and $-T$ (that is, in the opposite direction) on I_B. Now consider the nonrotating case when we take the two wheels, one in each hand, twist the shaft, and then release it. Initially the angular momentum of the system is zero and so it must remain. This is satisfied if the total momentum of the two wheels is zero; hence the momentum of the one must be equal and opposite to that of the other. (We neglect at present the mass moment of inertia of the shaft.)

There must be therefore some section N which remains at rest, and the frequency of oscillation of the two flywheels must be the same, so that the directions of motion continue to be opposite one another.

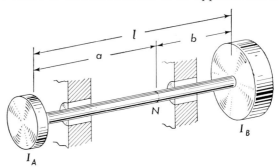

FIG. 3–20.

Suppose the flywheels A, B are distant a, b from N. We equate the frequencies (using eq. 3–31)

$$f = \frac{1}{2\pi}\sqrt{\frac{GJ}{I_A a}} = \frac{1}{2\pi}\sqrt{\frac{GJ}{I_B b}} \tag{3–32}$$

But only the denominators differ; therefore

$$I_A/I_B = b/a \tag{3–33}$$

Since $a + b = l$ this yields

$$a = \frac{I_B}{I_A + I_B} \cdot l \qquad \text{and} \qquad b = \frac{I_A}{I_A + I_B} \cdot l$$

and substituting this in either of expressions 3–32

$$f = \frac{1}{2\pi}\sqrt{\frac{GJ(I_A + I_B)}{l\,I_A I_B}} \tag{3–34}$$

The section N which remains at rest is called the *node* or *nodal section*. It is to be noted that the case considered before, with one end of the shaft anchored, is a particular case of the foregoing when (say) I_B becomes infinite. The node then moves over until $b = 0$ and $a = l$.

3–16. Shaft of Varying Diameters. Consider a shaft of two diameters, as in Fig. 3–21a. If we neglect the moment of inertia of the shaft, we have already from previous computations (eq. 3–29)

$$f = \frac{1}{2\pi}\sqrt{\frac{c}{I}}$$

The problem of finding the torsional spring constant c is the same as that considered in Art. 3–7 and so can be seen most easily by apply-

ing to the end of the shaft a unit torque and noting the angle change
between the ends.

For AB

$$\text{Torque applied} = 1 \text{ unit} = c_1\theta\Big]_A^B$$

$$\theta\Big]_A^B = \frac{1}{c_1} = \frac{32l_1}{\pi d_1^4 G}$$

Similarly,

$$\theta\Big]_B^C = \frac{1}{c_2} = \frac{32l_2}{\pi d_2^4 G}$$

Adding, total angle change

$$\theta\Big]_A^C = \theta\Big]_A^B + \theta\Big]_B^C = \frac{32}{\pi d_2^4 G}\left(\frac{d_2^4}{d_1^4}l_1 + l_2\right) \qquad (3\text{--}35)$$

This is the angle change due to unit torque; and the reciprocal will
be the required spring constant c (torque per radian) for the system.
But notice in eq. 3–35 that the factor before the bracket is the reciprocal
of the spring constant for a shaft of diameter d_2 only (except for the
length term). If we were to take a shaft of diameter d_2 and length
$\left(\dfrac{d_2}{d_1}\right)^4 l_1$ it would have the same characteristic, as concerns torsion, as
the shaft of diameter d_1 and length l_1. This would be an *equivalent shaft*.

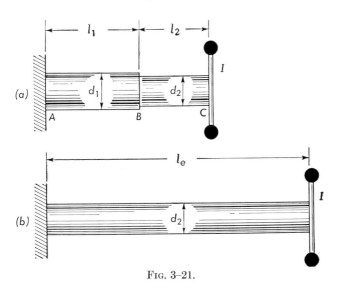

FIG. 3–21.

Figure 3–21b shows, below the original, the "equivalent shaft" for
the case considered above. From eq. 3–35 we obtain

$$l_e = \left(\frac{d_2}{d_1}\right)^4 l_1 + l_2 \qquad (3\text{-}36)$$

where the equivalent shaft is of diameter d_2. With this we can write the frequency directly, and so find an economy in the work.

$$f = \frac{1}{2\pi}\sqrt{\frac{c}{I}}$$

where

$$c = \frac{\pi d_2^4 G}{32 l_e}$$

The idea of the equivalent shaft of uniform diameter can be extended and is used, for instance, in determining the torsional vibration characteristics of even so complicated a shaft as an engine crankshaft. Formulae for converting cranks of various design have been calculated by W. Ker Wilson[*] in England, and by others.

3-17. Rayleigh's Method.[†] Distributed Mass. When a body cannot reasonably be assumed to have concentrated mass, we have to consider the effect of different elements of it vibrating different extents. An example would be the spring with the weight on the end, where the weight of the spring had also to be considered; or another example is the cantilever strip.

In such a system there are an infinite number of possible ways of vibration. That is, the spring can extend amounts proportional to the distance from the fixed end, quite uniformly, or the free end can go down when the middle goes up, or compression waves can be running up and down the spring as ripples on water. The body is said to have an infinite number of degrees of freedom.

However, at present we are studying only one degree of freedom. The *simplest* manner in which a body of distributed mass can vibrate always gives the slowest in the series of possible natural vibrations. Lord Rayleigh has shown that if *any reasonable assumption* is made as to the shape that a body keeps while vibrating, even though one makes a wrong assumption, yet the frequency found will be very close to the correct value. The method of maximum energies is used to obtain this frequency.

In many cases the simplest assumption for shape is that the body will have the same shape vibrating as with similar *static* loads. Thus for the spring we can assume linearly proportional extensions from the fixed end, and for the cantilever we can assume the shape is the statically deflected shape. These will give values of frequency often within 1 per

[*] W. Ker Wilson, *Practical Solution of Torsional Vibration Problems*, Vol. I (New York: John Wiley & Sons, Inc., 1935).

[†] Lord Rayleigh, *Theory of Sound* (1st ed.; London: Macmillan & Co., Ltd., 1877: reprint by Dover Publications, New York, 1945).

cent of the true value. The method is used greatly in the next chapter, but an example follows.

3–18. Torsional Vibration Including Moment of Inertia of Shaft. In Fig. 3–22 a shaft of length l and total mass moment of inertia I_s is fixed at its inner end and at the outer free end carries a disk with concentrated moment of inertia I_d. Consider that the shaft is divided into a large number of equal short lengths. Then since whatever torque T is applied

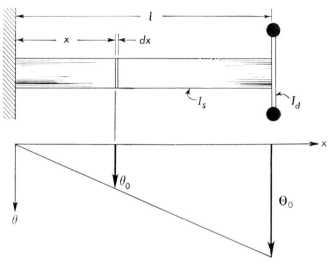

FIG. 3–22.

at the end will be the torque in each short length, each will be twisted through the same angle. Hence the total angular twist at any section distant x from the fixed end is given by

$$\theta = \frac{x}{l}\Theta \qquad \text{ASSUMPTION 1}$$

where Θ is the twist angle at the free end, and this we call our assumption of shape. It is shown in the graph below the figure. Now the simplest mode of vibration is for all parts to move together, all reaching their amplitude together; this means all parts have the same frequency or at any given position x

$$\theta = \theta_0 \sin \omega t \qquad \text{ASSUMPTION 2}$$

which includes the motion at the free end

$$\Theta = \Theta_0 \sin \omega t$$

The subscript "0" defines the amplitude values and so the first assumption includes

$$\theta_0 = \frac{x}{l}\Theta_0$$

In figuring the maximum potential energy of the system, the fact that we are including now some new mass has no effect. It is still only the same shaft which is twisted and contains strain energy, as was the case in Art. 3–14. So for an end amplitude of Θ_0,

$$\text{P.E.}_{\text{max}} = \tfrac{1}{2}T_{\text{max}}\,\Theta_0 = \tfrac{1}{2}c\Theta_0{}^2$$

To find the kinetic energy, it is necessary to reckon that every part of the shaft has mass and a different velocity. At a point x along the shaft there is an element of mass having moment of inertia

$$\frac{dx}{l}I_s$$

and this has a velocity $\dot{\theta}$ which has a maximum value $\theta_0\omega$, found by differentiating assumption 2.

$$\text{K.E.}_{\text{max}} \text{ of an element } = \frac{1}{2}\left(\frac{dx}{l}I_s\right)(\theta_0\omega)^2$$

We need to sum up the effect of all elements, which means an integral of dx from $x = 0$ to $x = l$. Since θ_0 is a function of x we have

$$\text{K.E.}_{\text{max}} \text{ of shaft } = \int_0^l \frac{1}{2}\frac{I_s}{l}\theta_0{}^2\omega^2\,dx = \frac{I_s\omega^2}{2l}\int_0^l\left(\frac{x}{l}\right)^2\theta_0{}^2dx$$

$$= \tfrac{1}{6}I_s\theta_0{}^2\omega^2$$

There is also the disk at the end which has K.E. involving its maximum velocity $\theta_0\omega$, so that equating K.E. and P.E. maxima:

$$\tfrac{1}{2}c\theta_0{}^2 = \tfrac{1}{6}I_s\theta_0{}^2\omega^2 + \tfrac{1}{2}I_d\theta_0{}^2\omega^2$$

$$\omega^2 = \frac{c}{I_d + \tfrac{1}{3}I_s}$$

$$f = \frac{1}{2\pi}\sqrt{\frac{c}{I_d + \tfrac{1}{3}I_s}} \qquad (3\text{–}37)$$

Thus it is seen that the effect of the mass moment of inertia of the shaft may most easily be included by using an equivalent system in which the disk has an inertia equal to that of the real disk *plus one-third that of the shaft.*

3–19. Free and Forced Vibration—Resonance.

The equations of motion derived so far have been based on the idea that a system is distorted and then only the internal forces tending to restore equilibrium have been acting. This is called a condition of *free vibration,* and the frequency of this motion is the *natural frequency.*

However, this is not the only type of vibration. External forces may be acting. For instance, some sort of *damping* is always present. Examples are air resistance and internal intermolecular friction in the metal. This will be considered later, and it will be seen that damping causes the vibration to die down, and also slightly changes the frequency.

Forced vibration is another sort. This occurs when an outside periodic force acts upon a body and forces it to oscillate. The frequency can be anything, and the amplitude will not die down as long as the outside force keeps doing work.

An important condition arises when the frequency of the forced vibration coincides with that of the free vibration. This is the condition of *resonance*. Consider a pendulum. A first outside push is given to it and it starts to swing naturally. Now if the outside force continues to push in the direction of the velocity, it is continuing to put work (energy) into the system. The second swing will be wider than the first, and so on.

In the case of machinery, even a small outside force can soon build up oscillations until something breaks. One of the primary reasons for investigating undamped free vibrations is to find the frequency at which resonance may occur, and to avoid it. For instance, if in an airplane the natural frequency of some part of an instrument on the panel coincides with that of the vibrations from the engine, that instrument is useless and will break on the first flight. The instrument must be re-designed, making some part a little heavier or lighter, or changing some stiffness, so that its natural frequency is changed.

3–20 Marine Installation. A ship has an engine and flywheel power unit, which drives a long shaft at the end of which is a propeller. This system will have a natural frequency of torsional vibration. Now if either the torsional impulses from the engine or the variations in the steady resistance of the propeller due to the blades passing the rudder occur at this same frequency, there will be a condition of resonance, and the amplitude of the oscillations will be increased until the shaft probably fails. If in designing a marine unit the resonant angular velocity of the shaft comes within the running speed range, the design should probably be changed, either by stiffening the shaft or by changing the magnitude or position of the moments of inertia.

To find the natural frequency it is necessary to calculate the moments of inertia involved and the shaft stiffness, as seen in eqs. 3–34 and 3–37.

First then the stiffness: if the shaft is solid, eq. 3–30 should be used; if the shaft is hollow then

$$c = \frac{\pi(D^4 - d^4)G}{32l} \tag{3-38}$$

when D, d are the outside and inside diameters. In merchant ships it is not unusual to have hollow shafts, but the Navy, anxious to keep down weight, always prefers hollow shafts.

The values of the torsional modulus

for steel $\qquad\qquad G = 12 \times 10^6$ lb/in.^{2}

for phosphor bronze $G = 6.25 \times 10^6$ lb/in.^{2}

Secondly the moments of inertia: if the engine is a diesel, the problem of finding its moment of inertia is not an elementary task; but it is often the case that it has a moment of inertia very large compared with that of the propeller. In this case the node in the shaft will be very close to the engine flywheel, and only small error will result if the whole length of shaft is taken to be on the propeller side of the node. We may then use the case of Art. 3–18 instead of Art. 3–15, and the eq. 3–37. But there is an adjustment to be made to the moment of inertia of the propeller: this moment of inertia is calculated or found experimentally by swinging it in air; when in water, an amount of water turns with the propeller, and it is reckoned that this increases the inertia by about 20 per cent.

If the motor is a steam turbine, the two moments of inertia are usually of the same order, so that we have the case of Art. 3–15. But the turbine is usually geared to the shaft through double-reduction gears, and this is beyond our present scope.

Example. A four-bladed marine propeller, 17 ft in diameter, weighing 15,000 lb, with radius of gyration 3.73 ft, is driven by a 12-cylinder 2-stroke diesel. The steel line shaft has 14.75 in. outside diameter and 8.75 in. bore, and is 150 ft long. The engine develops full power at 90 rpm.

Investigate for possible resonance.

$$I_{\text{prop}} = \frac{15,000}{32.2} \cdot (3.73)^2 = 6480 \text{ lb ft sec}^2$$

$$I_{\text{shaft}} = \frac{W}{g}\left(\frac{D^2 + d^2}{8}\right) = \frac{55,750(217.6 + 76.6)}{32.2 \times 8 \times 144} = 444 \text{ lb ft sec}^2$$

where $W = 0.28 \times 150 \times 12 \times \frac{\pi}{4}(14.75^2 - 8.75^2) = 55,750$ lb.

Effective $I = 1.2 I_{\text{prop}} + 1/3 I_{\text{shaft}} = 7928$ lb ft sec^2

$$c = \frac{\pi(14.75^4 - 8.75^4)12}{32 \times 150 \times 12} \times 10^6 = 27.11 \times 10^6 \text{ lb in./rad}$$

(by eq. 3–38)

$$= 2.260 \times 10^6 \text{ lb ft/rad}$$

$$\text{Natural frequency} = \frac{1}{2\pi}\sqrt{\frac{2.260 \times 10^6}{7928}} = 2.690 \text{ cps}$$

(by eq. 3–37)

$$= 161.4 \text{ cpm}$$

a) For resonance with blade frequency, i.e., 4 impulses per revolution:

$$\text{Resonant Speed} = \frac{161.4}{4} = 40.35 \text{ rpm}$$

Hence 40.35 rpm is in the running range, but assume that horsepower will vary as the cube of the rpm:

Since full horsepower occurs at 90 rpm, horsepower at 40.35 rpm is only $(40.35/90)^3$, or 9 per cent, of full load.

Hence trouble is not likely to be serious, because the shaft will have only a small steady torque from the horsepower and so can take quite a lot extra from vibration. The amplitude of vibration is not expected to be very large, for the propeller, when vibrating torsionally, has to swirl water back and forth.

b) For resonance with engine. A 12-cylinder 2-stroke engine produces 12 torsional impulses per revolution from firing. Hence to produce 161.4 impulses per minute it will be rotating at $\frac{161.4}{12} = 13.45$ rpm. This is lower than the above, and the engine probably would not even run so slowly.

Thus the design is satisfactory.

3-21. Small Variations and Experimental Errors. If in making a satisfactory design it is an accepted fact that natural frequencies must be avoided because of resonance, it is important that the natural frequencies be well reckoned at the start. However, the exact reckoning of natural frequencies of machine elements presents quite a problem. How much error is made in neglecting damping, in assuming concentrated masses, in reckoning structural corners as pin joints? This becomes quite a question.

It is well to reckon therefore the percentage error in frequency that certain known or suspected experimental errors in readings or reckonings can make. For example, suppose a "weightless" cantilever beam carries at its end a "concentrated" mass. It is decided that the formula

$$f = \frac{3.127}{\sqrt{\Delta}} \tag{3-11}$$

will suffice. The deflection Δ is measured as 0.0144 in. (cf. page 100). But there is no assurance in that last figure—it might be 0.0145 or 0.0143. This amounts to nearly 0.7 per cent error in data (relatively small as such data often go), and it is desired to find how much percentage error in frequency this involves.

Immediate use of the slide rule to find the three possible frequencies by eq. 3-11 and their differences will yield poor results. A very simple mathematical device is available; it involves only differentiation.

If Δ in eq. 3-11 is variable, find the variation in f due to Δ by obtaining the derivative of f with respect to Δ:

$$\frac{df}{d\Delta} = -\frac{3.127}{2\Delta^{3/2}}$$

or

$$\frac{df}{d\Delta} = -\left(\frac{3.127}{\sqrt{\Delta}}\right)\left(\frac{1}{2\Delta}\right) = -\frac{f}{2\Delta}$$

Therefore

$$\frac{df}{f} = -\frac{1}{2}\frac{d\Delta}{\Delta} \qquad (3\text{-}39)$$

or, reading the d's as δ's, the percentage change in frequency is of opposite sign and half the value of the percentage change in deflection. A reading of Δ that is 0.7 per cent high (that is, reading 0.0144 when really it is 0.0143) will give a frequency answer that is 0.35 per cent low.

Take a pendulum clock to a mountain-top home, or the Equator, where the value of g is slightly different, and it will need adjustment, for frequency varies as $\sqrt{g/l}$. But a spring-and-mass system will have the same frequency for though it can be written $\sqrt{kg/W}$ this really means $\sqrt{k/m}$, and mass is invariable. A torsional pendulum clock is therefore independent of location.

BIBLIOGRAPHY

CHURCH, A. H. *Elementary Mechanical Vibrations.* New York: Pitman Publishing Corp., 1948.

DEN HARTOG, J. P. *Mechanical Vibrations.* 3d ed. New York: McGraw-Hill Book Co., Inc., 1947.

FREBERG, C. R., and KEMLER, E. N. *Elements of Mechanical Vibration.* 2d ed. New York: John Wiley & Sons, Inc., 1949.

HANSEN, H. M., and CHENEA, P. F. *Mechanics of Vibrations.* New York: John Wiley & Sons, Inc., 1953.

MERIAM, J. L. *Mechanics.* (Part II, "Dynamics") New York: John Wiley & Sons, Inc., 1952, Chap. 14.

MYKLESTAD, N. O. *Vibration Analysis.* New York: McGraw-Hill Book Co., Inc., 1944.

RAMSAY, A. S. *Dynamics,* Part I. London: Cambridge University Press, 1929, Chaps. 7 and 17.

THOMSON, W. T. *Mechanical Vibrations.* New York: Prentice-Hall, Inc., 1948.

THORNTON, D. L. *Mechanics Applied to Vibrations and Balancing.* 2d ed. London: Chapman & Hall, Ltd., 1951, Chap. 3.

TIMOSHENKO, S. *Vibration Problems in Engineering.* 2d ed. New York: D. Van Nostrand Co., Inc., 1937.

TIMOSHENKO, S., and YOUNG, D. H. *Engineering Mechanics.* 2d ed. New York: McGraw-Hill Book Co., Inc., 1940, Chap. 10.

TOFT, L., and KERSEY, A. T. J. *Theory of Machines.* 6th ed. London: Sir Isaac Pitman & Sons, Ltd., 1949, Chaps. 3 and 14.

TUPLIN, W. A. *Vibration in Machinery.* 2d ed. London: Sir Isaac Pitman & Sons, Ltd., 1946.

PROBLEMS

3-1. A particle moves in a straight line, with simple harmonic motion, making 7 complete oscillations in 11 sec. The velocity of the particle is 4 ft/sec when its distance from the center of the oscillation is 5 in. Find the amplitude of the motion, the maximum velocity, and the maximum acceleration.   (C.U.)

3–2. A square steel slab weighing 100 lb is attached to and rests horizontally upon four equal springs of stiffness 20 lb/in. compression. At least how far must the slab be depressed (while remaining horizontal) so that some dried peas that are upon it shall bounce away on the rebound?

3–3. A Frahm Tachometer reed consists of a small weight w attached to the end of a cantilever steel strip 2 in. in length and $0.030 \times \frac{1}{4}$ in. section. Find w for a frequency of 1800 cycles/min. (Neglect the mass of the strip.)

3–4. A U-tube has internal cross section 1/20 sq in., and the bottom is a semi-circle of mean radius 1 in. The tube is filled with mercury (weight 0.49 lb/cu in.) to a height of 18.43 in. in each straight part of the tube. If the mercury is depressed in one tube and then released, find the natural period of oscillation.

3–5. The figure shows a drum, of radius r and moment of inertia I, about which is wrapped a light string. The string is attached to two unequal springs, k_1, k_2, which are anchored at the other ends. The drum is free to rotate about a fixed pivot. Assuming no slip of the string on the drum, and ignoring the weight of the two springs, find the natural frequency.

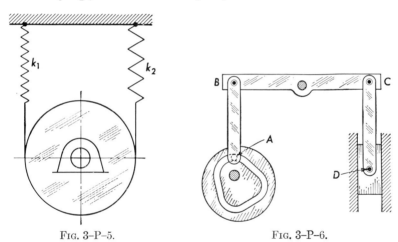

FIG. 3–P–5.   FIG. 3–P–6.

3–6. A cam follower system consists of push rod, rocker arm, connecting rod and a heavy sliding body, as in the figure. There is a guide not shown for the cam roll A. The sliding body weighs 70 lb, while the weights of all other parts are negligible. The system is disassembled; and experiment shows that a tension of 100 lb stretches the connecting rod CD by 0.0032 in., a compression load of 100 lb on the push rod AB shrinks it 0.0026 in., while loads of 100 lb down at both ends of the rocker, supported by its pivot, bend B by 0.0152 in. away from a straight line through C and the pivot. Assuming point A fixed, find the natural frequency of body D in oscillating against the cam.

3–7. A log, 10 ft in length and 6 in. in diameter, with specific gravity 0.8, floats vertically in a large body of water. If it is displaced vertically from the position at which it floats at rest, it will bob up and down. Find the natural period.

3–8. The log in Problem 3–7 floats in water contained in a tub of internal diameter 2 ft. Find the natural period of vertical oscillation.

3–9. The platen of a printing press, weighing 4 tons, slides horizontally on frictionless guides. It arrives at the end of its slide with velocity V, meets bumper springs having a combined stiffness of 8 tons per inch compression, and rebounds. Find the time of contact with the springs. Assume perfect elasticity, without mass to the springs.

3–10. The moving table of a planing machine slides upon horizontal guides. The table weighs 240 lb and the frictionless force opposing its motion is 40 lb. At a time when the speed of the table is 3 ft/sec, the driving mechanism is disconnected and the table is then brought to rest in a distance of $1\frac{1}{2}$ in. by collision with a spring buffer attached to the rigid frame of the machine. Calculate the time required for the spring to acquire its greatest compression. Assume that the spring is initially free from stress and neglect all loss of energy in the initial impact.   (C.U.)

3–11. A simple pendulum with weight 5 lb and length 9 in. is attached to the roof of an elevator which has an acceleration vertically downward of 22 ft/sec². What is the period of small amplitude swing of the pendulum?

3–12. A simple pendulum (weight W, length l) is inverted, as in the figure, and two equal springs, each of stiffness k, are attached at a distance s from the fixed center of oscillation.

Write the equation of motion by the inertia method and hence find the minimum stiffness of each spring so that the pendulum will oscillate with

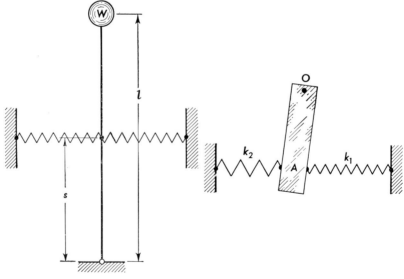

FIG. 3–P–12.   FIG. 3–P–13.

simple harmonic motion through small angles. Give a numerical answer for the case $W = 4$ lb; $s = 12$ in., $l = 24$ in.

3-13. A heavy bar OA is in a horizontal plane and pivots about a fixed vertical axis at O. At A two springs resist any motion of the bar: $k_1 = 10$ lb/ft, $k_2 = 20$ lb/ft. Find the period of small oscillations when the radius OA will be sensibly constant at 12 in. The bar weighs 30 lb; its center of gravity is 6 in. from O, and its radius of gyration around that point is 5 in.

3-14. Two large spheres of 3 in. diam are joined by a light thin rod so that their centers are 12 in. apart like a dumbbell. If the rod has a pivot 4 in. from one sphere's center, find the frequency of small-angle oscillation as a pendulum about this pivot.

3-15. The figure shows a light bar pivoted at the center and of length 6 in. At a point 1 in. from the center a weight of 2 lb is mounted. The ends of the lever are attached to two springs, one of stiffness $K_1 = 5$ lb/in., the other (on weighted side) of stiffness $K_2 = 7$ lb/in. Use the inertia method to find the frequency for small oscillations.

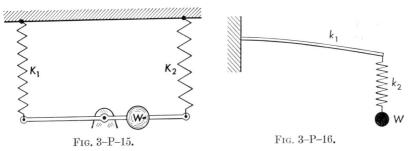

FIG. 3–P–15.   FIG. 3–P–16.

3-16. The figure shows a weight W of 5 lb hanging from the end of a coil spring of stiffness $k_2 = 10$ lb/in., the upper end of which is attached to a cantilever. A static weight of 4 lb will deflect the cantilever end $\frac{1}{2}$ in. Find the natural frequency of the motion of W; neglect the weights of spring and cantilever.

3-17. A wheel is mounted on an axle and its motion is controlled by a light spiral spring so that when it is displaced from its position of equilibrium it makes small rotational oscillations. The strength of the spring is such that a torque of $1/20$ lb in. will twist it through 1 radian. If the time of a complete oscillation is $\frac{1}{2}$ sec. find the moment of inertia of the wheel. Find also the maximum angular velocity if the maximum displacement from the position of equilibrium is 10°.
(C.U.)

3-18. A weight W hangs from the end of an inextensible string which is wrapped around a cylindrical drum of moment of inertia I and radius r in. The weight is supported in equilibrium by a spiral torsional spring on the drum's axle, which has a stiffness K measured as lb in. torque per radian. Find the frequency of vibration by the maximum energy method.

3-19. A weight W is attached to the end of a light rigid rod of length L pivoted freely at a fixed point as in the figure. In static equilibrium the rod is held horizontal by a spring of stiffness k located at a distance s from the pivot:

a) Find the natural frequency.

b) If a small body of weight w is dropped from a height h onto the weight W, and sticks to it, find the amplitude of the resultant vibration (assuming small angular motion of the rod).

Weights of rod and spring may be neglected but impact must be considered.

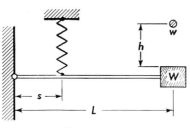

Fig. 3–P–19.

3–20. A simple pendulum is 36 in. long, and at its end is a bob weighing 10 lb. A horizontal spring is attached to the pendulum 12 in. down from the pivot; its stiffness is 5 lb per in., but it exerts no force when the pendulum hangs vertically.

A bullet weighing $\frac{1}{2}$ oz is fired into the bob, entering with velocity 2200 ft/sec, and lodges there. Find the amplitude and frequency of the ensuing motion. Neglect angularity in the spring. (C.U.)

3–21. A weight of 3 lb is attached to the end of a vertical spring, and the stretch is 4.5 in. Find the amplitude and frequency of the ensuing motion if 1 lb of the weight is suddenly removed.

3–22. An elevator weighing 10,000 lb is descending at 180 ft/min constant speed, but at the instant that it is hanging by 60 ft of cable the upper end of the cable is suddenly stopped. If for the steel cable $E = 15 \times 10^6$ lb/in.^{2} and cross-sectional area is 2.5 in.^{2}, find the maximum stress in the cable, and frequency of the resulting vibration. (Timoshenko)

Compare this with the stress caused by similar stoppage during upward travel. Neglect damping.

3–23. A clock is regulated by a pendulum whose period is supposed to be 2 sec. The clock is found to gain 40 sec in 24 hr. In order that the clock may keep correct time, should the pendulum be lengthened or shortened, and by what per cent? (U.L.)

3–24. A clock pendulum is so designed that it will measure seconds exactly when swinging with amplitude 10° either side of vertical. But it is installed in a clock in which it is permitted to swing 15° either way.

a) By how much will the clock be slow after 24 hr?

b) How much time will have elapsed when the clock strikes its 24th hour?

3–25. A cantilever spring, 4 in. in length, of 0.031 in. thickness, and 1 in. across the flat, carries a 3-lb weight on its free end. Find the percentage variation of frequency that results from calculations based on an error of 0.001 in. in measuring the thickness.

3–26. Show that the very large radius of curvature of a concave mirror or lens may be obtained in this manner: Lay the mirror with concave face up, and roll on it a steel sphere of radius r. The radius of curvature will be given by

$$R = r + \frac{5T^2g}{28\pi^2}$$

where T is the period of rolling of the sphere.

3–27. A solid cylinder of weight 20 lb, radius 6 in., rolls on a plane surface. To the cylinder is attached a weight of 3 lb at radius 4 in. Find the natural frequency of small oscillations.

3–28. A right conical solid of steel has a height of 4 in. and an apex half-angle of 15°. It is set upon a plane inclined at 15° to the horizontal. Find the period of small rolling oscillations.

3–29. In the figure the rack gear carries an integral drum on which is wound a thin steel tape. Find the natural frequency of oscillation of this body against the spring, which is attached to the end of the tape.

Pitch radius of gear = 5 in., radius of drum = 3 in., radius of gyration of gear and drum together = 4 in. about the center. Weight of gear and drum together = 24 lb; spring stiffness 9 lb per in.

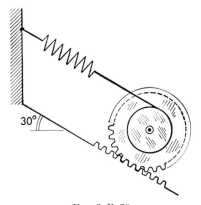

Fig. 3–P–29.

3–30. A semicylindrical shape of sheet metal as in Fig. 1–9 (page 16) lies upon a horizontal plane. Find its period of small-angle rolling.

3–31. A large mass of weight W and moment of inertia J about its center of mass is attached to the end of a horizontal cantilever spring of length L and stiffness $3EI/L^3$ lb per in. of lateral displacement. Find the frequency by the maximum energy method, ignoring the mass of the spring. For any small deflection δ, it may be assumed that the slope at the end is given by $\theta = 2\delta/L$.

3–32. The figure shows a light rod EF universally pivoted at E and carrying a concentrated mass at F. It is kept horizontal, when in its equilibrium position, by the inextensible string GH. Find the periodic time of small oscillations forward and back.

(C.U.)

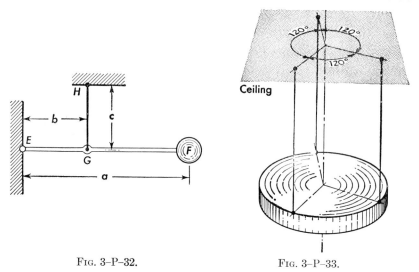

FIG. 3–P–32.   FIG. 3–P–33.

3-33. An important practical method of finding the moment of inertia of many bodies is indicated by the following. A 12-in. diam circular disk, weighing 5 lb, is suspended from the ceiling by three long wires of equal length, so that its normal axis is vertical. The wires are vertical and are attached at points equidistant from the center of gravity and 120° apart, as in the figure.

If the disk is twisted about its vertical axis and released, find the period of the motion.

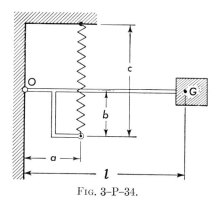

FIG. 3–P–34.

3-34. The figure shows the equilibrium position of a seismograph mechanism. The moving arm is pivoted at O, its center of gravity is at G, and its radius of gyration about a transverse axis through O is k. The spring, which is light, is freely pivoted at its ends and, when the system is in equilibrium, the extension of the spring is d.

Show that the system will oscillate if $a^2c > bd(c - b)$ and find the period of small oscillations.   (C.U.)

3-35. A uniform rod BC of mass m is hinged at the end C to a vertical wall and supported in an inclined position by a light spring AB attached to the end B and to a point A on the wall vertically above C. $BC = a$ and $CA = b$. The spring will extend a unit distance under tension λ. When the rod is in equilibrium AB is horizontal. Show that the periodic time of small oscillations of the rod in a vertical plane ABC will be $2\pi\sqrt{\dfrac{2ma^2}{6\lambda b^2 - 3mgb}}$.   (C.U.)

3-36. A plank of negligible thickness but of length 10 ft and weight 25 lb is set on top of a fixed circular drum of radius 2 ft. It proceeds to seesaw without slip. Use the maximum energy method to find the frequency of small oscillations.

3-37. Three identical gear wheels, each of effective radius a and radius of gyration $a/\sqrt{2}$ are supported in smooth bearings by a light arm AC, as shown in the figure. The system is supported with wheel A fixed and the arm AC hanging vertically. Show that the time of small oscillation about a mean vertical position is given by $2\pi\sqrt{11a/3g}$. Neglect friction. (C.U.)

3-38. Prove that the linear spring constant k of a coiled wire spring in tension is given by

$$k = \frac{Gd^4}{8nD^3}$$

where d is the wire diameter, D the mean coil diameter, and n the number of coils; it may be assumed that the deflection is due to torsion, the shear being negligible.

FIG. 3–P–37.

3-39. Two masses, $2m$ and m, are attached to the ends of a light inelastic string passing over a pulley of mass m with its axis fixed horizontally. From m is suspended another mass m by means of an elastic string of unstretched length a and spring constant mg. If the system is released from rest with the elastic string unstretched, and the pulley is considered as a solid circular disk of radius r, prove that each mass will move with S.H.M. (simple harmonic motion), and find the period and distance over which the mass $2m$ oscillates.   (U.L.)

3-40. Two railroad cars weigh 50,000 lb each and are connected by a coupling of stiffness 16,000 lb/in. Find the natural frequency of oscillation. *Note*: The stiffness of any coil spring is given by GJ/R^2L where J and R are moment and dimensions of the coil, and L is the length of wire in the whole spring.

3-41. A running pocket watch is placed on a perfectly frictionless horizontal table so that it may be regarded as free to rotate about its own center of gravity. It is composed essentially of a balance wheel, of moment of inertia i, and a body, of moment of inertia I, connected by a hairspring. The inertia of the hairspring and other parts of the mechanism may be ignored.

Show that if $I = 110$ gram $\cdot$ cm^2 and $i = 0.05$ gram $\cdot$ cm^2, the watch gains nearly 20 seconds a day in this position if its rate is correct when the body is rigidly held.

Show also that in general, in addition to its oscillations, the body of the watch rotates steadily with a small uniform spin.   (C.U.)

3–42. Two cylindrical disks are mounted on a shaft 12 in. in length, which is free to rotate about a horizontal axis. If one disk were held, the other end of the shaft would turn one radian if a torque of 4 lb in. were applied. The two disks, of moment of inertia $I_A = 0.20$ and $I_B = 0.16$ lb in. sec^2, are of radius $r_A = 5$ in., and $r_B = 4$ in. respectively. Two weights are then suspended by strings wrapped around the disks, as in the figure. On A the weight is 4 lb; on B, 5 lb. Find the natural frequency of the system and the position of the node in the shaft. Weights of shaft and strings are negligible.

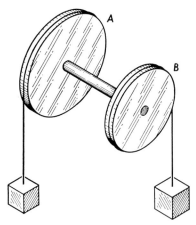

Fig. 3–P–42.

3–43. Two trucks, one weighing 1000 lb, the other 2000 lb, run without friction on a straight track. They are connected by a spring of stiffness 30 lb/in., equal in compression and tension, and of negligible weight.

If initially the 1000-lb truck is at rest and the heavier is suddenly given a velocity of 20 ft/sec toward the former, investigate completely the ensuing motion. Find the maximum and minimum velocities of both trucks.

3–44. A motor rotating at constant speed drives a flywheel through two shafts set at an angle and connected by a universal joint. The flywheel consists of a rim and four spokes. The rim weighs 10 lb and its mean radius is 6 in. Each spoke is flexible and a force of 40 lb at the 6-in. radius is required to twist the rim $1/10$ radian with respect to the hub.

If the motion transmitted through a universal joint is not uniform but is given by the equation

$$\omega_B/\omega_A = 1 + \lambda \cos 2\alpha$$

where A and B are the two shafts (A the driver), α is the angle through which A has turned, and λ is a constant, investigate possible resonances.

3–45. The armature shaft of an electric motor with six field-poles carries a pulley which is keyed to it. The moment of inertia of the pulley is 0.07 lb ft sec^2, that of the armature is 0.04 lb ft sec^2, and that of the shaft is negligible. The steel shaft is of 1 in. diameter, and the length between motor and pulley is 24 in. Find the speed (rpm) of the armature for resonance of torsional vibration.

Problems Including Mass of Spring

3-46. A truck of weight W moving freely on a horizontal plane is attached by a spring of weight w, free length l, and stiffness k, to a fixed point. Prove that the circular frequency of horizontal oscillation is given by $\omega^2 = kg/(W + \frac{1}{3}w)$.

3-47. A uniform cylindrical steel rod of $\frac{1}{2}$ in. diameter and 10 ft in length is fixed at one end, and given an initial twist at the other. Find by Rayleigh's method its natural frequency of torsional vibration.

3-48. The top end of a spring is attached to the ceiling. The spring weighs 6 lb and has a stiffness of 20 lb/in. extension. To its lower end is attached another spring weighing 3 lb and of stiffness 10 lb/in. To the bottom end of this lighter spring is attached a weight of 1 lb, which is constrained to move vertically. Use Rayleigh's method to find the lowest natural frequency of oscillation.

3-49. A 5-ft steel shaft is fixed at one end and to its free end is attached a flywheel with moment of inertia 10 lb ft sec². From the fixed end the first 2 ft of length are of 2 in. diameter and the next 3 ft of length are of 1 in. diameter. Find the natural torsional frequency.

3-50. A steel shaft is partly of tapered form: from its anchorage it diminishes in diameter uniformly from 2.5 in. to 1.5 in. in 3 in. of length. It is then of 1.5 in. diameter for a further 9-in. length. To the end is attached a disk with moment of inertia 2 lb in. sec². Find the natural frequency of torsional oscillation of this system, and compare it with the frequency of a plain 12-in. length of 1.5-in. shaft carrying the same disk.

Chapter 4

BALANCE OF ROTORS AND CRITICAL SPEEDS

4–1. The Effects of Lack of Balance. A simple single-throw crank-shaft as in Fig. 4–1a is rotating at constant speed. The center of gravity of the shaft lies on the axis of rotation, and therefore causes no inertia effect. But the crank has a center of gravity at some distance r from the axis, and the inertia effect is therefore a centrifugal force

$$F = \frac{W}{g} r \omega^2$$

acting at the center of gravity. Fig. 4–1b shows a simplified version of the crank with the mass concentrated at the center of gravity, and with the same inertia effects. This drawing shows the conventional representation of the original.

Fig. 4–1c shows the crank in end view, and in the position where the mass makes an angle of θ with the vertical. The centrifugal force is radially outward; the vertical and horizontal components of the force are

$$F_V = \frac{W}{g} r \omega^2 \cos \theta$$

$$F_H = \frac{W}{g} r \omega^2 \sin \theta$$

The vertical force therefore varies during each revolution from a maximum of $+\frac{W}{g} r \omega^2$ upward through zero to a minimum of $-\frac{W}{g} r \omega^2$, that is, of the same magnitude but downward; and similarly with the horizontal force. Now since the shaft is mounted in bearings which are part of some frame, shaking forces are acting on the frame. All materials are more or less elastic. If we consider the elasticity of the frame, or if the frame is supported by resilient mounts, such as are commonly used with automobile engines, it is apparent that these alternating forces will cause unpleasant vibrations in that frame and also probably noise, with undue wear and tear on the machinery. But we may go further by considering also that the shaft is flexible, and since the force acts at some point other than at the bearings, bending moments and shear forces will deform the shaft.

These two conditions will be considered in sequence here. The first

136

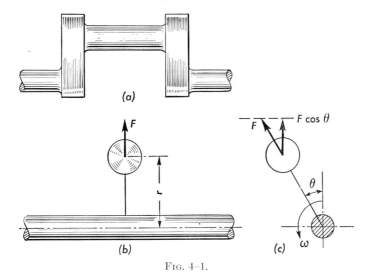

FIG. 4–1.

part will assume a rigid shaft and will consider the methods of eliminating the forces, merely bearing in mind that if they are not perfectly
eliminated, vibrations in the frame, and radial loads on the bearings,
will result. The second part will consider the effects of even small unbalanced forces on a flexible shaft.

(A) Rigid Shaft

4–2. Balancing a Single Mass. In Fig. 4–2 W is a weight at radius r
on a disk that rotates with a shaft at angular velocity ω. The rotation
creates a radial outward force $\dfrac{W}{g}r\omega^2$. But this force may be neutralized
by adding to the disk another balancing weight W_1 at radius r_1 such
that this will produce an equal and opposite force. Thus radius r_1 must
be at 180° from radius r while still in the plane of the disk, and

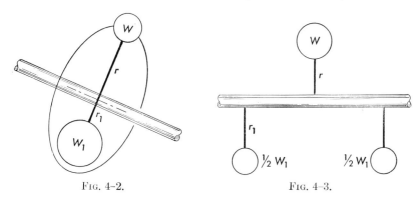

FIG. 4–2.   FIG. 4–3.

$$\frac{W_1}{g}r_1\omega^2 = \frac{W}{g}r\omega^2$$

or since ω^2/g can be factored out,

$$W_1 r_1 = Wr \tag{4-1}$$

With this the shaft is said to be in *dynamic balance* and it is seen that there is wide variety of choice for a balancing weight, since only the product $W_1 r_1$ is specified. The weight W may be balanced by a similar weight at the same radius, a larger weight at a smaller radius, or a smaller at a larger radius.

However, to place a balance weight exactly opposite in the same plane is not always a possible solution. In the case of the engine crank of the preceding article, a counterweight directly opposite the crank would interfere with the motion of the connecting rod. The solution in this case is to split the required counterweight into two halves, and move one half right, the other left along the shaft by the same distance, as shown in Fig. 4–3.

4–3. Several Masses in a Transverse Plane. Let W_1, W_2, W_3, $\cdots$ be any number of eccentric weights mounted on a disk (as in Fig. 4–4), which rotates at constant angular velocity ω. Each will produce a centrifugal force, and it is immediately evident from the vector diagram that if these forces are not already in equilibrium, one extra force will achieve it.

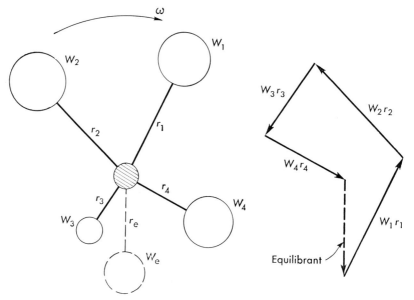

Fig. 4–4.

The angular position of the radius for this one equilibrant is given by the direction of the closing vector, and the magnitude of $W_e r_e$ is found from the length of this vector.

Inherently, graphical solutions suffer from being only approximately accurate, although in many cases their accuracy is quite sufficient in practical problems. But a more exact solution can be found analytically by equating the horizontal and vertical components of the vectors (including the equilibrant required) to zero. Where θ is the angle that each radius makes with the horizontal or x-axis, as shown in Fig. 4–5 we have

$$[W_1 r_1 \cos \theta_1 + W_2 r_2 \cos \theta_2 + \cdots + W_e r_e \cos \theta_e]\frac{\omega^2}{g} = 0 \quad (4\text{–}2)$$

$$[W_1 r_1 \sin \theta_1 + W_2 r_2 \sin \theta_2 + \cdots + W_e r_e \sin \theta_e]\frac{\omega^2}{g} = 0 \quad (4\text{–}3)$$

ω^2/g is shown as a factor common to all terms; hence it may be omitted.

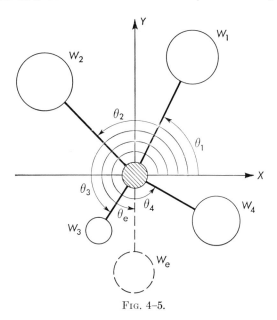

Fig. 4–5.

It may then be written, that for a number of weights to be in dynamic balance

$$\Sigma F_X = \Sigma W r \cos \theta = 0 \quad (4\text{–}4)$$

$$\Sigma F_Y = \Sigma W r \sin \theta = 0 \quad (4\text{–}5)$$

Note that these two equations are the same as those for *static balance*. By this is meant that if the shaft is laid on horizontal parallels, in any two positions, it will not roll. Two positions are obviously necessary, for consider the case of the crankshaft with a single throw: if the shaft is set on parallels with the crank vertically down, it will not roll. Another position (not 180° off) is needed to show the unbalance.

Take the case in Fig. 4–5 as it is shown. By summing moments of the gravity forces around the axis of the shaft, there will be static equilibrium if

$$\Sigma(\text{Static Moments})_Y = W_1 r_1 \cos \theta_1 + W_2 r_2 \cos \theta_2 + \cdots = 0$$

This is the same as eq. 4–4. Now, for the easiest analytical case, let the other position be when the shaft is turned 90° and again set on the parallels. Then for the static moments to be zero, eq. 4–5 is required.

So static equilibrium and dynamic balance in this case are exactly the same. For both, the requirement is that the center of gravity of the whole system be in the axis of rotation.

Example. W_1, W_2, W_3, located as in the table below, need an equilibrant or balancing weight W_e.

No.	W lb.	r in.	$\theta°$
1	10	4	0
2	15	6	90
3	20	5	225

To start the analysis, tentatively place W_e in the first quadrant: this makes eqs. 4–4 and 4–5 appear as follows:

$$10 \times 4 \cos 0° + 15 \times 6 \cos 90° + 20 \times 5 \cos 225° + W_e r_e \cos \theta_e = 0$$
$$10 \times 4 \sin 0° + 15 \times 6 \sin 90° + 20 \times 5 \sin 225° + W_e r_e \sin \theta_e = 0$$

So

$$W_e r_e \cos \theta_e = 20 \times 5 \times 0.707 - 10 \times 4 \times 1 = 30.7$$
$$W_e r_e \sin \theta_e = 20 \times 5 \times 0.707 - 15 \times 6 \times 1 = -19.3$$

Divide these to get

$$\tan \theta_e = -\frac{19.3}{30.7} = -0.629$$

This has two solutions, but observe that the sine is negative while the cosine is positive; thus θ_e must be in the fourth quadrant. The signs automatically show that the assumption of first quadrant as in Fig. 4–6 is wrong; instead

$$\theta_e = \text{arc tan } (-0.629) = 327° \, 50'$$

Now from the sum of the squares of the two expressions

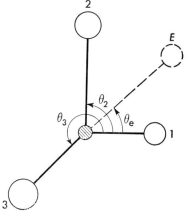

Fig. 4–6.

$$W_e r_e = \sqrt{30.7^2 + 19.3^2} = 36.2$$

say, for example, 7.24 lb at 5-in. radius.

4–4. Several Masses in an Axial Plane. Fig. 4–7 shows a number of weights (say three), all lying in a plane that includes the axis of rotation. In this case the requirements of eqs. 4–4 and 4–5 (that is, that the sum of forces in any direction must be equal to zero) are not enough. For, since the lines of action of the centrifugal forces do not pass through a point, they may also produce a couple tending to tilt the shaft; and this can only be balanced by an equal and opposite couple. Thus, in general, two extra weights are needed for balance.

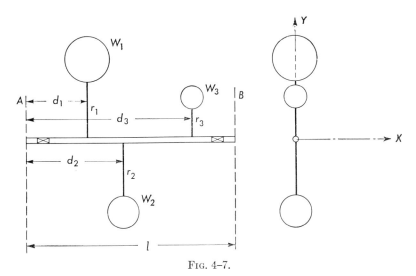

FIG. 4–7.

For instance, let us choose some transverse plane A (Fig. 4–7) in which it will be convenient to add one of these counterbalance weights. The dimensions d_1, d_2, d_3, $\cdots$ measure the axial distance from A to the planes of the weights, and dimension l is the distance to the second or B plane in which a counterbalance weight may be added. Now taking moments of the centrifugal forces about the axis of plane A,

$$\Sigma M_A = \frac{W_1}{g} r_1 \omega^2 d_1 - \frac{W_2}{g} r_2 \omega^2 d_2 + \frac{W_3}{g} r_3 \omega^2 d_3 + \frac{W_B}{g} r_B \omega^2 l$$

W_B properly chosen will cause this to vanish. Since ω^2/g is a common factor not equal to zero, we may write more shortly:

$$W_1 r_1 d_1 - W_2 r_2 d_2 + W_3 r_3 d_3 + W_B r_B l = 0 \qquad (4\text{–}6)$$

Now with the first counterweight B so chosen, the dynamic moments about A are balanced. A second weight is then added to balance the forces, and this must be placed in plane A so that it will not upset the moment equation. From eq. 4–4 for the centrifugal forces:

$$W_A r_A + W_1 r_1 - W_2 r_2 + W_3 r_3 + W_B r_B = 0 \qquad (4\text{–}7)$$

If in either eq. 4–6 or 4–7 the product $W_B r_B$ or $W_A r_A$ turns out negative, the meaning is that the weight is on the opposite side of the shaft from that assumed.

The location of planes A and B may be anywhere desirable. It frequently occurs in machines that there is some wheel, flywheel, or gear to which it is easy to attach a counterweight. The plane B for instance could also have been chosen coincident with plane 3, so that the weight B can become an addition to, or a subtraction from the weight W_3. A great variety of solutions are possible.

Example. A two-cylinder horizontal engine has two cranks between two flywheels, the cranks being at 180° to each other. Each crank has the dynamic effect of an 800-lb weight at a radius of 15 in. The cranks are symmetrically placed and 28 in. apart. The flywheels are 4 ft 8 in. apart, and the counterweights are to be attached inside the rim of the wheels at 58-in. radius.

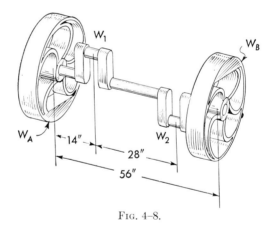

Fig. 4–8.

Let the left-hand wheel in Fig. 4–8 be the reference plane A. Then for the dynamic moments about the center of this wheel to be zero:

$$(800 \times 15 \times 14) - (800 \times 15 \times 42) + (W_B \times 58 \times 56) = 0$$

$$W_B = \frac{800 \times 15 \times 28}{58 \times 56} = 103.4 \text{ lb}$$

and is positive, that is, on same side as W_1.

Also, $\Sigma F = 0$, therefore guessing that W_A is probably on the same side as W_2,

$$- (W_A \times 58) + (800 \times 15) - (800 \times 15) + (103.4 \times 58) = 0$$
$$W_A = 103.4 \text{ lb}$$

Thus W_A and W_B are equal, which can also be seen by the symmetry.

Problem. A four-cylinder automobile engine has two cranks at $0°$ and two at $180°$. All crank throws and revolving masses are equal. There are therefore three possibilities of design, as in Fig. 4–9.

If no counterweights are to be added, which is/are the balanced crankshaft(s)? Think first; the answer is at bottom of the next page.

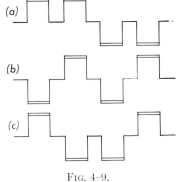

Fig. 4–9.

4–5. Certain Cases Where One Counterweight Is Enough.
It was shown in Art. 4–2 and Fig. 4–3 that two counterweights can balance one. Stated in reverse then, two masses on the same side of a shaft, or $180°$ apart, can be balanced by one.

Consider the cases shown in Fig. 4–10. On the left is the case where two weights, W_1 and W_2, are on the same side of the shaft, and on the right they are on opposite sides, or $180°$ apart.

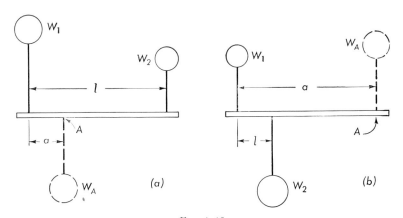

Fig. 4–10.

The counterweight W_A is not going to affect the moments about point A. This point is therefore located by the requirement that the moments from the weights W_1 and W_2 must cancel each other, or, in case (a)

$$W_1 r_1 a = W_2 r_2 (l - a) \qquad (4\text{--}8)$$

or in case (b)

$$W_1 r_1 a = W_2 r_2 (a - l) \qquad (4\text{--}9)$$

These equations give the location, i.e., dimension a. The size of W_A at some chosen radius r_A is given by the equation of forces (eq. 4–7) which is that for static balance.

It might be noted that eq. 4–8 can be solved for any weights, and the counterweight will always be between them. But in eq. 4–9 there is one exception, for if $W_1 = W_2$, dimension a becomes infinite (mathematically). In the practical case, W_1 and W_2 must be very different or dimension l short, so that the counterweight is not unreasonably far off.

4–6. Several Masses in Various Planes — First Method (Distribution). Any number of rotating weights in different planes can be balanced by adding counterweights in two previously chosen planes.

Referring to Fig. 4–11, it is desired to balance the three weights W_1, W_2, and W_3 by the addition of counterweights W_A and W_B in the planes A and B respectively.

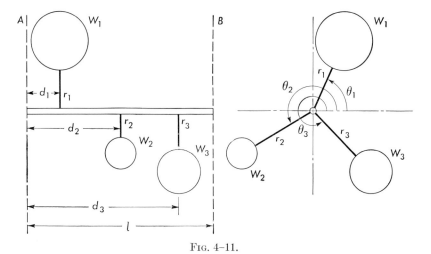

Fig. 4–11.

Consider the unbalanced weights separately and proceed as with the problem of the preceding Art. 4–5. Weight W_1 can be completely balanced by the addition of weights W_{1A} and W_{1B} in the A and B planes respectively. If these two are at radius r_1 in the A and B planes, we have

$$W_{1A} + W_{1B} = W_1$$

$$W_{1A} = \frac{l - d_1}{l} W_1 \quad \text{and} \quad W_{1B} = \frac{d_1}{l} W_1 \qquad (4\text{–}10)$$

Answer to problem on previous page:
Fig. 4–9(c) is the only balanced crank.
All are balanced for forces, but only type (c) for moments.

For instance, if $d_1 = 1$ ft and l is 5 ft, we have $W_{1A} = \frac{4}{5}W_1$ and $W_{1B} = \frac{1}{5}W_1$.

Proceeding in similar manner for each of the others separately, there result as many counterweights in each reference plane as there are weights. Now in Fig. 4–12 are shown the three counterweights in each plane, viewed from the right-hand end. Note that each counterweight

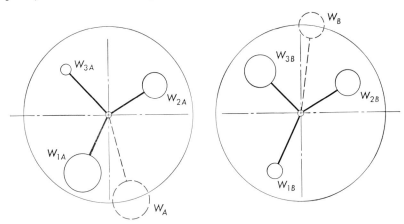

FIG. 4–12.

is displaced 180° from the weight it is balancing (since the planes A and B are outside all the others). All that remains of the problem is now to find a single weight in each of the planes which will produce the same force as the three found. In other words, W_A at the desired radius r_A must be the resultant of the three forces caused by W_{1A}, W_{2A}, and W_{3A}. This is merely the problem of balancing in a single transverse plane (refer to Art. 4–3), except that W_A is the resultant and not the equilibrant.

Example. The shaft with two weights, as shown in Fig. 4–13, is to be balanced by counterweights in the A and B planes by weights at a radius of 5 in. W_1 is vertical, and W_2 135° from it.

$$W_{1B} = \tfrac{6}{20} \times 5 = 1\tfrac{1}{2} \text{ lb} \quad W_{1A} = 5 - 1\tfrac{1}{2} = 3\tfrac{1}{2} \text{ lb}$$
$$W_{2A} = W_{2B} = \tfrac{10}{20} \times 6 = 3 \text{ lb}$$

In plane A (Fig. 4–13):

$$W_A \times 5 \cos \theta_A = 3\tfrac{1}{2} \times 2 - 3 \times 3 \cos 45°$$
$$W_A \cos \theta_A \quad = 0.1272$$
$$W_A \times 5 \sin \theta_A = 3 \times 3 \sin 45$$
$$W_A \sin \theta_A \quad = 1.2728$$

Dividing one by the other
$$\tan \theta_A = 10.005$$
$$\theta_A = 84°17'$$

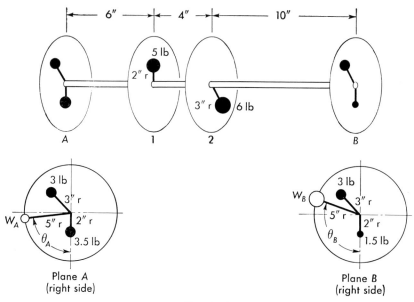

FIG. 4–13.

Taking the sum of the squares:

$$W_A = W_A\sqrt{\sin^2 \theta_A + \cos^2 \theta_A} = \sqrt{1.2728^2 + 0.1272^2}$$
$$= 1.28 \text{ lb}$$

In plane B:

$$W_B \times 5 \cos \theta_B = 1\tfrac{1}{2} \times 2 - 3 \times 3 \cos 45°$$
$$W_B \times 5 \sin \theta_B = 3 \times 3 \sin 45°$$

Whence

$$\theta_B = 117°7'$$
$$W_B = 1.44 \text{ lb}$$

4–7. Several Masses in Various Planes — Second Method (Graphical). A useful graphical method of solving the same type of problem was developed by W. E. Dalby. In Fig. 4–14 it is desired to find the counterweights to be added to the planes A and B to effect dynamic balance of the three weights W_1, W_2, and W_3.

By taking moments about the center of plane A, the size of the counterweight B may be determined immediately. This involves three-dimensional moments, and their vector representation. View the shaft from the end outside plane B, as shown in Fig. 4–14b. The centrifugal force $\dfrac{W_1}{g}r_1\omega^2$ due to weight W_1 acts at a distance d_1 along the shaft from plane A, so that its moment about A is $\dfrac{W_1}{g}r_1\omega^2 d_1$; but since ω^2/g will be common to all terms, we may call the moment $W_1 r_1 d_1$. The direction

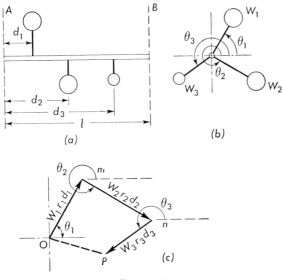

Fig. 4–14.

will be parallel to the arm on which the weight is mounted, that is, at angle θ_1 from the vertical, and so we may draw this moment as the vector $\overline{om}$ in Fig. 4–14c. Proceeding with the other two weights, the resultant may be found as the vector sum of the three moments or the vector $\overline{op}$. For the total moment on the shaft to be zero, the effect of the weight in plane B must be to close the vector polygon. Thus the moment to be produced by weight W_B is shown by the vector $\overline{po}$. Dividing this value by the length l between planes, we obtain the product $W_B r_B$ and then by arbitrarily choosing a radius, the required weight is determined.

Thus having the value of W_B, there remains to be found the other weight W_A. This is needed for the static balance of forces and so is solved by the method of Art. 4–3. Alternatively, W_A can be found by repeating the work outlined above, but with moments taken about the center of plane B.

A warning should be given of a possible pitfall. If either of the planes A or B lies inside one or more of the weights, as in Fig. 4–15, then, when moments are taken about the center point of plane B, the direction of the moment vector of that weight outside W_2 is reversed from the direction of the radius arm. This is seen to be so because the length d_2 is of opposite sense to the length d_1.

4–8. Several Masses in Various Planes — Third Method (Analytical). In the graphical solution just explained (Fig. 4–14), the condition for the closing of the vector polygons of moments about one end may be written:

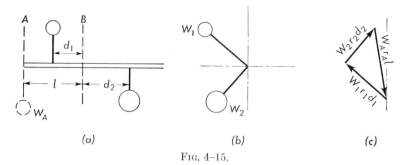

FIG. 4–15.

$$W_1 r_1 d_1 \cos \theta_1 + W_2 r_2 d_2 \cos \theta_2 + \cdots + W_B r_B l \cos \theta_B = 0$$
$$W_1 r_1 d_1 \sin \theta_1 + W_2 r_2 d_2 \sin \theta_2 + \cdots + W_B r_B l \sin \theta_B = 0$$

These may be expressed more concisely as:

$$\sum_{1, 2, \cdots, B} W r d \cos \theta = 0$$

$$\sum_{1, 2, \cdots, B} W r d \sin \theta = 0 \tag{4–11}$$

After these moment equations have determined W_B, then either we may use the fact that the sum of the forces must be zero, by using the eqs. 4–4 and 4–5 of static balance, or else moments may be taken about the other end, as represented by the equations below:

$$\sum_{1, 2, \cdots, A} W r (l - d) \cos \theta = 0$$

$$\sum_{1, 2, \cdots, A} W r (l - d) \sin \theta = 0 \tag{4–12}$$

In using the analytical procedure, a sketch of the vector diagram is of the greatest use.

An unusual example of unbalanced weights arranged to give balance follows:

Example. Four masses A, B, C, and D are mounted on a shaft, as in the Fig. 4–16. If the relative angular position of each about the axis of the shaft can be adjusted, and if the weight of mass C can be changed, show how to arrange the angles so as to secure complete balance, and state the required weight C.

The weights of the three masses, each at a radius of 1 ft, are

$$A = 180 \text{ lb} \qquad B = 250 \text{ lb} \qquad D = 160 \text{ lb}$$

and they are spaced along the shaft as shown.   (C.U.)

The relative angles are required; thus there are three to be found. The shaft may be rotated, and any one direction may be chosen as reference. Then let the radius of A be straight upward at $0°$.

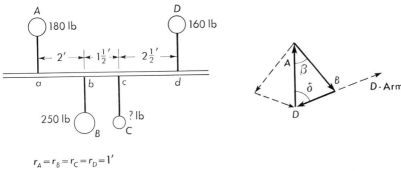

$$r_A = r_B = r_C = r_D = 1'$$

Fig. 4–16.   Fig. 4–17.

A force consideration, or moments about a, b, and d leave 3 or 4 unknowns. Moments about c leave only two. So first sketch the vector diagram of the moments: since the magnitudes (lengths) of each vector are known, *this diagram alone* (or the equations that go with it) must give solutions to θ_B and θ_D. It is seen there are two possible solutions (the second is shown by dotted lines).

Magnitude of moments about c, or length of vectors in Fig. 4–17:

$$A = 180 \times 1 \times 3\tfrac{1}{2} = 630$$
$$B = 250 \times 1 \times 1\tfrac{1}{2} = 375$$
$$D = 160 \times 1 \times 2\tfrac{1}{2} = 400$$

We may write the two equations:

$$B \sin \beta = D \sin \delta$$
$$B \cos \beta + D \cos \delta = A$$

But on eliminating one angle (say δ) these reduce to the "cosine rule" for the vector triangle:

$$D^2 = A^2 + B^2 - 2AB \cos \beta \qquad \text{(i)}$$
$$2 \times 375 \times 630 \cos \beta = (630)^2 + (375)^2 - (400)^2$$
$$\cos \beta = 0.798 \qquad\qquad \underline{\beta = 37°4'}$$

Similarly

$$2 \times 400 \times 630 \cos \delta = (630)^2 + (400)^2 - (375)^2 \qquad \text{(ii)}$$
$$\cos \delta = 0.826 \qquad\qquad \delta = 34°19'$$

Now notice that A and B are on the same side of C, hence if A is directed upward, B is downward. D is on the opposite side of C; thus for it to have a moment in the same general direction as B, the arm of D must be directed *upward*, as shown by the line "D arm."

Then the solutions for the positions of B and D relative to the 0° of arm A are:

$$(1) \quad \begin{aligned} \theta_B &= 142°56' \\ \theta_D &= 34°19' \end{aligned} \Big\} \quad \text{or} \quad (2) \quad \begin{aligned} \theta'_B &= 217°4' \\ \theta'_D &= 325°41' \end{aligned} \Big\}$$

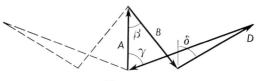

FIG. 4–18.

Note the advantage of the vector picture, which shows that these answers can only be paired in the above manner.

To find the angle and magnitude of C, sum forces (Fig. 4–18). It is seen there is only one solution (vector to close the polygon) for each of the above solutions. A, B, and D are now known in magnitude and direction.

$$\Sigma F_{\text{horiz}} = 250 \sin \beta + 160 \sin \delta - C \sin \gamma = 0 \qquad \text{(iii)}$$
$$\Sigma F_{\text{vert}} = 180 - 250 \cos \beta + 160 \cos \delta - C \cos \gamma = 0 \qquad \text{(iv)}$$

Setting the unknowns on the right-hand side and dividing:

$$\tan \gamma = \frac{250 \times 0.603 + 160 \times 0.564}{180 - 250 \times 0.798 + 160 \times 0.826} = \frac{240.7}{112.6} \qquad \underline{\gamma = 64°58'}$$
$$C^2 = 240.7^2 + 112.6^2 \qquad\qquad\qquad \underline{C = 265.5 \text{ lb}}$$

Hence there are two solutions, but one is merely the reverse of the other (i.e., where one measures the angles clockwise, the other is the same counterclockwise).

By this example the advantages of using the vector sketches even in the algebraic solution are clearly shown. To write down the algebraic equations, as eqs. 4–13, 4–14, 4–15, and 4–16, and blindly try to solve them simultaneously can lead to tremendous unnecessary work.

4–9. Summary. The cases considered in Arts. 4–3, 4–4 and 4–5 are apparently special cases of the general problem of Arts. 4–6 and 4–7. Thus, taking Fig. 4–14 for reference, the requirements that any system of eccentric weights be in balance may be stated in four equations.

For static balance, that is, balance of forces:

$$\Sigma Wr \sin \theta = 0 \qquad\qquad (4\text{–}13)$$
$$\Sigma Wr \cos \theta = 0 \qquad\qquad (4\text{–}14)$$

For dynamic balance, that is, balance of couples:

$$\Sigma Wrd \sin \theta = 0 \qquad\qquad (4\text{–}15)$$
$$\Sigma Wrd \cos \theta = 0 \qquad\qquad (4\text{–}16)$$

where, if the system is in balance, the axial distances d may be measured from any point.

If a certain system is to be checked for balance the equations above should equate to zero. If a system is known to be out of balance, then two unknown weights W_A and W_B in known planes A and B should be added to the system; then the equations above, with the sum (Σ) including W_A and W_B, may be solved simultaneously, and solutions will be found for $W_A r_A$, $W_B r_B$, θ_A, and θ_B.

It may be noted that in the preceding work, the planes A and B in which the balance weights were to be placed were generally assumed to be arbitrarily decided beforehand. The equations show that this is not the only possible procedure. From the equations the values of θ are never arbitrary. But it is possible to reverse the process, deciding first that we have weights W_A and W_B already mounted at given radii, and to find in what plane they should be placed.

In the case that the forces are not balanced, the resultant unbalanced centrifugal force causes an alternating force in any one direction on the shaft bearings; this alternating force is known as the *"hammer blow."* This name is particularly used in the case of a railroad locomotive, where the hammer blow occurs on the rails at regular intervals. When the couples are unbalanced, the resultant is called the *"tilting"* couple.

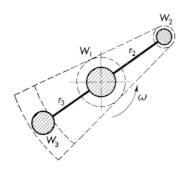

Fig. 4–19.

4–10. Slow-Speed Balance or Not?

An important practical point comes up for consideration in slow-speed machinery, which should form the basis for the decision of the designer as to whether to balance or not.

When an unbalanced crankshaft rotates, the maximum force to be carried by the bearings will occur when the centrifugal force and the weight augment each other. The balancing procedure is then regarded as one which removes the centrifugal force by adding further weight. In Fig. 4–19 then, the addition of W_3 is advantageous, by reducing the bearing loads, only when

$$\frac{W_2}{g} r_2 \omega^2 + W_2 + W_1 > W_3 + W_2 + W_1$$

Supposing that $r_3 = r_2$, then $W_3 = W_2$ and the condition of improvement by balancing becomes

$$\omega^2 > g/r_2$$

or $$N > \frac{187.7}{\sqrt{r_2}} \text{ rpm } (r_2 \text{ in in.})$$

Of course, if space permits a very large radius r_3 for the counterweight, then W_3 itself can be smaller, and then balancing is theoretically more desirable; however, this is not recommended. For all machines must start and stop, and the addition of a counterweight at a large radius will greatly increase the moment of inertia of the rotating body; and this means that larger torques are needed whenever the speed changes.

The consideration of moment of inertia together with dynamic balancing is of great importance in the design of all variable speed mechanisms, such as in the balancing of the cranks of a four-bar link mechanism.

4–11. Solid Rotors. Many rotating bodies are cylindrical in form. For instance, electric motor armatures may be regarded as solid cylinders; gears, fans, turbine rotors approximate cylindrical disks.

In the balancing of such bodies, two possible errors of mounting must be corrected. First the center of gravity may not be the center of rotation. This may occur as a result of a small error in machining, or because of the lack of symmetry in the design or lack of homogeneity of the material. Secondly the axis of the cylinder may be at a skew angle to the axis of rotation, as in Fig. 4–20.

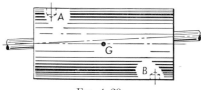

Fig. 4–20.

The eccentricity of the center will cause static unbalance which may be corrected by the methods already outlined. The skew mounting will cause dynamic unbalance, or centrifugal force couple unbalance. This may be eliminated by two counterweights, but their calculation involves the knowledge of the products of inertia of the body and is left for a later chapter (Chap. 6).

It may also be noted that when balancing such solid bodies, instead of adding extra counterweights, it is very common to subtract weight. This is accomplished by drilling holes on the heavy side of the rotor. In Fig. 4–20 two such holes are shown at A and B. A nice problem can then arise in deciding how large a drill to use, and how deep to make the hole; as a deeper hole will remove more weight but also will lessen the effective radius of the balance. Thus the larger the diameter of drill that is used, the less metal need be removed.

(B) Flexible Shaft

4–12. Critical Speed of Whirling. Let us now consider not only that a system of rotating bodies will probably have at least a small amount of unbalance, but that such unbalanced forces and couples will bend the shaft on which they are mounted.

Consider first a vertical shaft on which is mounted centrally a single disk of weight W. Due to errors in machining, the center of gravity is very slightly off the centerline of the shaft, by the eccentricity ϵ (maybe as small as a thousandth of an inch). Now as the shaft and disk revolve centrifugal force will start to bend the shaft. Due to the elasticity of the shaft this is resisted by a force called the restoring force; but this bending of the shaft means greater radius, thus producing greater centrifugal force which causes still more bending.

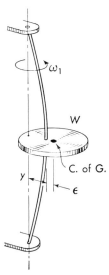

Fɪɢ. 4–21.

Equilibrium will be reached when the shaft is bent an amount y (Fig. 4–21) if we can write the equation that the two forces are equal and opposite. When the speed of revolution of the shaft is ω_1 rad/sec, the centrifugal force is

$$\frac{W}{g}(y + \epsilon)\omega_1^2$$

(if the mass of the shaft itself is neglected). The restoring force of a simply supported shaft or beam was considered before (page 99); since it is proportional to the deflection (if small) it may be abbreviated as ky, where

$$ky = \left(\frac{48EI}{L^3}\right)y$$

Hence we may find the equilibrium value of y from the balance of forces:

$$\frac{W}{g}(y + \epsilon)\omega_1^2 = ky$$

$$y + \epsilon = \frac{kg}{W\omega_1^2}y$$

$$y = \frac{\epsilon}{\dfrac{kg}{W\omega_1^2} - 1} \tag{4–17}$$

Now kg/W is recognizable as the square of the circular frequency ω of transverse vibration (without any revolution). To distinguish it from ω_1, we will call it ω_n, for natural free vibration,

$$\omega_n{}^2 = kg/W$$

and eq. 4–17 simplifies to

$$y = \frac{\epsilon}{(\omega_n/\omega_1)^2 - 1} \tag{4-18}$$

Thus if $\omega_1 = \omega_n$, the deflection y appears mathematically infinite, but at other values of the revolution ω_1, there is a more reasonable value of y.

Of course the infinite value is beyond the limits of our hypothesis of the proportional elastic property of the shaft—the meaning is therefore that the shaft will be permanently strained and probably fractured if run for long at this particular speed which is therefore called the "critical speed" (or better, the critical *whirling* speed or *whipping* speed, to distinguish it from other critical speeds, such as those in torsional vibration).

So there will be trouble if the shaft revolves at the critical value of ω_1 given by ω_c; that is, if

$$\omega_c = \omega_n \tag{4-19}$$

$$N_c = \frac{60\omega_c}{2\pi} = \frac{60\omega_n}{2\pi} = \frac{187.7}{\sqrt{\Delta}} \text{ rpm} \tag{4-20}$$

where Δ in. is the central deflection of the shaft due to a static load of W lb.

Now eq. 4–18 defines the equilibrant value of y. This is not reached immediately, but builds up as the shaft revolves. So it is possible to pass quickly through the critical speed to higher speeds.

As ω_1 increases from zero to ω_c, the deflection y increases from zero to infinity, as shown in the graph (Fig. 4–22).

For ω_1 higher than ω_c, y has a negative sense relative to the sense of

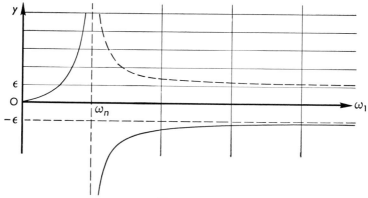

FIG. 4–22.

ϵ, and decreases again with increasing speed, until at very high speeds y tends to the value $-\epsilon$.

The phenomenon may frequently be observed in an ordinary electric fan when it is gaining speed after being turned on. The fan will pass through a tremulous phase of shuddering before it seems to gain reassurance and spin with increasing smoothness.

The meaning of the negative sense of y (above critical) is important. The center of gravity is now on the inside of the arch. The radius defined as $(y + \epsilon)$ in this case has the absolute value $|y| - |\epsilon|$. And, if the speed becomes very high compared to the critical, the ideal condition will be approached, in which the curvature of the shaft is just sufficient to bring the center of gravity of the disk exactly in the centerline between the bearings.

In Fig. 4–22 the dotted line in the higher speed range shows the absolute value of the shaft deflection, and is the commoner form reproduced. The change in sign of the amplitude y relative to the rotor is referred to as a phase change of $180°$.

In connection with the ability of the rotor to pass through the critical speed, and in doing so to incur the $180°$ phase change, two analyses have been published by Thearle* and Dent.† They assume a constant angular acceleration through the critical range, and show that the maximum deflection is finite and of an amount depending on the value of the acceleration. The phase change furthermore occurs gradually, the phase being $90°$ at the critical speed. Unfortunately both analyses contain errors.

4–13. Effect of Long Bearings. Long bearings will restrict the free turning at the ends of the rod, so that the spring constant k will show increased stiffness. As in all vibration problems, an increased stiffness will result in a higher natural frequency. The calculations of Art. 4–12 for the shaft carrying a single disk will still hold, as may be seen, and the critical speed is still given by

$$N = \frac{187.7}{\sqrt{\Delta}}\text{rpm}$$

but $\Delta = \dfrac{Wl^3}{192EI}$ in. in the case of a very long bearing. With ordinary bearings it is probably somewhere in between the two values.

As pointed out by Den Hartog‡ and by Myklestad§ it frequently

* E. L. Thearle, "The Rotating Disk," *Mechanical Engineering*, Vol. 46 (November, 1924), p. 670.

† J. A. Dent, "Deflection of a Shaft at Critical Speed," *Mechanical Engineering*, Vol. 47 (September, 1925), p. 724. See also Correspondence on the above by F. Hymans, *Mechanical Engineering*, Vol. 48 (August, 1926), p. 765.

‡ J. P. Den Hartog, *Mechanical Vibrations* (3d ed.; New York: McGraw-Hill Book Co., Inc., 1947), p. 275.

§ N. O. Myklestad, *Vibration Analysis* (New York: McGraw-Hill Book Co., Inc., 1944), pp. 77–79.

happens in practice that a given bearing has different restrictions in the horizontal and vertical planes. In this case there will be two whirling speeds, as shown graphically by Fig. 4–23, and a period of partial recovery between them.

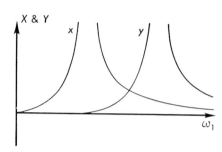

FIG. 4–23.

4–14. Automatic Self-Balancing Device. The fact that an unbalanced wheel on a shaft, when revolving above critical speed, revolves with its heavy side *inward*, can be used to secure an automatic self-adjusting balance of the wheel. A device to accomplish this was described by E. L. Thearle* in 1931, and in 1950 the Cincinnati Milling Machine Company† introduced commercially a similar device for their grinding wheels, a device which is very interesting, simple, economical, and effective.

In this machine the grinding wheel is mounted at the end of a shaft, which overhangs the bearings; the wheel acts therefore as a mass at the end of a cantilever. Inside the hub of the wheel there are three balls. Figure 4–24, which is a longitudinal section, shows that these balls are clamped by a mushroom-shaped plunger under spring pressure. But at the right-hand end, this plunger stem (*A*) forms a piston in a hydraulic cylinder chamber; that is, the turning of a con-

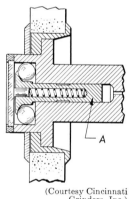

(Courtesy Cincinnati Grinders, Inc.)

FIG. 4–24.

trol valve will admit the hydraulic fluid to this chamber, move the plunger to the left, and release the balls.

The three balls are initially presumed to be spaced at 120° intervals, as in the transverse section (Fig. 4–25). A new grinding wheel is mounted and the machine brought up to a speed *above critical*. The cantilever shaft will whip, so that the center of the spindle and ball raceway will describe circles around the center of rotation (the centerline of the sup-

* Ernest L. Thearle, "A New Type of Dynamic Balancing Machine," *Trans. A.S.M.E.*, Vol. 54 (1932), Paper APM-54-12.

† Albert H. Dall, leaflet of the Cincinnati Milling Machine Co., Cincinnati, Ohio.

porting bearings). But the *light* side of the grinding wheel will be radially farthest outward. The clamp on the three balls is then released; due to centrifugal forces they begin to move around toward the light side of the wheel. This adjustment counteracts the initial unbalance. There will obviously be a period of oscillation of the balls, but this will die down quickly, and their equilibrium position (Fig. 4–26) will be such as to cause the geometric center of the wheel and raceway to coincide with the axis of rotation. For then the centrifugal forces acting on the balls will pass through their points of contact with the raceway.

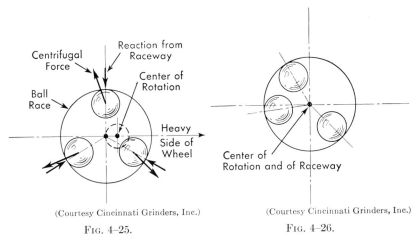

(Courtesy Cincinnati Grinders, Inc.)   (Courtesy Cincinnati Grinders, Inc.)

FIG. 4–25.   FIG. 4–26.

The balls are then clamped. After a truing cut is taken on the grinding wheel, removing any elliptical or eccentric irregularities, the wheel may be balanced again; and then at regular intervals, as the wheel wears away in use, perfect balance can be restored at the discretion of the operator.

An earlier scheme for automatic balancing was proposed by LeBlanc in 1913, and is referred to by Stodola.* It operates upon the same principles, but utilizes mercury inside a drum, instead of the three balls.

4–15. Whirling of a Shaft and Disk with Damping. A more complete study of the action of a single disk on a flexible shaft rotating at constant speed will involve the consideration of the effect of air friction in holding back the whipping.

Suppose that the disk in Fig. 4–27 is a turbine rotor with vanes around its periphery. Then on each elemental length δs of the circumference (point P) there will be acting a tangential force δF given by

$$\delta F = f u^2 \cdot \delta s \qquad (4\text{–}21)$$

* A. Stodola, *Steam and Gas Turbines*, Vol. II (New York: McGraw–Hill Book Co., Inc., 1927), p. 1134.

where u is the absolute velocity of the position chosen, and f is the frictional coefficient per unit length.

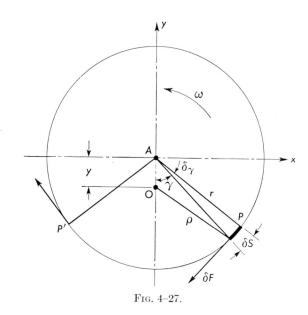

Fig. 4–27.

Now if O is the centerline of the shaft bearings, and A the geometric center of the disk of radius r which shows a deflection $y = \overline{OA}$ due to the curvature of the shaft, it follows that

$$\delta s = r\,\delta\gamma$$
$$u = \rho\omega$$
$$\rho^2 = r^2 + y^2 - 2ry\cos\gamma$$

where γ shows the angular position of the point P from the line AO. Substituting these into eq. 4–21, the element of tangential frictional force is

$$\delta F = fr\omega^2(r^2 + y^2 - 2ry\cos\gamma)\delta\gamma$$

To sum up the effects on the disk as a whole, it is necessary to resolve these forces in components in the x and y directions

$$\delta F_x = -\delta F \cos\gamma$$
$$\delta F_y = -\delta F \sin\gamma$$

By symmetry, since for each point P there is a point P', it is obvious that for the whole circumference

$$\Sigma\delta F_y = 0$$

Not so for the x component, however: by reducing the elements to the limit, we have

$$\Sigma\delta F_x = \int_{\gamma=0}^{\gamma=2\pi} dF_x = -fr\omega^2 \int_0^{2\pi} (r^2 + y^2 - 2ry\cos\gamma)\cos\gamma\, d\gamma$$

$$= fr\omega^2 \left[(r^2 + y^2)\sin\gamma + ry(\gamma + \tfrac{1}{2}\sin 2\gamma) \right]_0^{2\pi}$$

$$= 2\pi fr^2 y\omega^2 \tag{4-22}$$

This may be written in abbreviated form

$$F = cy\omega^2$$

where c is a constant. There is also a couple due to the sum effect of the tangential forces around the center A, which must be overcome by the torque through the shaft from the driving motor.

Turning the attention now to Fig. 4–28, this frictional force F appears at the center A in the direction $-x$, opposing the whirl. The deflection of the shaft $OA = y$ causes a restoring spring force R acting from A toward O

$$R = ky = \left(\frac{48EI}{l^3}\right)y$$

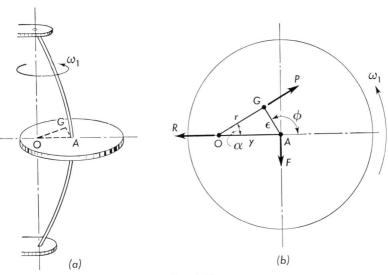

(a)   (b)

Fig. 4–28.

but the effect of F is to make the center A lag behind the center of mass G, which is still presumed, as in Art. 4–11, to be eccentric from A by the small amount ϵ. The angle of lag is ϕ, measured between AG and the radial line OA. The centrifugal force P, of course, acts at the center of mass G and is

$$P = \frac{W}{g} r \omega^2$$

if r is now meant to represent the radius OG.

Under the action of these three forces the disk must be in equilibrium; so by resolving

Radially: $P \cos \alpha - R = 0$

Tangentially: $P \sin \alpha - F = 0$

when the angle $AOG = \alpha$. These may then be written

$$\frac{W}{g} \omega^2 r \cos \alpha = ky$$

$$\frac{W}{g} \omega^2 r \sin \alpha = c\omega^2 y$$

But from the geometry of the figure

$$r \cos \alpha - \epsilon \cos \phi = y$$
$$r \sin \alpha = \epsilon \sin \phi$$

So substituting to eliminate r:

$$\frac{W}{g} \omega^2 (y + \epsilon \cos \phi) = ky \tag{i}$$

$$\frac{W}{g} \omega^2 \epsilon \sin \phi = c\omega^2 y \tag{ii}$$

Solving for ϕ by dividing

$$\tan \phi = \frac{c\omega^2}{k - \frac{W}{g}\omega^2} \tag{4-23}$$

and it may be noted that this is independent of y and ϵ.
Thus

$$\sin \phi = \frac{c\omega^2}{\sqrt{\left(k - \frac{W}{g}\omega^2\right)^2 + c^2\omega^4}}$$

which when placed in (ii) gives

$$y = \frac{(W/g)\omega^2 \epsilon}{\sqrt{\left(k - \frac{W}{g}\omega^2\right)^2 + c^2\omega^4}} = \frac{\epsilon}{\sqrt{\left(\frac{kg}{W\omega^2} - 1\right)^2 + \left(\frac{cg}{W}\right)^2}} \tag{4-24}$$

Now if we compare this with the natural speed of whirling without frictional damping, or $\omega_n = \sqrt{kg/W}$, we obtain

$$y = \frac{\epsilon}{\sqrt{\left(\frac{\omega_n^2}{\omega^2} - 1\right)^2 + \mu^2}} \tag{4-24a}$$

and

$$\tan \phi = \frac{\mu}{\dfrac{\omega_n^2}{\omega^2} - 1} \tag{4-23a}$$

where μ is the damping force ratio $F \colon \dfrac{W}{g} y\omega^2$.

The meaning of this equation may be found by comparing it with eq. 4-18, which was the undamped case. It is seen that eq. 4-24 becomes eq. 4-18 if $c = 0$ (or $\mu = 0$).

In the critical case of $\omega = \omega_n$, eq. 4-18 gave an infinite amplitude, but now this is modified: When $\omega = \omega_n$ eq. 4-24a gives the value of the critical speed amplitude as

$$y = \epsilon/\mu \tag{4-25}$$

With large damping, the amplitudes shown in Fig. 4-29 can be held fairly low. Nevertheless, this still remains the critical region.

Equation 4-23 is shown by the graph of Fig. 4-30. The phase, or

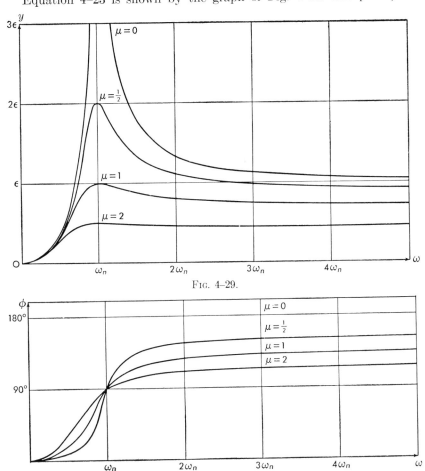

Fig. 4-29.

Fig. 4-30.

angle of lag of the center of mass, is seen to shift slowly over. At the critical speed it is always 90°, independent of damping, and it approaches $\tan^{-1}(-\mu)$ at very high speeds.

[It may be shown mathematically that eq. 4–25 exactly represents the maximum value of y in eq. 4–24a. This is unlike the case often considered, that has a viscous damping force $cy\omega$ (cf. Art. 5–3), in which the maxima occur at speeds slightly off critical.]

4–16. The Significance of Damping. We have now carefully developed formulae for whirling, taking account of damping. The question naturally arises—when do we have to use these longer equations, or when is it good enough to ignore damping?

In order to answer that question we shall proceed to find the approximate magnitude of the damping force and then reckon its effect. The engineering problems in which whirling has to be considered are principally those in the design of grinding wheels, fans, and superchargers which rotate in air; and in turbines, centrifugal pumps, and compressors which rotate in steam or water. Let us then find the damping for air and for water.

The impact force of air, as calculated already (page 34), was $0.0025v^2$ lb/sq ft, when the momentum was entirely lost. In the machines cited the momentum will not be lost, so that the force exerted may be from twice as much to a small fraction of the above. But let us use this anyhow, for it will at least give us the order of magnitude of the force. In eq. 4–21 the value of f is $0.0025b$ for rotor width b ft. Hence in eq. 4–22, $c = 2\pi(0.0025b)r^2$ lb sec²/ft, and so in eqs. 4–24a and 4–25

$$\mu = \frac{cg}{W} = \frac{cg}{\rho\pi r^2 b} = \frac{2(0.0025)32.2}{\rho}$$

where ρ is the weight per cu ft of material of the rotor. Suppose the rotor to be steel, this gives

$$\mu_{air} = 0.032$$

f and μ will both increase in proportion to the specific weights of the two fluids. So we expect

$$\mu_{water} = \left(\frac{62.4}{0.08}\right)0.032 = 25.8$$

Applying these now to eq. 4–25, it appears that the amplitude at critical speed will be very high for whirling in air, but even smaller than the static eccentricity when whirling in water. This leads to the first conclusion: in water pumps, the damping is so strong that we may forget that critical speeds occur at all. If the rotor is dynamically balanced—and of course all such machines must be—the value of ϵ must be very small, and at all speeds it can be expected that the whirling amplitude will not exceed twice this value.

In contrast, air has very little damping. Dry steam also has very little. As a result the critical speed is a severe one, and must be avoided. The engineering rule of thumb is that any critical speeds must be avoided by 10 per cent, and outside this range we examine eq. 4–24a and see that μ may as well be ignored. This then is the second conclusion. For if damping is ignored, the calculated bending and the stresses therefrom will be higher than the actual, which is on the safe side for designing purposes.

The reason for taking the trouble to make the calculations in Art. 4–15 is therefore to enable these conclusions to be made, as well as to explain the gradual changing over of the angle of lag ϕ, as shown in the graph (Fig. 4–30).

4–17. Critical Whirling Speed of a Shaft with Disks. As a result of the discussion of the preceding section, we may proceed to investigate the critical speeds of any system without reference to any damping. Consider then a slender shaft which carries several disks.

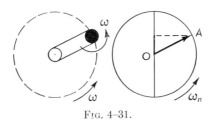

FIG. 4–31.

In Art. 4–12 it was proved that for a single rotor the rotational speed was critical when it synchronized with ω_n, the natural circular frequency of transverse vibration. That this will be true for all types of shaft and loading is apparent from Fig. 4–31. There the left circle represents the locus of any section of the bent shaft as viewed from one end while whirling, and the right circle is the auxiliary circle (ref. Art. 3–2) of the simple harmonic oscillation, with the vector OA rotating at speed ω_n, the natural circular frequency. Synchronism of the two involves resonance, the critical condition.

Therefore in order to find the critical speed of any arrangement of rotors on any shaft, it is necessary only to find the natural circular frequency of its free transverse plane vibration. The Rayleigh method, described on page 120, is a most useful attack.

The shaft in Fig. 4–32 is shown with four disks, but might have any number of them. It is assumed first that every part vibrates laterally with simple harmonic motion in the simplest mode. This mode is expressed when the shaft alternates between a single bow on one side and a symmetrical one on the other side. All disks therefore have the same frequency of motion, so that if y is the instantaneous deflection, with maximum A,

$$y_1 = A_1 \sin \omega t$$
$$y_2 = A_2 \sin \omega t$$
$$\cdots\cdots\cdots\cdots \text{ etc.}$$

This we call the Rayleigh motion assumption. Then there is need of the shape assumption: what precisely is this single bow shape, or what are the amplitudes A?

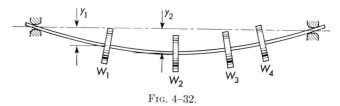

FIG. 4-32.

The merit of the Rayleigh method is that any reasonable shape may be assumed. The curve caused by the weights of the rotors under static conditions is commonly taken to be an adequate representation. Several methods of statics are available (one is outlined on page 174) to ascertain the static deflections: suppose they are found to be δ_1, δ_2, δ_3, δ_4. Now the amplitude of the various disks is not the same at all speeds of whirling, so let the dynamic deflections be $a\delta_1$, $a\delta_2$, $\cdots$ where a is a parameter.

Then for weight W_1, the motion is $y_1 = a\delta_1 \sin \omega t$, which shows a maximum velocity (by differentiation) of $a\delta_1\omega$. The maximum kinetic energy of this disk is then $\frac{1}{2}(W_1/g)(a\delta_1\omega)^2$, and for the whole system it is

$$K.E._{max} = \frac{1}{2}\frac{W_1}{g}(a\delta_1\omega)^2 + \frac{1}{2}\frac{W_2}{g}(a\delta_2\omega)^2 + \cdots$$
$$= \frac{a^2\omega^2}{2g}(W_1\delta_1^2 + W_2\delta_2^2 + \cdots) \qquad (4\text{-}26)$$

Now δ_1 is defined here as the static deflection of disk W_1, which means that with this deflection the restoring spring force of the shaft is W_1; and with deflection $a\delta_1$ the spring force is aW_1. The elastic potential energy of the shaft in its amplitude position is therefore the sum of the work done in deflecting each disk, or

$$P.E._{max} = \frac{1}{2}(aW_1)(a\delta_1) + \frac{1}{2}(aW_2)(a\delta_2) + \cdots$$
$$= \frac{1}{2}a^2(W_1\delta_1 + W_2\delta_2 + \cdots) \qquad (4\text{-}27)$$

Now by the theory of the maximum energy method (Art. 3-8) these are equated, to yield the expression for the natural circular frequency ω or

$$\omega^2 = g\frac{\Sigma W\delta}{\Sigma W\delta^2} \tag{4-28}$$

Since this is also the critical speed of the shaft in whirling, in number of revolutions it is approximately, but closely,

$$N_{\text{crit}} = 187.7\sqrt{\frac{\Sigma W\delta}{\Sigma W\delta^2}} \text{ rpm} \tag{4-29}$$

where the δ's are static deflections measured in inches; the weight of the shaft has been neglected. In this approximation the result will appear a little higher than the true critical. An example of the use of this formula appears in Art. 4-21.

4-18. Critical Whirling Speed of a Uniform Shaft. Suppose that the number of disks in the shaft of Fig. 4-32 became infinite; the separate disks would merge to form a uniform section shaft. In order to adapt the solution just found, the individual disks must be infinitesimally thin.

Let y continue to be the measure of transverse deflection at any point, and let x represent the distance along the shaft from the left-hand end when straight. At any position x (Fig. 4-33) there will be a disk of weight $(w\,dx)$ if w is the weight per unit length of the shaft.

Proceeding as before, we assume for any and every such disk a motion

$$y = (a\delta) \sin \omega t$$

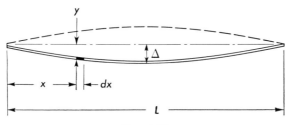

FIG. 4-33.

and then for the assumption of shape find some $a\delta$ for every x. This δ will now be a continuous function of x. Equation 4-26 will transform into

$$\text{K.E.}_{\text{max}} = \frac{1}{2}\frac{a^2\omega^2}{g}\int_{x=0}^{x=L} w\delta^2 \cdot dx \tag{4-30}$$

and eq. 4-27 becomes

$$\text{P.E.}_{\text{max}} = \tfrac{1}{2}a^2\int_{x=0}^{x=L} w\delta\,dx \tag{4-31}$$

Finally we obtain instead of eqs. 4–28 and 4–29

$$\omega^2 \int \delta^2 \, dx = g \int \delta \, dx \tag{4-32}$$

$$N_{\text{crit}} = 187.7 \sqrt{\frac{\int \delta \, dx}{\int \delta^2 \, dx}} \text{ rpm} \tag{4-33}$$

This has the proviso that δ is the statically deflected shape. For a uniform shaft simply supported we can look this up* and obtain the formula

$$\delta = \frac{w}{24EI}(x^4 - 2Lx^3 + L^3x)$$

On substitution into the integral of eq. 4–31

$$\int_0^L w\delta \, dx = \frac{w^2}{24EI} \int_0^L (x^4 - 2Lx^3 + L^3x) dx$$

$$= \frac{w^2}{24EI} \left[\frac{1}{5}x^5 - \frac{1}{2}Lx^4 + \frac{1}{2}L^3x^2 \right]_0^L$$

And for the integral in eq. 4–30

$$\int_0^L w\delta^2 \, dx = \frac{w^3}{(24EI)^2} \int_0^L (x^8 - 4Lx^7 + 4L^2x^6 + 2L^3x^5 - 4L^4x^4 + L^6x^2) \, dx$$

$$= \frac{w^3}{(24EI)^2} \left[\frac{1}{9}x^9 - \frac{1}{2}Lx^8 + \frac{4}{7}L^2x^7 + \frac{1}{3}L^3x^6 - \frac{4}{5}L^4x^5 + \frac{1}{3}L^6x^3 \right]_0^L$$

$$= \frac{31}{630} \cdot \frac{w^3L^9}{(24EI)^2}$$

so that eq. 4–32 becomes

$$\frac{31}{630} \frac{w^3L^9}{(24EI)^2}\omega^2 = g \cdot \frac{1}{5} \frac{w^2}{24EI}L^5$$

$$\omega^2 = \frac{1}{5} \cdot \frac{630}{31} \cdot \frac{24EI}{wL^4}g$$

$$= 97.54\frac{EIg}{wL^4} \tag{4-34}$$

Written in terms of the central static deflection Δ, which for a uniformly loaded shaft freely supported is

$$\Delta = \frac{5}{384} \frac{wL^4}{EI} \quad \text{(a constant for any one beam)}$$

the critical speed (eq. 4–33) becomes

$$N_{\text{crit}} = \frac{211.5}{\sqrt{\Delta}} \text{ rpm (approximately)} \tag{4-35}$$

* M. M. Frocht, *Strength of Materials* (New York: The Ronald Press Co , 1951), p. 435, for example.

4-19. Potential Energy from Bending Moment. The Rayleigh method, as has been stated, gives remarkably accurate results for the critical speed for many different assumed shapes. It will, of course, give the greater accuracy as the shape assumed is more nearly correct.

Suppose for the uniform shaft, as in Fig. 4–33, we assume that while whirling it takes on the form of a sine wave. This happens to be the actual shape, as will be proved later. The procedure follows along as before:

a) It is assumed that all parts move transversely in a plane with simple harmonic motions of the same frequency, so that they all reach the amplitude position together; this is to say that for all values of x

$$y = \delta \sin \omega t$$

so that $y_{\max} = \delta$ and the maximum velocity $\dot{y}_{\max} = \delta\omega$, where δ varies according to the station x.

b) At any station x there is an element of this shaft of weight $w\,dx$. Its maximum kinetic energy is then $(1/2)(w/g)(\delta\omega)^2\,dx$, and that for the whole bar is

$$\text{K.E.}_{\max} = \frac{1}{2}\frac{w\omega^2}{g}\int_0^L \delta^2\,dx \tag{4–36}$$

This is exactly the same as for eq. 4–30.

c) We need to express the assumed shape as a function of x. This time we wish to write a sine wave of one bow, which entails reaching $\sin 180°$ (i.e., $\sin \pi$) when $x = L$. This is

$$\delta = A \sin\left(\frac{\pi x}{L}\right) \tag{4–37}$$

where A gives the maximum deflection at midspan.

Then we turn to find potential energy. But the expression in eq. 4–27 is valid only when the shape assumed is the static deflection shape.

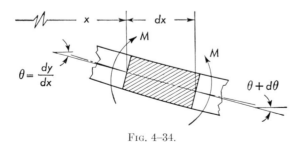

Fig. 4–34.

Consider the enlarged view of the element of length δx in Fig. 4–34. The bending moment acting on this element is shown as M. At the left end, at station x, the slope is dy/dx. At the right end, at station $(x + dx)$, the slope is $\dfrac{dy}{dx} + \dfrac{d}{dx}\left(\dfrac{dy}{dx}\right) dx$. The angle $d\theta$ through which the element is bent is therefore given by the difference in slope, or

$$d\theta = \frac{d}{dx}\left(\frac{dy}{dx}\right)dx = \frac{d^2y}{dx^2}\,dx$$

Now the potential energy of the element is equal to the work done in bending it from straight (with bending moment zero) through angle $d\theta$ (when resistance reaches a maximum M). Since M is proportional to the curvature

$$\text{P.E.}_{\text{element}} = \frac{1}{2}M\,d\theta$$

$$= \frac{1}{2}M\,\frac{d^2y}{dx^2}\,dx$$

The theory of beams gives

$$M = EI\,\frac{d^2y}{dx^2} \tag{4-38}$$

and in our case, the maximum y we have called δ, so that for the element

$$\text{P.E.}_{\text{max}} = \frac{1}{2}\left(EI\,\frac{d^2y}{dx^2}\right)\left(\frac{d^2y}{dx^2}\right)dx \quad \text{for } y = \delta$$

$$= \frac{1}{2}EI\left(\frac{d^2\delta}{dx^2}\right)^2 dx$$

and for the whole span

$$\text{P.E.}_{\text{max}} = \frac{1}{2}EI\int_0^L \left(\frac{d^2\delta}{dx^2}\right)^2 dx \tag{4-39}$$

This is a perfectly general result for any beam of uniform section.

Now by differentiating the assumed equation of shape (eq. 4–37) for this problem

$$\frac{d^2\delta}{dx^2} = -A\left(\frac{\pi}{L}\right)^2 \sin\left(\frac{\pi x}{L}\right)$$

$$\text{P.E.}_{\text{max}} = \frac{EI}{2}\int_0^L A^2\left(\frac{\pi}{L}\right)^4 \sin^2\left(\frac{\pi x}{L}\right) dx$$

Equate this to eq. 4–36 for the K.E.:

$$\frac{EI}{2}A^2\left(\frac{\pi}{L}\right)^4 \int_0^L \sin^2\left(\frac{\pi x}{L}\right) dx = \frac{1}{2}\frac{w}{g}\omega^2 A^2 \int_0^L \sin^2\left(\frac{\pi x}{L}\right) dx$$

$$\omega^2 = \pi^4 \frac{EIg}{wL^4} \tag{4-40}$$

If we convert this to reach revolutions per minute in terms of Δ, the static midspan deflection given on page 166, we obtain

$$N_{\text{crit}} = \frac{211}{\sqrt{\Delta}} \text{ rpm} \tag{4-41}$$

when Δ is in inches. This result should be compared with eq. 4-35; the earlier assumption gave a slightly higher answer, as all wrong assumptions of shape will by this Rayleigh method. But the difference is typically small.

Example 1. Find the critical whirling speed of a uniform steel shaft of $3\frac{1}{2}$-in. diameter held in bearings 7 ft apart.

Wt. of steel $= 0.28$ lb/in.³

wt. per inch run $= w = 0.28 \times \frac{\pi}{4}(3.5)^2 = 2.69$ lb

$E = 30 \times 10^6$ lb/in.²; $I = \pi(3.5)^4/64 = 7.36$ in.⁴

From eq. 4-40

$$\omega^2 = \frac{\pi^4 \times 30 \times 10^6 \times 7.36 \times 386}{2.69 \times (7 \times 12)^4} = 6.18 \times 10^4$$

$$\omega = 248 \text{ rad/sec}$$

$$N = \frac{60}{2\pi}\omega = 2375 \text{ rpm}$$

Alternately from eq. 4-41, using the formula for the central static deflection Δ:

$$\Delta = \frac{5}{384} \cdot \frac{2.69 \times (7 \times 12)^4}{30 \times 10^6 \times 7.36} = 0.0079 \text{ in.}$$

$$N = \frac{211}{\sqrt{0.0079}} = 2375 \text{ rpm}$$

Example 2. Derive an expression for the critical speed of a uniform shaft of weight w per unit length, and span L between bearings which do not permit any angular motion.

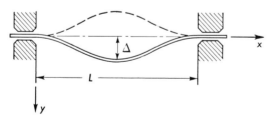

FIG. 4-35.

This is the problem of the shaft in "long bearings," and is the same as that of the beam built into supports at both ends (Fig. 4-35). It is much more rigid than a freely supported beam, and we expect a much higher frequency.

Make the motion assumption

$$y = \delta \sin \omega t$$

when δ is the maximum deflection at any x along the shaft.

Make the assumption of shape: it looks like a full cosine wave, or (what is the same thing) half of a sine-squared wave:

$$\delta = \frac{\Delta}{2} - \frac{\Delta}{2} \cos \frac{2\pi x}{L} = \Delta \sin^2 \frac{\pi x}{L}$$

where Δ designates merely the unknown central deflection. This is not the statically deflected shape, so for the P.E. we use eq. 4–39:

$$\frac{d}{dx}(\delta) = \frac{\Delta}{2} \cdot \frac{2\pi}{L} \sin \frac{2\pi x}{L}$$

$$\frac{d^2}{dx^2}(\delta) = \frac{\Delta}{2}\left(\frac{2\pi}{L}\right)^2 \cos \frac{2\pi x}{L}$$

$$\text{P.E.}_{\text{max}} = \frac{1}{2}EI\left(\frac{\Delta}{2}\right)^2\left(\frac{2\pi}{L}\right)^4 \int_0^L \cos^2 \frac{2\pi x}{L}\, dx = \frac{\pi^4 E I \Delta^2}{L^3}$$

where $\displaystyle \int_0^L \cos^2 \frac{2\pi x}{L}\, dx = \frac{1}{2}\int_0^L \left(1 + \cos \frac{4\pi x}{L}\right) dx = L/2$

Next for the K.E. given by eq. 4–36:

$$\text{K.E.}_{\text{max}} = \frac{1}{2}\frac{w\omega^2}{g}\left(\frac{\Delta}{2}\right)^2 \int_0^L \left(1 - \cos \frac{2\pi x}{L}\right)^2 dx = \frac{3}{16}\frac{wL\Delta^2}{g}\omega^2$$

for

$$\int_0^L \left(1 - \cos \frac{2\pi x}{L}\right)^2 dx = \int_0^L dx - 2\int_0^L \cos \frac{2\pi x}{L}\, dx + \int_0^L \cos^2 \frac{2\pi x}{L}\, dx = \frac{3}{2}L$$

Equating the energies

$$\omega^2 = \frac{16\pi^4}{3}\frac{EIg}{wL^4} \tag{4–42a}$$

Comparison with the eq. 4–40 shows that the inflexibility of the support bearings increases the critical speed in the ratio $4/\sqrt{3}$, and instead of eq. 4–41 we have

$$N = \frac{217}{\sqrt{\Delta}} \text{rpm} \tag{4–42b}$$

The decision as to which expression, eq. 4–41 or 4–42, is proper in a given design is a matter for the discretion of the engineer. All actual cases, except perhaps those of spherically seated ball bearings, lie somewhere between the two, but experience shows that generally eq. 4–41 is closer to fact, because of the clearance between the dimensions of any shaft and its journal for a running fit.

4–20. Dunkerley's Formula. When a shaft (as in Fig. 4–36) carries a certain number of disks upon it, and the effect of the weight of the shaft is to be reckoned together with those of the disks, the mathematical procedure becomes very tedious, for at each disk station there is a discontinuity in the slope of the shaft due to the sudden change in shear force.

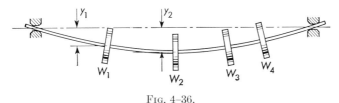

FIG. 4–36.

An empirical formula that gives excellent results is named after Professor Dunkerley:*

$$\frac{1}{\omega^2} = \frac{1}{\omega_s^2} + \frac{1}{\omega_1^2} + \frac{1}{\omega_2^2} + \frac{1}{\omega_3^2} + \cdots \qquad (4\text{--}43)$$

where ω is the result sought (in radians per sec),

ω_s is the circular frequency of the shaft due to its own mass, if all disks were removed,

ω_1 is the circular frequency of the shaft, regarded as stiff but massless, carrying disk W_1 alone,

ω_2 is the circular frequency of the shaft carrying W_2 alone.

Example 1. A steel shaft, $3\frac{1}{2}$-in. diameter, with a span of 7 ft between bearings, carries at midspan a turbine wheel weighing 1170 lb.

The shaft in this problem was taken as the subject of Example 1 in the last article. The solution to this, found by the integration process, gives us

$$\omega_s^2 = 6.18 \times 10^4$$

Now for ω_1, the only mass to be considered is that of the turbine wheel, and for this reason no integration (summation) is entailed in obtaining the kinetic energy. It is simply

$$\text{K.E.}_{\text{max}} = \frac{1}{2}\frac{W_1}{g}(A_1\omega)^2$$

* *Phil. Trans. Royal Soc.* (London) 1894, Vol. 185, p. 270.
A mathematical demonstration of the approximations involved in Dunkerley's formula is due to Hahn (1918) and referred to by Stodola, *op. cit.* (Vol. II), pp. 1110–1112.

if A_1 is the amplitude of oscillation of the wheel. For the potential energy the static deflection method is easiest; and reference to p. 164 shows that eq. 4–28 reduces to

$$\omega_1{}^2 = \frac{48EIg}{W_1L^3} = \frac{48 \times 30 \times 10^6 \times 7.36 \times 386}{1170 \times (7 \times 12)^3} = 0.590 \times 10^4$$

Then by Dunkerley's formula, for the shaft and wheel together

$$\frac{1}{\omega^2} = \left(\frac{1}{6.18} + \frac{1}{0.59}\right) \times 10^{-4}$$
$$\omega^2 = 0.538 \times 10^4$$
$$\omega = 73.3 \text{ rad/sec}$$
$$N_{\text{crit}} = 700 \text{ rpm}$$

It is reported that under test this rotor had a critical speed close to 770 rpm—higher than reckoned—probably because of restriction at the bearings, as discussed at the end of the preceding article.

A further example is given below to show that Dunkerley's equation has a fairly general application to problems in which several masses vibrate upon a single spring.

Example 2. A string attached to the free end of a spring is wrapped around a drum before being tied to a weight W. This weight oscillates vertically and the drum, with inertia I, rotates freely about a fixed horizontal axis, as shown in Fig. 4–37.

(i) Suppose W alone is on k; the equation of motion is

$$\frac{W}{g}x'' + kx = 0$$

and the circular frequency

$$\omega_1{}^2 = kg/W$$

(ii) Suppose I is with k alone; the equation is, by moments,

$$I\theta'' + (kr\theta)r = 0$$

so that the circular frequency

$$\omega_2{}^2 = kr^2/I$$

(iii) Applying Dunkerley's formula

$$\frac{1}{\omega^2} = \frac{W}{kg} + \frac{I}{kr^2}$$

This gives the natural frequency

$$f = \frac{1}{2\pi}\sqrt{\frac{kg}{W + Ig/r^2}}$$

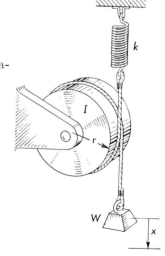

Fig. 4–37.

And it agrees with the solution on pages 101-2.

4–21. Graphical Method for Shafting of Varying Section. Among practical designs it is of common occurrence to find a shaft varying in diameter between bearings. For instance, there is the arbor that has greater diameter in the center than at the ends, and there is the turbine shaft that increases in diameter as it picks up torque from successive disks (Fig. 4–38).

To find the critical speed of such an assembly, eq. 4–29 is most easily applied. There are however adaptations of the mathematical analysis and integration methods, such as Myklestad's adaptation of the Holzer method,* which is more accurate, though it tends to take longer unless an expert on a calculating machine is available.

To use the Rayleigh method (to be described) the shaft, with any disks upon it, is thought of as divided into a series of discrete masses, concentrated at intervals along the shaft, and joined by massless shafts of a stiffness corresponding to the real shaft between these intervals. The greater the number of such intervals chosen, the more accurate will be the result, but also more work will be involved.

Then the problem becomes merely that of the calculation of the deflections δ at each station of such a shaft carrying these concentrated static loads; for this several methods are available, such as the funicular polygon method,† the area-moment method,‡ and the conjugate beam method,§ which are well described in various texts on strength of materials under the title "Deflection of Beams"; for this reason the detailed explanation is not elaborated here. The funicular polygon method is particularly favored in drafting offices.

Example. The steel shaft of Fig. 4–38(i) carries two turbine disks which appear on the figure as concentrated loads. The weight of the shaft itself provides a distributed load. With running-fit bearings of length about $1\frac{1}{2}$ diameters, the shaft is regarded as simply supported between points on the bearing centers.

Fig. 4–38(ii) shows the loading on the beam; only four stations are chosen which is perhaps an oversimplification. They are chosen as follows: the 95-lb rotor (which is disk and hub) is located midway on a

---

* N. O. Myklestad, *Vibration Analysis* (New York: McGraw-Hill Book Co., Inc., 1944), pp. 184–210.

† C. D. Albert, *Machine Design Drawing Room Problems* (3d ed.; New York: John Wiley & Sons, Inc., 1940), pp. 324–30; A. Morley, *Strength of Materials* (7th ed.; London: Longmans, Green & Co., 1928), pp. 112–13, 200; E. L. Richmond and R. H. Feng, "Graphical Methods for Determining Beam Deflections," *Machine Design* (Vol. 25 No. 9, September, 1953), pp. 177–83; S. Timoshenko and D. H. Young, *Theory of Structures* (New York: McGraw-Hill Book Co., Inc., 1945), pp. 17–34.

‡ M. M. Frocht, *Strength of Materials* (New York: The Ronald Press Co., 1951), pp. 282–324; P. G. Laurson and W. J. Cox, *Mechanics of Materials* (New York: John Wiley & Sons, Inc., 1938), pp. 153–72.

§ Frocht, *op. cit.*, pp. 325–27.

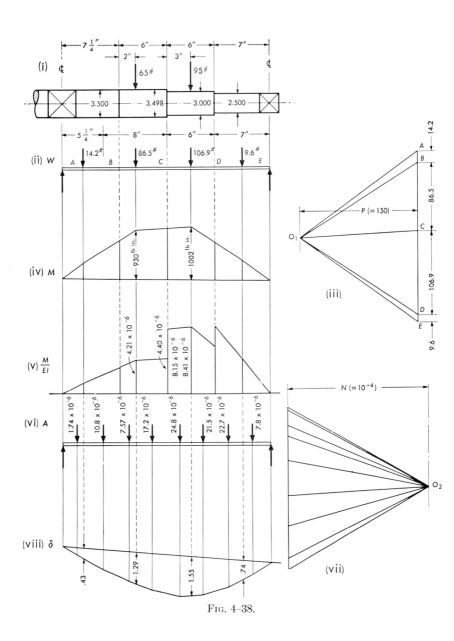

Fig. 4–38.

6-in. piece of shaft, and so the weight of this is added to the 95 lb. This leaves 4 in. of shaft to the right of the 65 lb, and for symmetry 4 in. to the left must also be taken for the center of mass to remain on the line of the 65 lb (the change from 3.498 to 3.500 diam is here regarded as negligible). There remain 5.25 in. of shaft at the left end and 7 in. at the right end to give the other two loads, and these four divisions of the shaft are near enough to being equal to each other. The loads are then:

$$W_{AB} = 0.28 \times \frac{\pi}{4}(3.5)^2 \times 5.25 \qquad = 14.2 \text{ lb}$$

$$W_{BC} = 0.28 \times \frac{\pi}{4}(3.498)^2 \times 8 + 65 = 86.5 \text{ lb}$$

$$W_{CD} = 0.28 \times \frac{\pi}{4}(3.0)^2 \times 6 + 95 \qquad = 106.9 \text{ lb}$$

$$W_{DE} = 0.28 \times \frac{\pi}{4}(2.5)^2 \times 7 \qquad = 9.6 \text{ lb}$$

The four loads are drawn as vectors added in order down the right side of the figure at (iii). A pole O_1 is chosen near the middle of this and rays drawn to the pole. Lines parallel to these rays span the respective spaces $A, B, \cdots$ between loads to form the bending moment diagram (iv).

The ordinate at every point of (iv) is divided by the value of EI of its section to produce figure (v)—the M/EI diagram, and this is treated as a new loading diagram. The areas of diagram (v) are shown as the eight "loads" of diagram (vi), the line of action being through the centroids. Because of the shape of this diagram eight parts are more convenient. These area loads appear as vectors down the side of diagram (vii), and by drawing parallels to the rays we produce the curve (viii) which is both the bending moment diagram of the area "loads" of (vi) and the desired deflected shape of the shaft.

Now as to the scales and interpretation of the resultant figure. Suppose the (horizontal) inch scale of the original shaft (i) and the others (iv, v, viii) is full-size. Any convenient scale is chosen for the loads in (iii) and, to this scale, the normal pole distance will represent P lb. Then the ordinate scale of (iv) will be P lb in. per in. (1 in. $= P$ lb in.).

In figure (v) the ordinates M/EI are read in inches per square inch; thus the areas under it are pure numbers, and these are entered down the vertical side of (vii). This scale enables the pole distance to be read as a number N, and the ordinate scale of the deflections (viii) will then be 1 in. $= N$ in.

[If the horizontal scale of (i) should be say half-size, then in (iv) the ordinate scale will be 1 in. $= 2P$ lb in. If then, in reckoning areas of (v) to enter as (vi) and on (vii), the real horizontal distance (not drawing widths) is used, the figure (viii) will also appear half-size so that its ordinate scale will be 1 in. $= 2N$ in.]

The results of this construction (the printed figure is of course reduced in size) are the four values of δ to correspond to the four loads, and they appear in the table below:

No.	W lb	δ in.	$W\delta$	$W\delta^2$
1	14.2	0.000043	0.0006	2.4×10^{-8}
2	86.5	0.000129	0.0112	144×10^{-8}
3	106.9	0.000155	0.0166	256×10^{-8}
4	9.6	0.000074	0.0007	5.3×10^{-8}
		$\Sigma =$	0.0291	408×10^{-8}

The summations of the last two columns are inserted in eq. 4–29 to give

$$N_{\text{crit}} = 187.7\sqrt{\frac{0.0291 \times 10^8}{408}} = 15,850 \text{ rpm}$$

4–22. The Stodola Method. An improved method similar to that just described is due to Stodola;* it takes cognizance of the fact that the shape of the shaft during whirling is due to centrifugal forces rather than plain gravity loads. It is capable of much greater accuracy than the Rayleigh method, for it may be applied several times over, each time getting nearer the truth.

Suppose, without actually making the construction, we were to draw a curve for the deflected shape of the shaft of Fig. 4–38. It is probable that a reasonable guess would come fairly close, that is, to shape not to amplitude. Luckily, any amplitude may be chosen, for as has been pointed out before the frequency of an oscillation does not depend on its amplitude. We call this guessed curve (similar to Fig. 4–38(viii)) the δ curve. While whirling, each part of the shaft, divided as before into discrete weights W_1, W_2, etc., is loaded by the forces $W_1\delta_1\omega^2/g$, $W_2\delta_2\omega^2/g$, etc., of which we have the W values and the δ values. Now, if by premonition we could guess the right ω value for the critical speed, and proceeded by the graphical method of Fig. 4–38 to find the deflection, we would necessarily come out with a deflection curve δ' equal to the δ curve that we started with, except that it would be of a more accurate shape than the guess; the average ordinate would agree. Such foresight is not common, but note that if a (wrong) guess such as that the speed is ω_g is made, the magnitudes of the resultant δ' curve will differ from the δ curve in the proportion ω_g^2/ω_c^2, where ω_c is the true critical sought, for (under small deflections) deflection is proportional to the load.

* Stodola, *op. cit.*, Vol. I, pp. 449–55; Den Hartog, *op. cit.*, pp. 194–98.

Thus the procedure is: make a guess at a reasonable δ, calculate $W\delta/g$ for each station, guess ω_g, apply this loading instead of that shown in Fig. 4–38(ii), and by the same procedure there shown find deflections δ' as in Fig. 4–38(viii). Then

$$\omega_c^2 = \left(\frac{\Sigma\delta}{\Sigma\delta'}\right)\omega_g^2$$

Den Hartog suggests that this is simplified if we always choose $\omega_g = 1$. Stodola himself suggests that often the ratio of the maximum ordinates is as good as the ratio of the average ordinates.

A second application of the method using the curve δ' as the guess, and thereby finding a more accurate δ'', will give a closer value to ω_c. A third application will rarely show any improvement, as the convergence is very rapid.

4–23. Higher Modes of Vibration. It is plain that when a uniform shaft is whirling, the single bow shape is not the only possible shape it may assume. In Fig. 4–39 there are shown greater numbers of bows, within the limits of the same span between bearings, all of which might

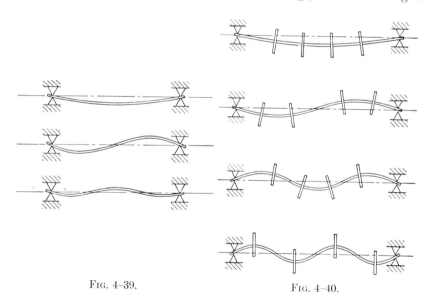

FIG. 4–39.   FIG. 4–40.

arise. There are in fact an infinite number of such possible shapes, and the uniform shaft is then said to have an infinite number of *degrees of freedom*.

Consider the shape with two bows, or what is the full sine wave. Each half of the sine wave is the same, and the shaft will therefore whirl in this second mode exactly as if the bearing span were halved.

Substitution of $L/2$ for L in eq. 4–40 shows that the critical speed in the second mode occurs at four times the critical speed of the first mode. The third-mode critical (seen by substituting $L/3$) occurs at nine times the critical of the first mode.

These are the higher modes of vibration. The critical we have been investigating by assuming the simplest shape has been always the lowest critical.

Where a shaft, as in Fig. 4–40, carries four disks, there are principally four criticals, as shown, but the shaft between the disks may still have an infinite number more. Criticals up as far as the third and fourth mode are sometimes of importance, but for higher than that they are rarely of interest because they are very difficult to induce in practice.

For the uniform shaft simply supported, as mentioned, the higher criticals are multiples of the first, according to the sequence of squares, 1, 4, 9, 16, 25, $\cdots$. For other arrangements this is not so simple. For example, in Fig. 4–41, there appear the shapes of the first and second modes of vibration of a uniform beam with long bearings. It is clear that the shape of the half span of the second mode is not a cosine wave, as for the first mode; and thus the second critical will not be four times the speed of the first. This problem will be solved in the next article.

In general, higher criticals are much more difficult to find. The Rayleigh and Stodola methods will give results, but they err by much wider margins than with the first mode. An interesting example is to be found given by Den Hartog,* and the convergence of his own method is discussed by Stodola.

4–24. Analytic Method for Uniform Beams. In the theory of structures, the slope, bending moment, shear, and loading of any beam are proved to be proportional to successive derivatives of the deflection. Thus

$$w = \frac{d^2}{dx^2}\left(EI\frac{d^2y}{dx^2}\right) \qquad (4\text{--}44)$$

when w is the load per unit length, follows directly from eq. 4–38. For a shaft that is whirling with deflection y, the loading w must be replaced by the centrifugal force per unit length, which is $(w/g)y\omega^2$ if w is the weight per unit length.

We shall follow here only the simplest case of a uniform shaft, in which w, E, and I are constants. The formulation is valid when these vary across the span with x, but the solutions become rather elaborate. For any uniform shaft, then

$$EI\frac{d^4y}{dx^4} = \frac{w}{g}\omega^2y \qquad (4\text{--}45)$$

* Den Hartog, *op. cit.*, pp. 202–5; Stodola, *op. cit.*, pp. 455–57.

This is a differential equation of the linear type, so that we guess for its solution and substitute for confirmation,

$$y = Ae^{\lambda x} \tag{4-46}$$

The guess is correct, then, provided

$$EI\lambda^4 = w\omega^2/g$$

Write this as

$$\lambda^4 - k^4 = 0$$
$$(\lambda^2 + k^2)(\lambda^2 - k^2) = 0$$
$$\lambda = \pm k \text{ and } \pm ik$$

where $k^2 = \omega\sqrt{\dfrac{w}{EIg}}$ and i is the imaginary $\sqrt{-1}$. Reference now to page 79 will show that these four values of λ in eq. 4–46 may be combined to give the general solution of eq. 4–45 as

$$y = A \sin kx + B \cos kx + C \sinh kx + D \cosh kx \tag{4-47}$$

Since no conditions have been imposed, such as the manner of support, or length of shaft, this result is good for any uniform shaft between any sort of bearings. It also will show all higher modes of whirling.

(1) SIMPLY SUPPORTED SHAFT. The conditions of simple support are that there shall be no deflection and no bending moment at either end. For span L

$$\left. \begin{array}{c} y = 0 \\ \dfrac{d^2y}{dx^2} = 0 \end{array} \right\} \text{ at } \left\{ \begin{array}{c} x = 0 \\ x = L \end{array} \right.$$

The second derivative of eq. 4–47 is

$$\frac{d^2y}{dx^2} = -Ak^2 \sin kx - Bk^2 \cos kx + Ck^2 \sinh kx + Dk^2 \cosh kx$$

so the conditions require

$$B + D = 0$$
$$A \sin kL + B \cos kL + C \sinh kL + D \cosh kL = 0$$
$$-Bk^2 + Dk^2 = 0$$
$$k^2(-A \sin kL - B \cos kL + C \sinh kL + D \cosh kL) = 0$$

These reduce to $B = D = 0$ and

$$C \sinh kL + A \sin kL = 0$$
$$C \sinh kL - A \sin kL = 0$$

Now $\sinh kL$ cannot be zero, so $C = 0$, but $\sin kL$ can vanish for kL any multiple of π. The particular form of eq. 4–47 that applies for this type of shaft is therefore

$$y = A \sin kx$$

where $k = \pi/L,\ 2\pi/L,\ 3\pi/L$, etc. These are the shapes of successive modes, and from the value of k^4 we obtain the critical speeds at which the shaft naturally falls into these shapes, or

$$\omega = k^2\sqrt{\frac{EIg}{w}} \qquad (4\text{-}48)$$

First critical:

$$\omega_1 = \pi^2\sqrt{\frac{EIg}{wL^4}}$$

Second critical:

$$\omega_2 = 4\pi^2\sqrt{\frac{EIg}{wL^4}},\ \text{etc.}$$

These form a harmonic series.

(2) LONG-BEARING SUPPORTS. In eq. 4-47 the conditions for no deflection or slope at either end may be stated

$$y = \frac{dy}{dx} = 0 \quad \text{at } x = 0 \quad \text{and } x = L$$

Thus

$$B + D = 0$$
$$A + C = 0$$
$$A(\sin kL - \sinh kL) + B(\cos kL - \cosh kL) = 0$$
$$A(\cos kL - \cosh kL) - B(\sin kL + \sinh kL) = 0$$

which reduce to the equation of shape

$$y = A(\sin kx - \sinh kx) + B(\cos kx - \cosh kx)$$

(of which those in Fig. 4-41 are two samples), and also to the equation for frequencies

$$(\cos kL - \cosh kL)^2 + \sin^2 kL - \sinh^2 kL = 0$$

which reduces to

$$\cos kL \cosh kL = 1 \qquad (4\text{-}49)$$

The solutions of this equation must be found by a graphical method; the solutions are $kL = 0,\ 4.730,\ 7.853,\ 10.996,\ \cdots$. They are very close to the values $0,\ 3\pi/2,\ 5\pi/2,\ 7\pi/2,\ \cdots$. From eq. 4-48, the critical speeds are

First critical: $$\omega_1 = (4.730)^2\sqrt{\frac{EIg}{wL^4}} = 22.4\sqrt{\frac{EIg}{wL^4}}$$

Second critical: $$\omega_2 = (7.853)^2\sqrt{\frac{EIg}{wL^4}} = 61.7\sqrt{\frac{EIg}{wL^4}}$$

Successive criticals lie close to the series $9,\ 25,\ 49,\ 81,\ \cdots$, that is, to the squares of odd integers, in their ratio to the first.

(3) CANTILEVER. Though the derivation will be left to the reader, it may be shown that the frequency equation (corresponding to eq. 4–49 in the preceding case) becomes

$$\cos kL \cosh kL = -1 \tag{4–50}$$

which has solutions $kL = 1.875, 4.694, 7.853, 10.996, \cdots$, and thus the criticals are

$$\omega_1 = 3.516 \sqrt{\frac{EIg}{wL^4}}$$

$$\omega_2 = 22.03 \sqrt{\frac{EIg}{wL^4}}$$

$$\omega_3 = 61.7 \sqrt{\frac{EIg}{wL^4}}$$

and thereafter very nearly the same as in the preceding case. The successive shapes assumed by the shaft are shown in Fig. 4–42.

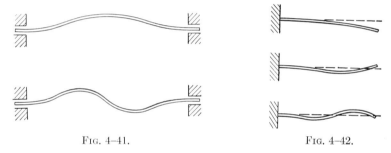

FIG. 4–41.   FIG. 4–42.

This series of critical speeds of whirling is the same as the natural frequencies of a cantilever beam vibrating. Since the prongs of a tuning fork vibrate as cantilevers, the interesting observation emerges that the overtones of a tuning fork are not harmonics of the principal tone.

4–25. Tension and Compression Effects. Tension applied to a beam, shaft, or wire will increase its natural frequency; this is common knowledge in music. Compression on a beam or shaft will, contrariwise, decrease the frequency, and this we shall proceed to show.

A slender column of length L rotating between simply supporting bearings is shown in Fig. 4–43. At a station x along the shaft the bending moment due to curvature is $EI(d^2y/dx^2)$ as usual and there is also the moment of the compressive end-load P on a moment arm y. Thus instead of eq. 4–45 we have

$$\frac{d^2}{dx^2}\left(EI\frac{d^2y}{dx^2} + Py\right) = \frac{w}{g}\omega^2 y$$

$$EI\frac{d^4y}{dx^4} + P\frac{d^2y}{dx^2} = \frac{w}{g}\omega^2 y \tag{4–51}$$

Since the shaft is simply supported, the general solution of this, involving both trigonometric and hyperbolic functions, must reduce to

$$y = A \sin \frac{n\pi x}{L}$$

and substitution confirms this, and shows moreover the essential frequency equation

$$EI\left(\frac{n\pi}{L}\right)^4 - P\left(\frac{n\pi}{L}\right)^2 = \frac{w}{g}\omega^2$$

$$\omega = n\pi\sqrt{\frac{g}{wL^2}\left[EI\left(\frac{n\pi}{L}\right)^2 - P\right]} \qquad (4\text{-}52)$$

Increased load P will therefore decrease the frequency. The first natural frequency, with the single bow, as in Fig. 4–43, obtains when $n = 1$, and for this the limiting pressure P is

$$P = EI\frac{\pi^2}{L^2}$$

above which there is no oscillation. This is the well-known Euler critical column load.

If, on the other hand, the shaft were under tension P, the only change is in the sense of P, and eq. 4–52 expresses the frequency if the minus before P is changed to plus.

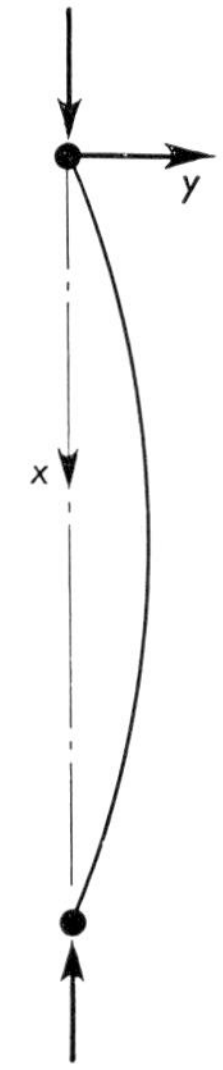

(C) Balancing Machines

4–26. Principle of Operation. Two balancing weights are known to be sufficient to balance any rigid rotor. Their angular position and the magnitude of their unbalance, Wr, can be found for any arbitrary planes—the two correction planes—that may be chosen.

FIG. 4–43.

But in order to draw out any dynamic unbalance, consisting of centrifugal couples, the rotor must be rotating; dynamic unbalance just does not appear in a static rotor.

A further point that was brought out in the earlier part of this chapter is that if a rotor is brought into dynamic balance, it is then necessarily in static balance also. And the easiest way to determine the balance weight needed in one correction plane is to take moments about the other correction plane. Moments about any other point, or a reckoning of forces, will produce an equation involving both correcting weights, and this necessitates solution of two simultaneous equations.

Figure 4–44 is an isometric drawing of the essential parts of a Tinius

Olsen* balancing machine that operates on these mechanical principles. No rotor is shown, but an electric motor armature, for instance, might be imagined laid across the top of the roller bearings and connected to the driver; the bearings may be of the two-roller type shown, the three-

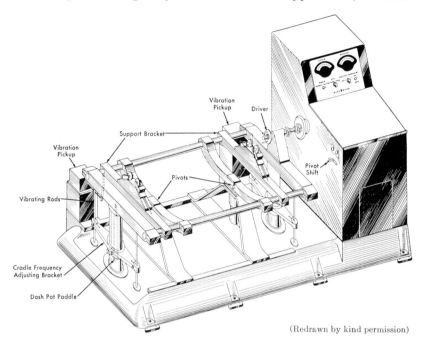

Vibration Pickup

Driver

Support Bracket

Vibration Pickup

Pivot Shift

Pivots

Vibrating Rods

Cradle Frequency Adjusting Bracket

Dash Pot Paddle

(Redrawn by kind permission)

Fig. 4–44.

roller type of Fig. 4–45, or the half-cylindrical type; it is important that they are not the source of any rough running of the rotor. The rotor is then driven by an electric motor either through flexible couplings, as shown, or as in another design by means of a belt passing over the rotor and a pulley below it in the rigid base of the machine.

The top layer of the machine—bearings and supporting brackets—forms a cradle which is attached to the base by four vertical columns (vibrating rods); these allow the cradle to move forward and backward in a horizontal plane. But there are also two pivots, one of which is locked to provide a fulcrum, while the other is free; these two pivots are movable along the vertical centerline under the bearings of the rotor and cradle.

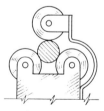

Fig. 4–45.

Suppose two planes, L and R, have been chosen as the correction planes for the addition or removal of weight for balancing. The two

* Tinius Olsen Testing Machine Co., Willow Grove, Pa.

pivots are set in these correction planes, first one pivot is locked, say the one in plane R, to provide the fulcrum, and the motor is started. If the rotor is not balanced it will oscillate horizontally about the vertical axis of the fulcrum under the influence of the horizontal component of the unbalanced centrifugal moment. Then an indicator connected to the left-hand bearing will measure the amplitude of this oscillation; the indicator can be mechanical or electrical—in Fig. 4–44 it is shown as "vibration pick-up,"—and its maximum reading can be interpreted to give the balance weight needed in plane L. Next, by shifting the fulcrum over to the pivot in plane L, the reading on another indicator at the right bearing can tell the balance weight needed in plane R.

But to determine the angular location for these counterweights is not quite so simple. It was pointed out in Art. 4–13 that when a rotor is whirling there is an angle of lag between the heavy side and the radially outermost side. Here we are not considering whirling in the sense that the rotor will bend between its bearings, in fact we must assume a rigid rotor. But the rotor revolves at the end of a cantilever suspension, on which it has a natural frequency of horizontal vibration, and a similar angle of lag is involved here. In the early days an approximate location for the counterweight was found by a scriber or a piece of chalk. As the rotor revolved at any speed in one direction the chalk was held against it and left a short line on the surface which would (for low speeds) be lagging behind the heavy side. Then the rotation was reversed, another chalk mark was made; and it is plain that the heavy side of the rotor would be half-way between the two marks. The angle of lag is small at very low speeds, at exactly the critical speed (synchronism of the rotational speed with the natural oscillation about the fulcrum) it is 90 degrees, and far above critical it is nearly 180 degrees, so that the light side is outermost.

The use of electrical devices is a great improvement over the mechanical indicator, for they can give a very accurate reading of angular location and show also very sensitive response to the magnitude of unbalance. With the same mounting of the rotor as in Fig. 4–44, the two horizontal rods from the bearings each move a small electric coil in the field of a permanent magnet, in place of the indicator. The oscillation then generates a current proportional to the velocity, and after any appropriate amplifications, this can be read as the magnitude of unbalance on a meter. The amplification allows very slight unbalance to be measured. To find the angle, one method is to use a stroboscope. The cradle support is made very flexible, so that the natural frequency is slow. Then at a speed of rotation around 1000 rpm, the condition is far above critical and the phase lag is very close to, and assumed to be, 180 degrees. Zero induced current in the coil will occur instantaneously with maximum horizontal motion, when the heavy side of the rotor is

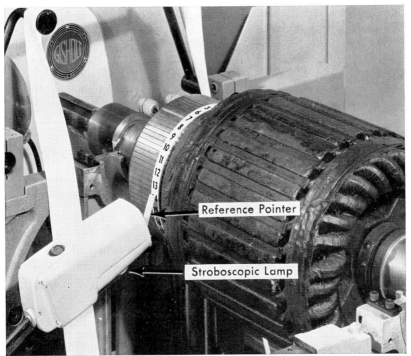

FIG. 4–46.   (Courtesy Gisholt Machine Co.)

horizontal; a flash from the stroboscope will therefore show this instantaneous position of the rotor, if some identification scheme is used, such as putting numbers around the rotor (Fig. 4–46).

Two alternatives to the stroboscope method are the wattmeter method and the rectifier method. In the latter, two cams are mounted on the motor shaft which is connected to the rotor, and these provide through their followers alternative paths for the electric current, for the circuit passes through one cam follower for 180 degrees of rotation and through the other for the second 180 degrees in each revolution. If the second is coupled in reverse electrically, mechanical rectification of the simple sinusoidal current from the pick-up is achieved. Now by turning the followers around relative to the machine base the phase of rectification can be shifted, with the two principal results shown in Fig. 4–47. When this current is fed into a D.C. ammeter, the current in the figure at (a) will give a maximum reading, and the form of (b) will give zero reading. The zero is easiest to find accurately, and then the cam followers are shifted 90 degrees to get curve (a); the reading of the ammeter is then proportional to the unbalance and the mass correction needed can be determined, while its angular location is found directly from the cam setting.

The wattmeter method also requires a device on the motor shaft by which the phase can be shifted. In place of the cam commutator, a two-pole sine-wave generator runs with the rotor, and its phase depends on the angular location of its stator. The current from the pick-up and the voltage from this small generator are then together fed into a watt-meter. Different phase positions will give either zero or maximum readings to accomplish the same results.

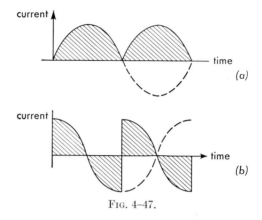

Fig. 4–47.

4–27. Elimination of the Fixed Fulcrum. The trouble with the fixed fulcrum (Fig. 4–44) is that the rotor has to be mounted in a cradle; and the cradle has a considerable mass which has to be moved by the unbalance. Therefore the sensitivity of the machine is impaired. However, without a fulcrum fixed under one of the chosen correction planes, it is necessary for the balancing machine to solve two simultaneous equations.

Such a system has been developed by the cooperation of Gisholt* and Westinghouse,† and is described in their literature. Its great advantage is the elimination of a large part of the cradle. Its disadvantage is that it requires an extra pair of operations in the calibration of its dials. The mechanical arrangement is very similar to that described already, and the solution of the simultaneous equations is accomplished electrically.

4–28. Balance of Flexible Rotors. Unfortunately all rotors are flexible, and only "rigid" rotors can be perfectly balanced. Thus in every case we are faced with a compromise. For instance, take the single crank of Fig. 4–48, and suppose that on the basis of the assumption of rigidity two counterweights $W/2$ have been added so that everything is nicely balanced. Then let this rotate at speed; under the influence of the two

---

* Gisholt Machine Company, Madison, Wis.
† Westinghouse Electric Corporation, Baltimore, Md.

internal centrifugal couples, the shaft will flex, so that the radius of weight W will increase slightly, and those of the two counterweights $W/2$ will decrease, and the shaft is balanced no longer.

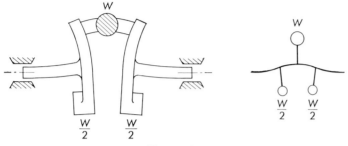

Fig. 4–48.

The distinction is therefore brought out between external centrifugal couples and forces, which may be balanced when rigidity can be assumed, and internal couples and forces which can spoil the rigidity and thus the balance. The external are those transmitted to the body of the machine.

Any method which helps to preserve the rigidity then helps the balance. In crankshafts for multicylinder engines the ideal condition is a journal bearing between each cylinder, and each crank throw balanced as in Fig. 4–49b. In a fourcylinder engine crankshaft, as in Fig. 4–49a, which is assumed rigid, there is theoretically no need for any balance weights, as external forces and couples are zero. Yet the two opposite internal couples C tend to bend the shaft as shown by the dotted line, and so it is essential to have at

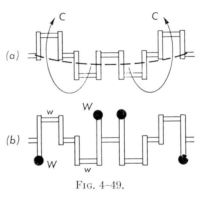

Fig. 4–49.

least a center bearing; each half is then treated as a unit to be balanced by the addition of two counterweights W.

Another source of trouble, occurring especially in electric generator rotors, is heat. Temperature differentials will cause warping, leading to unbalance.

As a result, for the best possible balance in any particular case, after the first balancing in a production machine, further balancing "in the field" is undertaken. That is, final adjustments to balance are made on the rotor running under normal operating conditions in its own bearings. Readings are taken of the vibration of the housing by means of vibration pick-ups, and either the wattmeter or rectifier method is used to find the angular position of unbalance. Several runs are always needed, for without controlled flexibility of the support the natural frequency may be high, and the phase angle between the "high spot" and "heavy side" of the rotor must be reckoned with. To calibrate the meter readings for magnitude of unbalance, known weights are generally added to the rotor temporarily to throw it out of balance. And when all is done, the rotor is only in balance for those particular speed and temperature conditions under which it was tested.

BIBLIOGRAPHY

Rigid Rotor

DALBY, W. E. *The Balancing of Engines.* 4th ed. London: Longmans, Green & Co., 1929.

DENT, J. A., and HARPER, A. C. *Kinematics and Kinetics of Machinery.* New York: John Wiley & Sons, Inc., 1921, Chaps. 6 and 9.

HAM, C. W., and CRANE, E. J. *Mechanics of Machinery.* 3d ed. New York: McGraw-Hill Book Co., Inc., 1948, Chap. 14.

Critical Speeds

DEN HARTOG, J. P. *Mechanical Vibrations.* 3d ed. New York: McGraw-Hill Book Co., Inc., 1947, Chap. 6.

FREBERG, C. R., and KEMLER, E. N. *Mechanical Vibration.* 2d ed. New York: John Wiley & Sons, Inc., 1949, Chap. 7.

INGLIS, SIR CHARLES. *Applied Mechanics for Engineers.* Cambridge: University Press, 1951, Chap. 17.

McLACHLAN, N. W. *Theory of Vibrations.* New York: Dover Publishing Co., 1951.

MYKLESTAD, N. O. *Vibration Analysis.* New York: McGraw-Hill Book Co., Inc., 1944, Chaps. 3 and 5.

STODOLA, A. *Steam and Gas Turbines.* Trans. by L. C. LOEWENSTEIN. New York: McGraw-Hill Book Co., Inc., 1927, Vol. I, Chap. 5, and Vol. II, Chap. 10.

TIMOSHENKO, S. *Vibration Problems in Engineering.* 2d ed. New York: D. Van Nostrand Co., Inc., 1937, Chaps. 1 and 5.

TOFT, L., and KERSEY, A. T. J. *Theory of Machines.* 6th ed. London: Sir Isaac Pitman & Sons, Ltd., 1949, Chaps. 12 and 14.

Balancing Machines

FLETCHER, C. NORMAN. *The Balancing of Machinery.* London: Emmott & Co., Ltd., 1931.

Catalogs and leaflets of:
Gisholt Machine Co., Madison, Wis.
Losenhausenwerk Düsseldorfer Maschinenbau A. G., Düsseldorf-Grafenberg, Germany.
Tinius Olsen Testing Machine Co., Willow Grove, Pa., and others.

PROBLEMS

(A) Rigid Shaft Problems

4–1. Four weights, 5 lb, 10 lb, 15 lb, and 20 lb, are disposed in the order listed, 90° apart around the circumference of a 48-in. wheel. How much weight must be used to effect static balance, and where on the circumference must it be placed?

4–2. A disk, mounted normal to its axis of rotation, carries three weights: W_1 of 30 lb at 12-in. radius, radius vector at 0°; W_2 of 10 lb at 24-in. radius, at 120°; and W_3 of 5 lb at 24-in. radius at 240°. Find the size and angular position of the balance weight needed at 12-in. radius.

4-3. Given the three weights below mounted upon a disk

No.	W	r				
1	100	12 in.	Angle between 100-lb and	80-lb	weights	= 60°
2	80	24 in.	" "	80-lb	" 120-lb "	= 120°
3	120	6 in.	" "	120-lb	" 100-lb "	= 180°

Find the magnitude and location of the balance weight required at a radius of 20 in. for static balance.

4-4. A 3-ft 6-in. railroad car wheel is out of balance by an amount equivalent to an eccentric weight of 3 lb at a radius of 18 in. What is the "hammer blow" on the rails at speeds of 0 to 100 mph? Plot on Cartesian and on logarithmic coordinates.

4-5. A locomotive has cylinders 18 in. by 24 in., two pairs of driving wheels, each 62 in. in diameter, weight of crankpin 110 lb, crankpin boss 150 lb, side rod 400 lb, and connecting rod 340 lb. Assuming no counterbalance weight, what would be the dynamic augment ("hammer blow") of each main driving wheel of this locomotive on the rails at speeds from 0 to 90 mph? Plot on both Cartesian and logarithmic coordinates; assume half the weight of the connecting rod is applied to the main crankpin.

4-6. A cam consists of a circular steel disk of 4-in. diameter, $\frac{1}{4}$ in. thick, mounted eccentrically by $\frac{1}{2}$ in. on a $\frac{1}{2}$-in. diam shaft. Investigate whether the cam can be balanced by drilling through the cam.

4-7. A garage mechanic is balancing an automobile wheel. He attaches a 3-oz lead to the rim, and then feels a 2-oz weight is needed 150° from the first. The finishing touch is provided by a 1-oz weight placed 45° from the 3-oz on the opposite side to the 2-oz.

What cheaper method could have been used, to obtain the same balance using only integral ounces of lead weights?

4-8. A shaft carries a single crank equivalent to 100 lb at 3-in. radius. The shaft is mounted in bearings 10 in. apart, and the crank is 4 in. from the left-hand bearing. Two counterweights, A and B, are to be added: A is 2 in., and B 7 in. along the shaft from this bearing; A is at 6-in. radius but B can only be at 5-in. radius. Find A and B.

4-9. Two cranks 180° apart around a shaft and 24 in. apart along the shaft are equivalent to 20-lb weights at 12-in. radius. Two counterweights are added at 12-in. radius, 10 ft apart, the nearer being 3 ft from one crank. Sketch the positions and find the magnitudes of these counterweights.

4-10. Between two pulleys, A and B, is a crankshaft 6 ft long. Two feet from A the first crank causes 10-lb unbalance at effectively 12-in. radius. Four feet from A the second crank, 90° out of phase with the first, causes 8-lb unbalance at 15-in. radius. If the pulleys are 3 ft in diameter, find the position and size of counterbalance weights to be added to their rims for complete balance.

4-11. A crankshaft, with three cranks 6 in. apart, has the second crank at

90° from the first, and the third making an angle of 135° with both the others. The two cranks at 90° are each equivalent to an unbalance of 10 lb at 3-in. radius; the third crank has an unbalance of 14.14 lb at the same radius. The shaft is mounted in bearings 2 ft apart, and rotates at 600 rpm. What forces must the bearings endure?

4–12. In Fig. 4–14 let $W_1 = 50$ lb, $W_2 = 200$ lb, $W_3 = 100$ lb, $r_1 = 10$ in., $r_2 = 18$ in., $r_3 = 12$ in., $\theta_1 = 120°$, $\theta_2 = 210°$, $\theta_3 = 330°$, $d_1 = 2$ ft, $d_2 = 5$ ft, $d_3 = 6$ ft, and $l = 10$ ft. Find the location and magnitude of a single balance weight to be added in each of the (A) and (B) planes, at 24 in. from the shaft.

4–13. Four weights A, B, C, and D, in that order, are mounted eccentrically on a shaft rotating at 427 rpm. The size and location of each are as follows:

	A	B	C	D
Weight, lb	3.5	5.0	5.0	W
Radius, in.	4.7	3.0	4.0	5.0
Angular position	64° 10'	180°	227° 44'	ϕ

Spacing along shaft: A to $B = 12$ in.; B to $C = 8$ in.; C to $D = x$ in. Find the hidden quantities W, ϕ, and x for complete balance.

4–14. The armature of an electric motor, originally balanced, had to have some soldering done on it. This involved adding weights as follows:

No.	W (lb)	r (in.)	θ (deg.)	x (in.)
1	0.3464	3	120	4
2	0.100	3	30	8
3	0.200	1.5	270	16

θ is measured in the right-hand end view of the armature; x is measured along the shaft from the left-end slip ring. There is also a slip ring at the right end, 20 in. from the other. By drilling a hole in each slip ring at 2-in. radius, find the weight to be removed, and its position, in order to restore balance.

4–15. A rotor mounted between centers for machining is given static balance by two weights, W_1 and W_2, bolted on near the ends. The rotor weighs 500 lb; W_1 of 18 lb and W_2 of 25 lb are at 14 in. and 10 in. radius respectively, are at 135° to each other, and at 15 in. on either side of the rotor mass center which is midway between the supporting centers. Determine the eccentricity of the mass center of the rotor, and the magnitude of the unbalanced couple acting on the supporting centers when the rotor is run at 30 rpm.   (U.L.)

4–16. a) A crankshaft has three cranks of 5-in. radius set at 120° to each other and equally spaced with a pitch of 12 in. The revolving mass for each crank is equivalent to 35 lb at crank radius. The shaft is supported in two bearings symmetrically placed relative to the cranks, and 38 in. apart. If the shaft rotates at 400 rpm, determine the dynamical load on each bearing.

b) Determine the magnitudes of the weights required to balance the shaft, one at a radius of 7 in. in the plane of the left-hand crank, and the other at a radius of 9 in. rotating in a plane 8 in. beyond the right-hand bearing. State angular positions relative to the left-hand crank.   (U.L.)

4–17. Experimental work on a perfectly balanced rotor involves adding weights of 0.4 lb at the point A and 0.6 lb at each of the points B and C, as shown in the figure. Find the position and weight of metal that must be drilled out of balancing rings at D and E in order to compensate for the added masses and restore dynamic balance. The drillings at D and E are to be at 4-in. radius and 3-in. radius respectively. (C.U.)

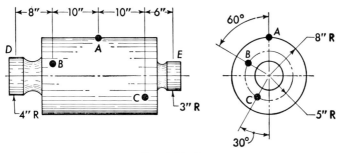

FIG. 4–P–17.

4–18. Prove by using only two equations that a system of three eccentric masses rotating can never be in dynamic balance if they are not in one plane.

4–19. A single weight will balance the system below. Find it.

No.	W (lb)	θ	d (in.)
1	3.0	0°	0.713
2	2.598	90°	3.213
3	2.0	240°	5.713

All radii are equal. d is measured along the shaft from some arbitrary reference point.

4–20. The following loaded shaft may be balanced by one weight, set at a radius of 4 in. Where and what must it be?

No.	W (lb)	r (in.)	θ (deg)
1	6	3	0°
2	8	5	90°
3	2	3	180°
4	5	4	270°

Distances between all adjacent planes, W_1 to W_2, W_2 to W_3, W_3 to W_4, are all 2 ft.

(B) Flexible Shaft Problems

4–21. Plot the graph (Fig. 4–22) of amplitude due to resonance; i.e., y/ϵ against ω_1/ω_n for $0 \leq \omega_1/\omega_n \leq 3$. Draw $-y$ as $+y$.

4–22. Find the critical speed of a belting line shaft, $1\frac{1}{2}$-in. diameter, carried by two bearings (simply supporting) 6 ft apart. The two pulleys on the shaft are neglected because they are close up against the bearings. The shaft is of steel.

4–23. A fan weighing 2 lb is attached to the end of a $\frac{1}{4}$-in. steel shaft, which projects as a cantilever $2\frac{1}{2}$ in. from its bearings. Find its lowest critical speed; the shaft mass may be neglected.

4–24. A blower weighing 100 lb is mounted on a 2-in. diam steel shaft, and is midway between two bearings 2 ft apart. The bearings achieve a simple support for the shaft. Find the lowest whirling critical (a) neglecting the weight of the shaft; (b) including the shaft weight (use Dunkerley's formula).

4–25. Demonstrate the validity of the assertion that any reasonable curve may be assumed in the Rayleigh method. Assume for a simply supported uniform beam a parabolic shape and apply the method of Art. 4–19 to obtain an expression similar to eq. 4–41.

4–26. Derive an expression for the critical speed of any uniform cantilever by using its statically deflected shape.

4–27. Assume a sinusoidal shape for a uniform cantilever and by the method of Art. 4–19 determine its critical speed of whirling.

A 12-in. length of $\frac{3}{4}$-in. diam steel shaft projects from its bearings as a cantilever. Find its lowest critical speed.

4–28. A locomotive side-rod weighs w lb per ft length and the ends are mounted to the driving wheels at radius r. These wheels have a rolling radius R, and their centers are L ft apart. Find the linear speed of the locomotive in miles per hour at which transverse whipping of the side-rod will occur. Assume the side-rod uniform with rigidity EI.

4–29. A shaft 24 in. long and supported in flexible bearings at the ends carries three loads of 5 lb each, spaced 6 in. from each other and from the bearings. The shaft is $\frac{1}{2}$-in. diameter and weighs 1.3 lb.

a) Taking the modulus of elasticity of the shaft as 30×10^6 psi, calculate approximately the lowest whirling speed.

b) The deflection of the shaft under gravity is 0.039 in. at the center, and 0.028 in. at the positions of the other two loads. Use these figures to obtain the whirling speed by another method.   (U.L.)

4–30. A steel shaft $\frac{1}{2}$ in. in diameter rotates in long fixed bearings, and a disk of weight 40 lb is secured to the shaft at the middle of its length. The span of the shaft between bearings is 24 in. The mass center of the disk is 0.02 in. from the axis of the shaft.

Neglecting the mass of the shaft and damping, determine its central deflection in terms of the speed of rotation in rpm. If the stress in the shaft due to bending is not to exceed 18,000 psi, find the range of speed over which this stress would be exceeded.   (U.L.)

4–31. Stirring blades are to be attached to the end of a long (cantilever) shaft which projects down into a vat. The blades weigh 5 lb, and the shaft projects 6 ft from its bearings. Find the diameter of the shaft for which the critical speed shall be over 600 rpm.

4–32. Two steam-turbine rotors are mounted on a 2-in. diam shaft between bearings 26.5 in. apart. The first rotor weighs 58 lb and is 9.25 in. from one bearing; the second rotor weighs 101 lb and is 15.25 in. from the same bearing. Find the lowest critical speed. The shaft weight may be neglected.

4–33. Required: the first, second, and third critical speeds of a uniform steel shaft of $1\frac{1}{2}$-in. diameter between bearings 6 ft apart.

a) Presume the bearings are simply supporting.

b) Presume the bearings allow no angular deflection.

4–34. A uniform steel shaft, of 2-in. diameter, is simply supported between bearings 30 in. apart and carries at midspan a turbine rotor of 50 lb weight. Consider the shaft as five 6-in. lengths, and determine the critical speed by the graphical method of Art. 4–21. Compare the result with that obtained by Dunkerley's formula.

4–35. A steel shaft is of three diameters as shown in the figure, and is held by simply supporting bearings 6 ft apart. Find its critical speed.

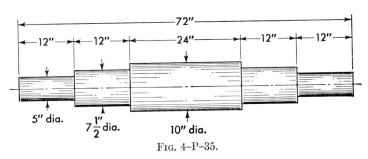

FIG. 4–P–35.

4–36. By the method of Art. 4–24, determine the critical speeds and the shape of a uniform shaft which is encastered (restrained by a long bearing) at one end and simply supported at the other.

4–37. A uniform rod of length l and mass m per unit length is encastered (zero slope) at one end and fixed laterally at the other end with rotation (slope) at this end resisted elastically by a bending moment equal to k times the angular rotation, where k is a constant. Show that the natural frequency n of natural vibrations of the rod is given by

$$(1 - \cosh z \cos z) = \frac{EIz}{kl}(\sinh z \cos z - \cosh z \sin z),$$

where

$$z^4 = \frac{4\pi^2 n^2 m l^4}{EI}$$

In connection with turbine-blade design, describe how this equation might be used to guard against resonance of shrouded blades due to frequency of nozzle impulses, and describe a means for suppressing this type of vibration.   (C.U.)

4–38. A solid steel shaft of diameter d in a certain design is to be replaced by a hollow shaft of which the outside diameter is D and the inside kD. The hollow shaft is to have equal strength in torsion (equal boundary shear stress). Express as a ratio (in terms of k only) the effect of this change on the critical whirling speed.

Then show that if $k = 0.5$ this indicates the hollow shaft will have a critical about 14 per cent higher than the solid shaft it replaces, though the outside diameter is only increased by 2 per cent.

4–39. A 1-in. diam steel shaft 20 ft long is simply supported in two bearings, one 5 ft, the other 15 ft, from one end. Find the lowest natural frequency of transverse vibration.

4–40. The figure shows a wooden 2 × 4 of length 10 ft attached to two 2 × 4 posts 4 ft high. The bottoms of the posts are rigid. Find the natural frequency of the horizontal vibration of the long member.

Fig. 4–P–40.

Chapter 5

VIBRATIONS—DAMPED AND FORCED

5-1. Damped Free Vibration. Suppose a body oscillates upon a spring. In Chapter 3 there were considered the force of the spring and the inertia force of the body; and, with these only considered, it appeared that the body moved with simple harmonic motion.

Such motion maintains a constant amplitude; but it is generally observed that all actual free vibrations diminish and in time disappear. This is due to friction of some kind.

The friction is called a damping force and is most commonly found in either or both of two kinds: (1) "solid friction," that is a more or less constant force which keeps changing its direction to oppose the velocity; (2) "viscous damping," that is a force which opposes and is proportional to the velocity; it occurs when a body moves with fairly low velocity in air, but much more so when the motion is through a liquid. We consider now the effect of the second variety.

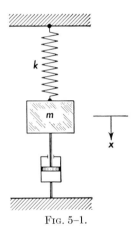

Figure 5-1 shows a mass m on a spring of stiffness k. Between the mass and the ground a small piston in a cylinder is the conventional representation of viscous damping: there is supposed to be a small by-pass between the top and bottom ends of the cylinder, so that any motion x of the mass will involve pumping the liquid through the by-pass, and cause a force $c\dot{x}$ lb. Coefficient c is the damping constant of proportionality.

FIG. 5-1.

If x (positive) is measured downward, mathematically $\dot{x}$ (positive) and $\ddot{x}$ (positive) are also down. Thus the spring force vector kx is up: the damping $c\dot{x}$ opposing $\dot{x}$ is up; the inertia $m\ddot{x}$, the reversed effective force from $\ddot{x}$, is up; and the sum of these forces gives

$$m\ddot{x} + c\dot{x} + kx = 0 \tag{5-1}$$

This equation is of a type called linear with constant coefficients* and the solution may be found among exponential functions. So guess a solution

$$x = Ae^{rt} \tag{5-2}$$

* Refer to the Appendix in Chapter 2, page 78.

where A and r are some constants still to be found. Then differentiate twice

$$\dot{x} = Are^{rt}$$
$$\ddot{x} = Ar^2e^{rt}$$

and substitute:

$$Ae^{rt}(mr^2 + cr + k) = 0 \qquad (5\text{–}3)$$

This is the "characteristic equation," and shows that though any value of A will be satisfactory, r must satisfy

$$mr^2 + cr + k = 0$$

$$r = (-c \pm \sqrt{c^2 - 4km}) \div (2m) \qquad (5\text{–}4a)$$

We prefer this in another form, using the fact that the natural (free) circular frequency is given by

$$k/m = \omega_n^2$$

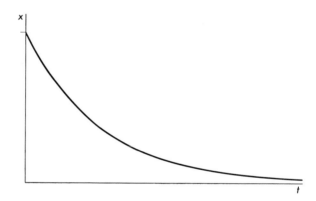

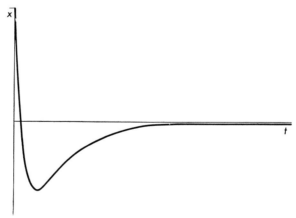

Fig. 5–2.

and also define

$$c/2m = n$$

Then

$$r = -n \pm \sqrt{n^2 - \omega_n^2} \tag{5–4b}$$

So r is dimensionally an angular velocity, and there are two values to satisfy the supposition (eq. 5–2). Equation 5–1 therefore has the solution

$$x = Ae^{r_1 t} + Be^{r_2 t} \tag{5–5}$$

A and B are each arbitrary. Now this needs some physical interpretation. Three cases must be distinguished that depend upon whether the radical in eq. 5–4 is real or imaginary.

CASE 1. STRONGLY DAMPED MOTION. When n is greater than ω_n, the radical in eq. 5–4b is real, but it will of course be smaller than n itself. Therefore there are two real values for r, both negative. Suppose they are $-a$ and $-b$. This allows eq. 5–5 to be written

$$x = Ae^{-at} + Be^{-bt} \tag{5–6}$$

The curve representing the motion will therefore appear in one or other of the forms shown in Fig. 5–2. It is the type of motion associated with the closing of a door fitted with a pneumatically damped spring, and also the so-called "dead-beat" response of instruments such as an automobile speedometer.

The motion is not a vibration at all—it is called aperiodic.

CASE 2. LIGHTLY DAMPED MOTION. When n is less than ω_n, the radical is imaginary. Equation 5–4b may be written

$$r = -n \pm i\omega_d$$

where

$$\omega_d = \sqrt{\omega_n^2 - n^2} = \sqrt{\frac{k}{m} - \frac{c^2}{4m^2}} \tag{5–7}$$

Equation 5–5 then may be transformed by factoring the real exponential:

$$x = e^{-nt}(Ae^{i\omega_d t} + Be^{-i\omega_d t}) \tag{5–8}$$

Using Euler's equations previously referred to (page 79), this becomes

$$x = e^{-nt}(A_1 \sin \omega_d t + B_1 \cos \omega_d t) \tag{5–9}$$

And Fig. 5–3 shows the curve of this type of motion. It is called a damped sinusoidal motion. The frequency of the oscillation remains constant throughout and is

$$f = \omega_d / 2\pi \text{ cps}$$

where ω_d is a little less than ω_n (eq. 5–7). The exponential curves $\pm e^{-nt}$ in the figure become the envelopes to the motion.

Now the sine and cosine part of eq. 5–9 may be written rather more neatly as a cosine with a phase difference as has been suggested before

$$x = e^{-nt} C \cos (\omega_d t - \phi) \qquad (5\text{-}10)$$

From this, the initial displacement of the body appears in general as $C \cos \phi$, although in Fig. 5–3 we have arbitrarily shown the special case of $\phi = 0$.

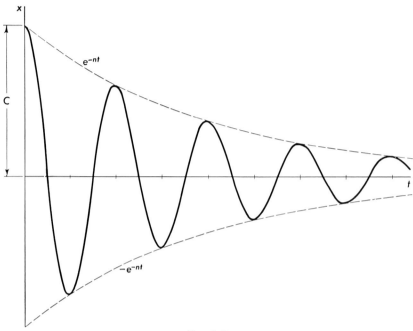

FIG. 5–3.

We cannot speak of a period, for the motion is not periodic (because it does not repeat exactly); nevertheless note that the time interval τ

$$\tau = 2\pi/\omega_d$$

will cause a repeat of the cosine part. Thus

after τ the displacement $x = e^{-n\tau} C \cos \phi$

after 2τ the displacement $x = e^{-2n\tau} C \cos \phi = (e^{-n\tau})^2 C \cos \phi$

which shows the displacement during each oscillation to bear a fixed ratio to the displacement in the preceding oscillation. The ratio is

$$\frac{x_{t + \tau}}{x_t} = e^{-n\tau} = e^{-\delta}$$

where x_t means the value of x at any specified time t. The natural logarithm of this ratio is δ, which is called the "logarithmic decrement."

$$\delta = n\tau = \frac{2\pi n}{\omega_d} = \frac{2\pi n}{\sqrt{\omega_n^2 - n^2}} = \frac{2\pi c}{\sqrt{4km - c^2}} \qquad (5\text{-}11)$$

Though (in eq. 5–10) the values of t for $\cos{(\omega_d t - \phi)} = 1$ will give the points of contact and tangency with the exponential curve, yet these will not be the points of greatest displacement x from equilibrium. However, in most practical cases the maximum is not much different from this, and the displacements at the tangent points are called successively the amplitudes. The ratio of consecutive amplitudes must be $e^{-\delta}$.

Measurement of successive amplitudes experimentally is frequently the best method of arriving at a quantity for the damping force coefficient c in eq. 5–1.

Example. A body of weight $W = 30$ lb is suspended on a spring which exerts a restoring force $k = 600$ lb per foot displacement from the position of static equilibrium, and its motion is subjected to a damping force of c lb per (foot per second) velocity. Experiment shows that the amplitude of the vibration diminishes to one-tenth of its original value in two complete oscillations. Find the frequency of oscillation and the value of the damping force c. (U.L.)

The equation of the damped oscillation is

$$\frac{W}{g}\ddot{x} + c\dot{x} + kx = 0$$

And since it is stated that the motion is an oscillation, the damping must be less than critical, and the solution as eq. 5–10

$$x = e^{-nt}\,C\,\cos{\omega_d t}$$

There is no need of the phase ϕ: we assume that the clock is started when the body is at an amplitude position.

At time $t = 0$ the displacement is C.

After two periods $t = 2\tau$, and the displacement is $Ce^{-n2\tau}$ and this is given as $C/10$. Therefore, taking the reciprocal of the ratio

$$e^{2n\tau} = 10$$
$$2n\tau = \log_e 10 = 2.303$$

or the logarithmic decrement is 1.15. Now $\tau = 2\pi/\omega_d$ and

$$\omega_d = \sqrt{\omega_n^2 - n^2} \quad \text{(eq. 5–7)}$$
$$4\pi n = 2.303\sqrt{\omega_n^2 - n^2}$$

Squaring

$$\left(\frac{4\pi}{2.303}\right)^2 n^2 = 29.8n^2 = \omega_n^2 - n^2$$

$$n^2 = \omega_n^2 \div 30.8 = \frac{600 \times 32.2}{30 \times 30.8} = 20.9 \ (\text{rad/sec})^2$$

Since ω_n^2 the free circular frequency (squared) is $kg/W = 644$, thus the damped circular frequency is

$$\omega_d = \sqrt{644 - 20.9} = 25$$
$$f_d = \omega_d \div 2\pi = 3.98 \text{ cps}$$

(For comparison f undamped $= 4.04$ cps.)

From the value of n^2, and the relation of n to c (see eq. 5–4b)

$$c = 2mn = \frac{2 \times 30}{32.2} \sqrt{20.9} = 8.52 \text{ lb sec/ft.}$$

CASE 3. CRITICAL DAMPING. There is lastly the middle case between the two previous cases, in which the damping is just enough to make the radical in eq. 5–4 equal to zero. The motion that results from this case is much the same as in Case 1—it is an aperiodic gradual return to the equilibrium.

The motion itself is not very important, but it is useful to pick out this critical value of the damping:

$$n_{crit} = \omega_n$$

or

$$c_{crit} (= c_c) = \sqrt{4km} \tag{5–12}$$

We may now summarize the cases 1 and 2 by saying

(1) for $c > c_c$ the motion is aperiodic

(2) $c < c_c$ the motion is exponentially damped harmonic.

Some of the equations derived in Case 2 may be written more neatly by expressing the damping c as a ratio of c_c.

Equation 5–7 for the damped circular frequency becomes

$$\omega_d = \sqrt{\omega_n^2 - n^2} = \sqrt{\omega_n^2 - c^2\omega_n^2/c_c^2} = \omega_n \sqrt{1 - (c/c_c)^2} \tag{5–13}$$

Equation 5–11 for the logarithmic decrement becomes

$$\delta = n\tau = 2\pi/\sqrt{(c_c/c)^2 - 1} \tag{5–14}$$

It may be noted that this type of damping explains satisfactorily the dying down of an oscillation, but it does not show its disappearance. The elimination is caused generally by the other type mentioned—solid friction. But this will not be taken up here; the reader can find it in texts on vibration.

5–2. Forced Vibration. In addition to the three forces due to inertia, damping, and the spring, let a spring-mounted body have applied to it an alternating force, of magnitude F varying sinusoidally with circular frequency ω rad/sec. The equation of motion will then be

$$m\ddot{x} + c\dot{x} + kx = F \cos \omega t \tag{5–15}$$

The mathematical procedure for solving this equation is outlined on page 79. It consists of two parts. First the left-hand side of the equation is set equal to zero, which equation is called the "homogeneous equation"

$$m\ddot{x} + c\dot{x} + kx = 0$$

This is identical to eq. 5–1 of this chapter with solution in the form either of eq. 5–6 or eq. 5–9 according as the value of the damping coefficient c is greater or less than critical. The solution is generally called the "complementary function."

But this does not satisfy eq. 5–15: so secondly it is necessary to make a good guess at any function which will satisfy eq. 5–15 as it stands. Such a guess when verified will be a "particular integral."

Because of the $c\dot{x}$ term, to guess a function involving solely $\cos \omega t$ would not be satisfactory, for the second term would produce $\sin \omega t$. Take therefore

$$x = P \cos \omega t + Q \sin \omega t \qquad (5\text{–}16)$$

where ω is the same as in the right-hand side of eq. 5–15.

Differentiate this twice and substitute:

$$\dot{x} = -P\omega \sin \omega t + Q\omega \cos \omega t$$
$$\ddot{x} = -P\omega^2 \cos \omega t - Q\omega^2 \sin \omega t$$
$$[(-m\omega^2 + k)P + c\omega Q] \cos \omega t + [(-m\omega^2 + k)Q - c\omega P] \sin \omega t$$
$$= F \cos \omega t \qquad (5\text{–}17)$$

Now if eq. 5–16 is a good guess for a particular integral, there must be values for P and Q implicit in eq. 5–17 which will hold for any and all values of time t. This necessitates that the coefficients of the sine and cosine terms on the right- and left-hand sides of eq. 5–17 are independently equal, or

$$(k - m\omega^2)P + c\omega Q = F \qquad \text{(cos coeff.)}$$
$$(k - m\omega^2)Q - c\omega P = 0 \qquad \text{(sin coeff.)}$$

Cross-multiplying to eliminate Q will produce

$$P = \frac{(k - m\omega^2)F}{(k - m\omega^2)^2 + c^2\omega^2}$$

From the second of the two simultaneous equations, this value of P will give

$$Q = \frac{c\omega F}{(k - m\omega^2)^2 + c^2\omega^2}$$

And these may be put in place in eq. 5–16. But it may better be written as a single wave

$$x = P \cos \omega t + Q \sin \omega t = R \cos (\omega t - \phi) \qquad (5\text{–}18)$$

where the amplitude R is

$$R = \sqrt{P^2 + Q^2} = \frac{F}{\sqrt{(k - m\omega^2)^2 + c^2\omega^2}} \qquad (5\text{-}19)$$

and the phase angle ϕ is found by the following equation and plotted for various magnitudes of damping c in the lower part of Fig. 5–4.

$$\tan \phi = \frac{Q}{P} = \frac{c\omega}{(k - m\omega^2)} \qquad (5\text{-}20)$$

Now this eq. 5–18 will be the particular integral. The reason for the need of both the complementary function and a particular integral is that in the particular integral, as explained before, there are no arbitrary constants. Since the solution of eq. 5–15 involves two integrations, two such arbitrary constants must appear, in order to cover all possible conditions of starting the oscillation, for instance for substitution of an initial displacement and an initial velocity.

The general solution of eq. 5–15 is therefore either

$$x = (Ae^{-at} + Be^{-bt}) + R \cos (\omega t - \phi)$$

or

$$x = e^{-nt} (A_1 \sin \omega_d t + B_1 \cos \omega_d t) + R \cos (\omega t - \phi) \qquad (5\text{-}21)$$

according as the damping is great or small. By substitution it may be verified that either will satisfy the equation

$$m\ddot{x} + c\dot{x} + kx = 0 + F \cos \omega t$$

5–3. Transient and Steady-State Motions. Examination of eq. 5–21 reveals that the first two terms represent an oscillation which diminishes (generally fairly quickly) as time passes. This part is therefore called the "transient" part of the solution.

The last term, which is the particular integral of eq. 5–18, will not change. After the transient has faded away, that which remains is called the "steady state solution," and it will continue as long as the excitation $F \cos \omega t$ continues.

The steady-state solution of eq. 5–15 is therefore eq. 5–18, or

$$x = \frac{F/k}{\sqrt{\left(1 - \frac{m\omega^2}{k}\right)^2 + \frac{c^2\omega^2}{k^2}}} \cos (\omega t - \phi) \qquad (5\text{-}22)$$

Since $k/m = \omega_n^2$ the (free) natural circular frequency, and since F/k is the static deflection x_{st} which would be caused by F applied statically to the springs k

$$x = \frac{x_{st}}{\sqrt{\left(1 - \frac{\omega^2}{\omega_n^2}\right)^2 + \frac{c^2\omega^2}{k^2}}} \cos (\omega t - \phi) \qquad (5\text{-}23)$$

The coefficient of the term x_{st} or $\dfrac{1}{\sqrt{\left(1 - \dfrac{\omega^2}{\omega_n{}^2}\right)^2 + \dfrac{c^2\omega^2}{k^2}}}$ is called the

"magnification factor" of the forced oscillation.

If the damping is very slight, the transients may take a long while to disappear, but eq. 5–23 may be written closely as

$$x = \frac{x_{st}}{1 - \dfrac{\omega^2}{\omega_n{}^2}} \cos\,(\omega t - \phi) \qquad (5\text{--}24)$$

(except in the region near $\omega = \omega_n$ because then the first term under the radical, eq. 5–23, may be as small as the term with the damping coefficient c).

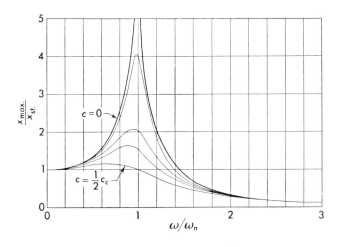

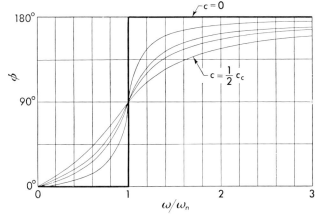

FIG. 5–4.

The curves in the upper part of Fig. 5–4 show the value of the magnification factor for various values of the ratio that the exciting frequency ω bears to the natural frequency ω_n.

The topmost curve reaches infinite value at $\omega = \omega_n$ (i.e., at resonance), and represents the amplitude of eq. 5–24, or the case of no damping. In all actual vibrations damping exists, so that the denominator of the amplitude term (eq. 5–22 or 5–23) is no longer zero when $\omega = \omega_n$, but depends on c. The more damping in the system the lower is the peak of the resonance curve.

When the frequency of the excitation is very low, the response of the spring-supported body is merely to move back and forth harmonically with a displacement the same as that which would be caused by the same static force, almost independently of the amount of damping.

When the frequency of the excitation is very high in comparison with the natural frequency, the response is small in all cases, and in a sense negative to the excitation.

The late Professor Sir Charles Inglis* had a description of these responses, which we quote—

In the behavior of this spring-supported mass there is something almost human; it hates to be rushed. If coaxed gently it responds docilely and moves in the direction it is asked to take. But, if urged to hurry faster than its natural gait, it develops a mulish obstinacy. Such movement as it condescends to make is in a retrograde direction, and the more it is rushed the more stubborn is its resistance. But if it is invited to vibrate with the frequency inherent to its nature, it shows its satisfaction by bouncing up and down with an exuberance of spirits which can be most embarrassing.

5–4. Spring Mounting for a Machine (No Damping). Fig. 5–5 represents diagrammatically a machine of mass m, mounted on springs whose purpose is to isolate within the machine as much as possible of any vibratory forces, to the benefit of floor and building.

Now coil springs will move with very little damping effect, and thus the response of the machine on such mounts is given by eq. 5–24 (except near resonance as noted before). This contrasts with the action of rubber or cork mounts, which always cause considerable damping due to internal intermolecular friction, and with these eq. 5–23 must be applied.

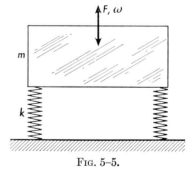

FIG. 5–5.

The mass of the machine m, and the magnitude and frequency of the

* *Applied Mechanics for Engineers* (Cambridge: University Press, 1951), p. 306.

vertical force $F \cos \omega t$ are presumed known. The problem is to choose certain springs of combined stiffness k.

Any force F_τ transmitted to the floor must pass through the springs, and this will be the cause of the deflection of the springs. If a is the amplitude of the vertical motion of m, the maximum force F_τ is

$$F_\tau = ka \tag{5–25}$$

But from eq. 5–24

$$a = \frac{F/k}{1 - \dfrac{\omega^2}{\omega_n{}^2}} \tag{5–26}$$

and this is shown by Fig. 5–4. So therefore we must arrange $k/m = \omega_n{}^2$ so that the amplitude a is as small as possible. From the graph (Fig. 5–4) it appears that this may be accomplished when ω the forcing frequency is very much higher than ω_n, the natural frequency. Or stated in reverse: the value of k must be so chosen as to make ω_n very much smaller than ω. Soft springs are needed.

By combining eqs. 5–25 and 5–26 the fraction of the force F which is transmitted to the floor is

$$\frac{F_\tau}{F} = \frac{1}{1 - \dfrac{\omega^2}{\omega_n{}^2}} \tag{5–27}$$

and this factor is called the "transmissibility."

Of course this must be qualified, as eq. 5–24 was qualified—that it does not apply near resonance when even slight damping becomes a significant factor. But there are other reasons implicit above to stay away from resonance.

The negative sense involved in eq. 5–27 when $\omega > \omega_n$ merely means that the maximum F_τ upward occurs when F is a maximum downward. The two forces vary in harmonic manner, with 180° phase difference.

When damping is a significant factor, it is necessary to reckon that the

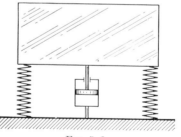

Fig. 5–6.

damping force as well as the spring-extension force is transmitted to the floor, as shown in Fig. 5–6. F_τ is in that case

$$F_\tau = \left[\sqrt{(kx)^2 + (c\dot{x})^2} \right]_{\max} \tag{5–28}$$

It is the vector sum of two components at right angles, because the two forces kx and $c\dot{x}$ are 90° out of phase. With this and eq. 5–22 the ratio of the maximum values of F_τ and F can be found. The analysis is fully developed by Myklestad and by Freberg and Kemler, to mention two texts.

The general conclusions from the analysis including damping are that whereas some damping is advantageous—for instance, while passing through the resonance at low speeds when the machine starts up, yet at all other speeds the damping is a disadvantage, for it not only transmits more force to the floor, but also absorbs power from the machine for a reduction in efficiency.

Example. A machine weighing 3 tons is mounted on four springs each of stiffness 1000 lb per inch compression. A piston within a vertical cylinder, reciprocating at 800 cycles per minute, causes a force of maximum value 200 lb. What is the maximum force transmitted to the floor? Is the mounting suitable?

800 cycles per min. is equal to a circular frequency

$$\omega = 800 \times \frac{2\pi}{60} = 83.7 \text{ rad/sec.}$$

$$\omega^2 = 7020$$

The natural frequency (in the vertical direction) of the machine on its mounts is given by

$$\omega_n{}^2 = \frac{k}{m} = \frac{386 \times 4 \times 1000}{6000} = 257$$

The forcing frequency is over five times the natural frequency. The transmitted force by eq. 5–27 is

$$F_\tau = \frac{200}{1 - (7020/257)} = (-)\frac{200}{26.3} = 7.6 \text{ lb}$$

As to suitability, (1) the static deflection of the machine on its springs is

$$\frac{W}{k} = \frac{6000}{4 \times 1000} = 1.5 \text{ in.}$$

(Note this is not x_{st} used in eqs. 5–23 and 5–24.); (2) the amplitude of oscillation due to F is from eq. 5–25

$$a = F_\tau/k = (-)\frac{7.6}{4000} = 0.0019 \text{ in.}$$

Hence the mounting is very suitable for most cases.

For comparison, suppose the springs chosen were four times stiffer, this would bring $\omega_n{}^2$ near 1000, making F_τ 34 lb; the oscillation will change very little—since both F_τ and k are increased: the amplitude a becomes about 0.0021. The principal advantage would be in the length of springs necessary, for their static deflection W/k would be only one-fourth as much (or $\frac{3}{8}$ in.) as with the springs originally considered.

On the other hand, for certain delicate machining operations or instruments, an oscillation of two-thousandths of an inch would be too much and springs softer than those originally suggested might be indicated. Softer springs produce both less oscillation and less transmitted force.

5–5. Two or More Excitations; Harmonics. In many machines several shafts rotate at different speeds, and all these will probably be unbalanced to a small extent. There may therefore be several forces with different frequencies exciting the machine to vibrate upon its mounting.

Now suppose, for example, that one of these unbalanced shafts rotates at three times the speed of another. If the latter produces a force $F_1 \sin \omega t$, the former will produce $F_2 \sin 3\omega t$, if ω has the same meaning in both cases. There will be a speed of rotation $\omega = \omega_1$ at which there will be resonance between the force of magnitude F_1 and the natural frequency of vibration of the machine on its mounting—which is shown mathematically by $\omega = \omega_n = \omega_1$.

But then also at one-third of this critical speed (or at $\omega_2 = \omega_1/3$) there must be another critical speed. For since the impulses from the force F_2 come with three times the rapidity of those from F_1, at one-third the critical ω_1 there will again be synchronism with the natural frequency ω_n.

So there are two resonances—one corresponding to each excitation. Since the second force has a frequency that is a multiple of the other, it is called a harmonic of the first—in this case the third harmonic.

In many cases the exciting force is periodic but cannot be expressed in the form of a few harmonics. Mathematically it may always be expressed as an infinite series of harmonics, called a Fourier series. An example of this sort is the force that occurs from the reciprocating motion of the pistons in an engine, and this will be taken up in a later chapter. But if a force may be expressed as

$$F = \Sigma F_n \sin n\omega t$$

then there will be an infinite number of resonances, and critical speeds at ω_1, $\frac{1}{2}\omega_1$, $\frac{1}{3}\omega_1$, $\frac{1}{4}\omega_1$, $\frac{1}{5}\omega_1$, etc.

There will never be any harmonics* of resonance, however, but just one resonance, when a single simple harmonic force is acting on such a spring-mounted body.

The amplitude of oscillation of a mass on springs, caused by two or more harmonic forces, is not the arithmetic sum but rather the vector sum of the amplitudes caused by each force separately. The phase of each induced vibration and also its frequency relative to the others must be considered.

---

* Another case of harmonics may arise, though only a simple harmonic force acts upon it, if a body is mounted on springs which have a nonlinear response, i.e., if deflection is not directly proportional to the force applied.

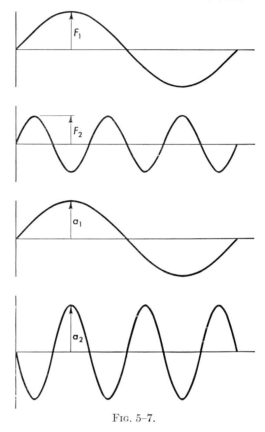

FIG. 5-7.

For example, from the previous analysis of forced undamped oscillation, the equation of motion for the illustrative example used is

$$m\ddot{x} + kx = F_1 \sin \omega t + F_2 \sin 3\omega t$$

and after the transient has been dissipated by friction, the steady-state motion will be

$$x = a_1 \sin \omega t + a_2 \sin 3\omega t$$

where the amplitudes are

$$a_1 = \frac{F_1/k}{1 - \left(\dfrac{\omega}{\omega_n}\right)^2}$$

$$a_2 = \frac{F_2/k}{1 - \left(\dfrac{3\omega}{\omega_n}\right)^2}$$

There will be a range of speed below both resonances when the motions a will be in phase with their own F; then a range of speeds between the

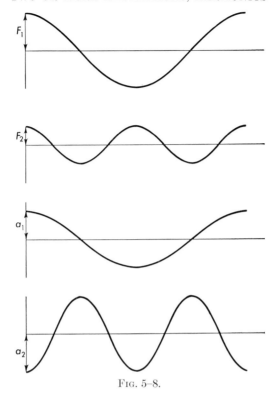

FIG. 5–8.

two resonances when a_1 is in phase with F_1, but a_2 180° out from F_2 being above its resonate speed; finally above the second resonance both are opposite in phase.

Figure 5–7 illustrates the two induced motions for that range between resonances. There is an instant of time that the two motions come into phase, so that in this range the two amplitudes may be added arithmetically.

As another example, Fig. 5–8 shows the response from first and second harmonic forces

$$F_1 \cos \omega t + F_2 \cos 2\omega t$$

and again it is seen that the maximum deflections come into phase at one instant so that the two amplitudes are added arithmetically.

Figure 5–9, however, shows the effect of first and second forces out of phase with each other, expressed as

$$F_1 \cos \omega t + F_2 \sin 2\omega t$$

The oscillations from these never come into phase; the maximum amplitude in this case happens to occur very near the 225° position, so that its value is about $a_2 + a_1 \cos 45°$.

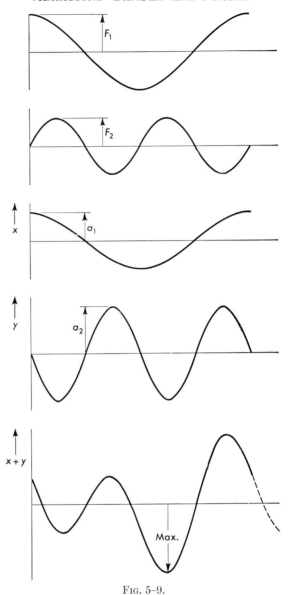

Fig. 5–9.

5–6. Oscillations from Centrifugal Forces and from Shaking. A frequent cause of the vibration of a machine upon its mounting is the lack of balance in some rotating member of the machine.

Suppose in Fig. 5–10 a shaft or rotor revolving with a varying speed ω rad/sec is out of balance to the extent of mrg lb ft. Then if the axis of the rotor were rigid, the vertical component of acceleration of m

would be $mr\omega^2 \cos \omega t$. We presume that the machine (of total mass M) is so mounted that it can only move vertically, and that this motion is measured by x upward. The inertia force of the mass m is then

$$m(r\omega^2 \cos \omega t - \ddot{x})$$

and the equation of vertical motion of the machine is

$$(M - m)\ddot{x} + kx = m(r\omega^2 \cos \omega t - \ddot{x})$$

or

$$M\ddot{x} + kx = mr\omega^2 \cos \omega t \qquad (5\text{–}29)$$

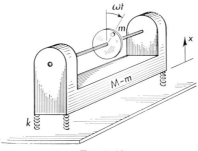

FIG. 5–10.

This is exactly as eq. 5–15, where $mr\omega^2$ replaces F except that damping has been neglected; the solution will therefore be as eq. 5–22 for the steady-state oscillation,

$$x = \frac{mr\omega^2/k}{1 - M\omega^2/k} \cos (\omega t - \phi)$$

Since $k/M = \omega_n^2$, this may be written

$$x = a \frac{\left(\dfrac{\omega}{\omega_n}\right)^2}{1 - \left(\dfrac{\omega}{\omega_n}\right)^2} \cos (\omega t - \phi) \qquad (5\text{–}30)$$

where $a = (m/M)r$. Now we find a variant on the previous magnification factor: it is

$$\text{Magn.} = \frac{\dfrac{\omega^2}{\omega_n^2}}{1 - \dfrac{\omega^2}{\omega_n^2}} = \frac{1}{\dfrac{\omega_n^2}{\omega^2} - 1} \qquad (5\text{–}31)$$

This is represented in Fig. 5–11, and should be compared with the (undamped) curve of Fig. 5–4. The earlier form starts with unit value, passes through resonance, and tends to return to zero, while this does the reverse.

Physical reasoning will explain the two cases. For instance, with constant force F at very low frequencies, the deflection is the same as that caused statically by F or $F/k = x_{st}$ so that the magnification is unity; whereas with a force $mr\omega^2$ varying with the speed, at no speed there is no force, no deflection.

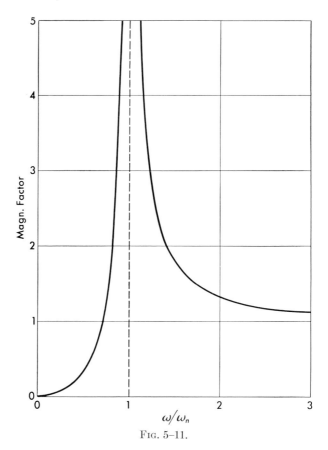

FIG. 5–11.

It should be noted that the curve in Fig. 5–11 is the same as that encountered in the study of the whirling of a disk upon a flexible shaft (Fig. 4–22). There is a direct correlation between the two types of vibration.

A further case where the magnification factor is of this type (eq. 5–31) arises when the base of a machine is shaken with an oscillatory motion (instead of an applied force) and the *relative* motion is studied. An example follows.

Example. A truck of mass M (Fig. 5–12) has mounted upon it a mass m which is attached by a spring. Some force F applied to the truck causes it to move with simple harmonic motion of circular frequency ω. It is desired to find an expression for the motion of the mass m *relative* to the truck. All friction and the mass of the truck wheels may be ignored. Find also the force F needed.

Let the motion of mass M caused by F be

$$x = x_0 \sin \omega t$$

and the displacement of m from its static position be y (relative to M). Both are measured in a positive sense to the right in the figure. A displacement y will then cause a spring tension pulling M to the right, and m back to the left.

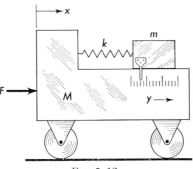

FIG. 5–12.

From the forces acting on m and on M respectively:

$$-m(\ddot{y} + \ddot{x}) = ky$$
$$F + ky = M\ddot{x}$$

Substituting for x (and therefore $\ddot{x}$) as known, we have

$$m\ddot{y} + ky = mx_0\omega^2 \sin \omega t \tag{5–32}$$

$$F = -Mx_0\omega^2 \sin \omega t - ky \tag{5–33}$$

The first of these is the equation of the forced oscillation of m; its solution of steady state is

$$y = \left(\frac{mx_0\omega^2}{k - m\omega^2} \right) \sin \omega t$$

or after $\div m\omega^2$

$$y = \left(\frac{x_0}{\dfrac{\omega_n^2}{\omega^2} - 1} \right) \sin \omega t$$

Therefore at low frequencies ω, the relative motion will be very small; at resonance it will become infinite (damping excepted) and then if the frequency of excitation increases to very high values, the amplitude will die down until it reaches a minimum value $-x_0$. Above resonance the response of the small weight will always be opposite to the motion of the large one.

The relative motion is explained by common sense: imagine the mass M as a horse. Then when it moves slowly, m sits securely upon its back: relative motion is small. When the mass M shivers rapidly, the rider cannot respond but stays almost stationary (in the absolute sense) so that the relative motion is equal and opposite to that of the mount. It is much easier to sit a galloping horse than a trotting one.

The force F that must be applied is found now from eq. 5–33.

$$F = -Mx_0\omega^2 \sin \omega t - \frac{kmx_0\omega^2}{k - m\omega^2} \sin \omega t$$

$$= -\left(M + \frac{m}{1 - \dfrac{\omega^2}{\omega_n^2}}\right) x_0\omega^2 \sin \omega t \qquad (5\text{–}34)$$

5–7. The Electrical Analogy in A-C Circuits. An alternating emf is to cause a current to pass around a series circuit containing resistor, induction coil, and capacitor (condenser) as in Fig. 5–13.

The counter-emf due to the passage of a current i amps through a resistance R ohms is always instantaneously the same as the product of current and resistance. Thus if i is sinusoidal it appears as in Fig. 5–14a and is given by

$$e_R = -iR \quad \text{(volts)}$$

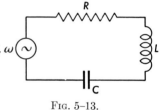

FIG. 5–13.

The counter-emf due to a current i passing through a coil of inductance L henrys is proportional to the inductance and the rate of change of the current. Figure 5–14b shows therefore that if i is a sine wave, e_L will be a negative cosine, or

$$e_L = -L\frac{di}{dt}$$

In a circuit containing solely a condenser, the charge contained is proportional to the impressed voltage and the capacitance C farads.

$$Ce_{\text{imp}} = q$$

Thus the counter-emf is (Fig. 5–14c)

$$e_C = -q/C$$

Now always $i = \dfrac{dq}{dt}$. And if the impressed emf $e = E \cos \omega t$ is to cause the current i, it must exactly overcome all the counter-emf's of the circuit (Fig. 5–13), or

$$E \cos \omega t = iR + L\frac{di}{dt} + \frac{q}{C} \tag{5-35}$$

$$= L\frac{d^2q}{dt^2} + R\frac{dq}{dt} + \frac{1}{C}q$$

This equation in q corresponds exactly to the form of the equation of forced oscillation of a mechanical system (eq. 5–15). From the solu-

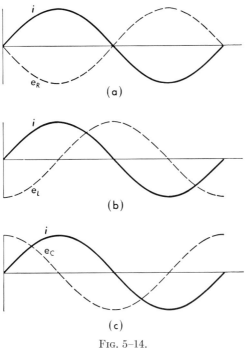

(a)

(b)

(c)

Fig. 5–14.

tion to that equation already obtained, we write for the steady-state electrical oscillation

$$q = \frac{E \cos (\omega t - \phi)}{\sqrt{\left(\frac{1}{C} - L\omega^2\right)^2 + R^2\omega^2}} \tag{5-36}$$

It is seen that the resistance is the agent damping out the transients formed when the circuit is first closed. Then the current appears from the derivative of eq. 5–36.

$$\frac{dq}{dt} = i = \frac{E\omega \sin (\omega t - \phi)}{\sqrt{\left(\frac{1}{C} - L\omega^2\right)^2 + R^2\omega^2}}$$

or

$$i = \frac{E \sin (\omega t - \phi)}{\sqrt{\left(\dfrac{1}{C\omega} - L\omega\right)^2 + R^2}} \qquad (5\text{-}37)$$

in which the radical, being the ratio of maximum voltage E to maximum current, is the impedance Z

$$Z = \sqrt{R^2 + \left(\frac{1}{C\omega} - L\omega\right)^2}$$

From the comparisons of the analogy, parallels are drawn between:

MECHANICAL			ELECTRICAL		
Applied force	F	lb	Applied emf	E	volts
Displacement	x	in.	Charge	q	coulombs
Velocity	$\dot{x}$	in./sec	Current	i	amperes
Spring stiffness	k	lb/in.	Reciprocal of capacitance	$1/C$	1/farads
Mass	m	lb sec²/in.	Inductance	L	henrys
Damping	c	lb sec/in.	Resistance	R	ohms

If it were possible to arrange an electric circuit without resistance resonance is induced when

$$\frac{1}{C} = L\omega^2$$

or

$$\omega = 1/\sqrt{LC}$$

just as we assume no damping in a mechanical system and obtain free resonance when

$$\omega = \sqrt{k/m}$$

This analogy is frequently used as a method of obtaining solutions for the response of mechanical systems; for it is generally cheaper and easier to set up an equivalent electric circuit for analysis and take readings of currents or voltage drops, especially in the case of networks of masses and springs. Electronic analogue computers are constructed on this principle.

5–8. Motion Caused by Constant Velocity or Acceleration. In many machines a component member of the mechanism is caused to move with constant velocity or acceleration by a neighboring member. For example, a cam is designed to give its follower such a motion. Since all members are compressible within the limits of the elastic properties of their material, the center of mass will have a motion that at first lags behind that of the surface being forced into motion.

It will be of interest to study just what the motion is. The problem

in analysis appears to be that shown in Fig. 5–15 in which the free end
A of the spring is given the specified motion x, and we wish to find the
resulting motion y of the mass center G.
Internal damping and friction will be neglected.

CONSTANT VELOCITY APPLIED. The motion of A is made to be

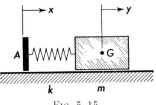

FIG. 5–15.

$$x = vt$$

where v is a constant from time $t = 0$
onward, but starts suddenly at zero time.

If the motion of G is assumed as y, the compression of the spring at
any time is $(x - y)$ and the spring force acting on mass m, causing its
acceleration, is $k (x - y)$. Hence

$$k(x - y) = m\ddot{y}$$

or writing

$$k/m = \omega_n^2$$
$$\ddot{y} + \omega_n^2 y = \omega_n^2 vt \qquad (5\text{–}38)$$

For solution of this equation we need to divide the work into finding
the complementary function and the particular integral. The former is
the solution of the homogeneous equation (right-hand side of eq. 5–38
set as zero)—

$$\ddot{y} + \omega_n^2 y = 0$$

or

$$y = A \sin (\omega_n t + \phi) \qquad (5\text{–}39)$$

For the particular integral, note that the right-hand side of eq. 5–38
still contains a t after two differentiations. Hence y might have started
as a cubic in t: and we make the guess

$$y = pt^3 + qt^2 + rt + s \qquad (5\text{–}40)$$

By differentiating and substituting in eq. 5–38 to see if this will
satisfy, obtain

$$(6pt + 2q) + \omega_n^2(pt^3 + qt^2 + rt + s) = \omega_n^2 vt$$

This must be true for any and all values of t; so coefficients of powers
of t must agree:

$$
\begin{aligned}
(t^3) \qquad & p\omega_n^2 = 0 \\
(t^2) \qquad & q\omega_n^2 = 0 \\
(t\ ) \qquad & 6p + r\omega_n^2 = \omega_n^2 v \\
(t^\circ) \qquad & 2q + s\omega_n^2 = 0
\end{aligned}
$$

This results in

$$p = q = s = 0$$
$$r = v$$

which is substituted in the guess (eq. 5–40) as a verified particular solution. The complete solution of eq. 5–38 and of the problem is the sum of these two parts, or

$$y = A \sin (\omega_n t + \phi) + vt$$

This is a sine wave based on a straight line with upward slope v. From the initial condition that $y = 0$ and the velocity $\dot{y} = 0$ at zero time,

$$A = -v/\omega_n \quad \text{and} \quad \phi = 0$$

so that the equation is exactly

$$y = vt - \frac{v}{\omega_n} \sin \omega_n t \tag{5–41}$$

and is represented in Fig. 5–16. Note the zero slope at the start, and after each period of oscillation.

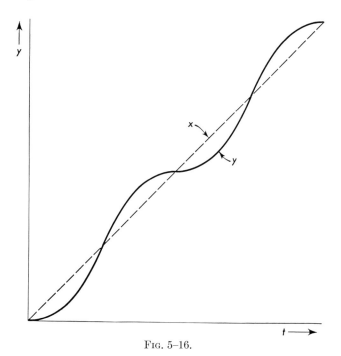

FIG. 5–16.

The stretch of the spring (and that will correspond to the stress in it) is $x - y$, or the sine part of eq. 5–41. The maximum stretch and compression are therefore the same and of magnitude v/ω_n. The mass, in trying to follow the motion required of it, continually overshoots the mark and then drops back.

CONSTANT ACCELERATION APPLIED. For this case Fig. 5–15 will apply as in the previous problem, but the acceleration of the point A

starting suddenly at $t = 0$, with no initial velocity of that point, will produce

$$x = \tfrac{1}{2} at^2$$

so that

$$\ddot{y} + \omega_n^2 y = \omega_n^2 \frac{at^2}{2} \tag{5–42}$$

This yields a complementary solution as before, but a particular integral of the general form

$$y = nt^4 + pt^3 + qt^2 + rt + s$$

should be a guess. This is substituted in eq. 5–42:

$$(12nt^2 + 6pt + 2q) + \omega_n^2(nt^4 + pt^3 + qt^2 + rt + s) = \omega_n^2 \frac{at^2}{2}$$

and from the coefficients of the powers of t, it appears that

$$
\begin{aligned}
&n = 0,\; p = 0 \\
&12n + q\omega_n^2 = a\omega_n^2/2 \qquad \text{or} \qquad q = a/2 \\
&6p + r = 0 \qquad\qquad\qquad\qquad\quad r = 0 \\
&2q + s\omega_n^2 = 0 \qquad\qquad\qquad\quad s = -a/\omega_n^2
\end{aligned}
$$

The complete solution is therefore

$$y = A \sin (\omega_n t + \phi) + \frac{1}{2} at^2 - \frac{a}{\omega_n^2}$$

Then from the initial conditions

$$\cos \phi = 0 \qquad \text{and} \qquad A = a/\omega_n^2$$

so that this motion is represented by Fig. 5–17, and the equation

$$y = \frac{a}{\omega_n^2} (\cos \omega_n t - 1) + \frac{1}{2}at^2 \tag{5–43}$$

The compression in the spring $(x - y)$ therefore will vary from zero to a maximum of $2a/\omega_n^2$; there is never any tension in the spring. The mass is always a laggard. It manages to catch up at intervals, only to drop back again. Unlike the case with constant velocity, it never overshoots the mark.

It might be asked how much force must be applied to the spring at point A (Fig. 5–15) in order to give that point constant acceleration. Since there is taken to be no mass at point A but only further up the spring at G, the only force required is that to overcome the spring compressive forces, or

$$
\begin{aligned}
F &= k(x - y) \\
&= k\left[\frac{a}{\omega_n^2}(1 - \cos \omega_n t) \right] \\
&= ma(1 - \cos \omega_n t) \tag{5–44}
\end{aligned}
$$

Thus the force at the start is zero, but it builds up to a value $2ma$. Its average value is ma.

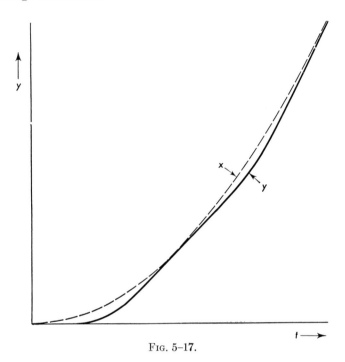

FIG. 5–17.

5–9. The Idea of Equivalent Mass. When two or more parts form an assembly which moves, it is often convenient to reduce the masses of the individual parts to one expression.

In this manner we have already found, for example, that when a simple spring-and-weight system oscillates freely, the effect of the spring mass is approximately the same as if one-third of it were added to the mass of the weight (refer to Problem 3–46).

As another example consider the following:

Example. In Fig. 5–18a a string, attached to the free end of a spring of stiffness 20 lb per in., passes once or twice around a drum (of weight 14 lb, radius 7 in., radius of gyration 5 in.) before being attached to a weight of 5 lb. The drum rotates freely about a fixed axis, and the string is assumed not to slip. Find the equivalent weight to be added to the pendant weight to account for the drum, during free vibration, as Fig. 5–18b.

This problem has been solved before, as a simple oscillation, in both Chapters 3 and 4. By taking moments about the drum axis, if the displacement of the pendant weight is x, and of the drum θ radians,

$$\left(kx + \frac{W}{g}\ddot{x}\right)r = -I\ddot{\theta}$$

By geometry

$$\ddot{\theta} = \ddot{x}/r$$

Simplify the equation of motion to

$$\frac{W}{g}\ddot{x} + \frac{I}{r^2}\ddot{x} + kx = 0$$

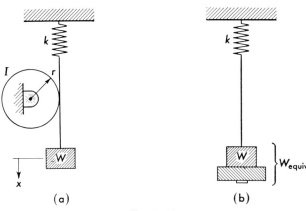

$$(a) \qquad\qquad (b)$$

Fig. 5–18.

The drum may be included in the simpler, equivalent, system of Fig. 5–18b if

$$W_{\text{equiv}} = W + Ig/r^2$$
$$= 5 + 14(\tfrac{5}{7})^2 = 12.143 \text{ lb}$$

Even in the event of a number of masses not moving together but merely coupled by springs to form a system, we may generally find some expression for the mass of the system in terms of its constituent parts.

Suppose then that a mysterious box encloses a number of unknown parts. The equivalent mass of the box and its contents will be equal to the force required to give it a unit acceleration, or

$$M_{\text{equiv}} = F/a \text{ lb sec}^2/\text{ft or lb sec}^2/\text{in.}$$

It is not usually equal to the sum of the masses of the items. For instance, in the last section we found the force required to accelerate such a box of light weight, containing a spring and one mass (all relative velocities being frictionless), so that from eq. 5–44 the equivalent mass of the body or bodies together (Fig. 5–19) is

$$M_{\text{equiv}} = F/a = m(1 - \cos \omega_n t)$$

when $\omega_n = k/m$. It is a variable. Alternatively, if the box itself has a mass M, Fig. 5–20, an additional force Ma is required, so that

$$M_{\text{equiv}} = M + m(1 - \cos \omega_n t)$$

Such a box as Fig. 5–20 will, however, have a different equivalent mass for different types of acceleration. The expression above is valid

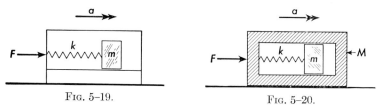

FIG. 5–19.   FIG. 5–20.

for any value of *constant* acceleration; but if the motion impressed is (say) sinusoidal, it is necessary to start once more with analysis as in the preceding section.

This analysis was made in an example (page 213). In order to produce a motion

$$x = x_0 \sin \omega t$$

of the box M, eq. 5–34 showed that a force F given by

$$F = -\left(M + \frac{m}{1 - \dfrac{\omega^2}{\omega_n^2}}\right)x_0\omega^2 \sin \omega t$$

was necessary. The acceleration found by double differentiation of x was

$$\ddot{x} = -x_0\omega^2 \sin \omega t$$

So the equivalent mass of the system in this harmonic motion is the ratio $F/\ddot{x}$ or

$$m_{\text{equiv}} = M + \frac{m}{1 - \dfrac{\omega^2}{\omega_n^2}} \tag{5–45}$$

Some very peculiar concepts arise from this. First suppose that the frequency of the motion x is above the resonance value ω_n of the attached k—m system: the second term in eq. 5–45 is negative. If ω is only slightly higher than ω_n, $\left(1 - \dfrac{\omega^2}{\omega_n^2}\right)$ is a very small negative quantity, so that the second term is a very large negative quantity and it may easily happen that the whole m_{equiv} is negative.

Thus we have a *negative mass!*

This concept is explained through the equation $F = ma$. A usual (positive) mass, when pushed by F, moves off in the direction pushed. A negative mass moves *toward* the force pushing it, as a vicious animal when "shooed" away may attack one.

Secondly, suppose that the oscillation of the box M being forced is of a frequency equal to that of the enclosed k—m system. The second term in eq. 5–45 becomes infinite and thus the whole m_{equiv} is infinitely large.

Now an *infinitely large mass* is one which requires an infinitely large force to accelerate it. In other words, under any ordinary finite force it *will not move at all.*

This possibility can be put to great use, for by so arranging a small addition to a machine, the machine itself can be made impervious to the excitation of a force of given frequency. Such an addition is called a *Frahm dynamic absorber*, after the man who first demonstrated it.

For an example of its use, think of the nuisance of the noise and vibration of beams in a ship or airplane, excited by the engines. Attach a small mass m by a spring k to the offending beam or panel, arranging the ratio $k/m = \omega^2$, and the beam vibration may be eliminated, or at least reduced to a very minor amount. The same device is used in railroad bridges to avoid serious stresses from the passage of locomotives whose wheels will be the cause of periodic "hammer-blows."

In rotary washing-machines the speed of rotation is known. Forces from the uneven distribution of clothes in the cylinder will be transmitted to the floor unless such an absorber is incorporated within the machine. For two principal speeds (washing speed and spin-dry speed) two absorbers would be necessary, each "tuned" to eliminate one of the frequencies from transmission.

BIBLIOGRAPHY

Reference should be made to the listing at the end of Chapter 3.

PROBLEMS

Solve the following two problems as mathematical exercises, and sketch the resulting curve.

5–1. $\ddot{x} + 10\dot{x} + 16x = 0$
Find x for $0 < t < 2$ if $x = -3$, $\dot{x} = 30$ when $t = 0$.

5–2. $2\ddot{x} + 12\dot{x} + 50x = 0$
Find x for $0 < t < 4$ if $x = 10$, $\dot{x} = 0$ when $t = 0$.

5–3. An oscillographic record of the motion of a machine table on being struck by a hammer shows oscillations which diminish in the ratio $1:0.25$. Their frequency is 20 cps. Find the ratio of the damping to critical damping. If it is also known that the table moves 0.040 in. under a static load of 100 lb, find the natural frequency and the approximate mass of the table top.

5–4. A weight of 12 lb is suspended by a light spring of stiffness 8 lb per inch and is free to move vertically. Its motion is damped by a dashpot which produces a force proportional to the velocity of the mass, the force being 3 lb when the velocity is 1 ft/sec. Starting with the system at rest, the upper end of the spring is moved vertically upward with a constant velocity of 5 ft/sec. Find the velocity and acceleration of the mass after $\frac{1}{20}$ second. (C.U.)

5–5. A rod, guided to move vertically with S.H.M. (simple harmonic motion), has a stroke of 1 in. A helical spring is attached to its bottom end and a weight is suspended from the spring. Under steady conditions, the weight is observed to have a travel of 4 in. Find the percentage alteration in the weight of the suspended mass required to reduce its travel to 3 in. (U.L.)

5–6. In the figure, AB is a uniform rod 16 in. in length, weighing 9 lb, and pivoted on a fixed pin at A. A tension spring is attached to the end B of the rod. In the position of equilibrium the rod is inclined at 30° from the vertical, and the axis of the spring is perpendicular to the rod. The stiffness of the spring is $\frac{1}{4}$ lb per in. Neglecting friction, calculate the natural frequency of small oscillations of the system. If the point of anchorage C of the spring is now given a S.H.M. in the line of the spring, making one complete oscillation per second with total travel $\frac{1}{2}$ in., what is the travel of B in its forced vibration? Neglect damping. (U.L.)

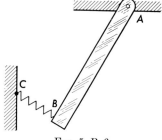

FIG. 5–P–6.

5–7. A mass of 1 lb weight is supported by a spring and its vertical movement is damped by a force proportional to the velocity so that in a free oscillation the ratio of successive displacements on the same side of the equilibrium position is 0.5 and the frequency is 5 cps. A vertical alternating force $3 \sin 30t$ lb is applied to the mass. Show that the amplitude of its oscillation will eventually be about 5 in. (C.U.)

5–8. A mass suspended on a spring has a natural frequency of 10 complete oscillations per second, and its motion is damped by a force proportional to its velocity so that the amplitude of the oscillation is reduced in the ratio 2:1 in every two seconds. If the point of support of the spring is given a vertical simple harmonic motion of frequency 10 and amplitude a, show that the resulting oscillation of the mass will reach an amplitude of about $91a$. (C.U.)

5–9. A weight suspended by a coil spring has a natural period of 0.8 sec for vertical oscillations when the upper end of the spring is fixed. If the weight is initially at rest, and the upper end of the spring is then given a vertical oscillation which continues for 3 sec and then ceases, the displacement during that time being given by the expression, in inches, $\frac{1}{2}(1 - \cos 2\pi t)$, calculate the resulting oscillation of the weight. Ignore damping. (C.U.)

5–10. The rotor of an indicating instrument is controlled by a spring and by a viscous damper. The rotor weighs 0.10 lb and its radius of gyration about the center of rotation is 0.45 in. When set in vibration the rotor makes one complete oscillation in 4.5 sec and the amplitudes of consecutive swings (in opposite directions) are in the ratio 100:24.

a) What would be the periodic time of the vibration if there were no damping?

b) If the rotor, initially at rest, receives a sudden impulse which causes it to swing through an angle of 20°, what amount of energy has been supplied by the impulse?

c) In what ratio must the damping be increased to make the motion aperiodic?
(L.U.)

5–11. The body of a two-wheeled trailer would have a natural period of vertical oscillation on the spring of $\frac{1}{3}$ sec were it not for the damping. The damping is viscous and just over critical value. The trailer is towed at 30 mph over a road which is worn into sinusoidal corrugations of wave-length 5 ft and depth 1 in. from crest to hollow. Find the amplitude of the vertical oscillations of the body when the motion has become steady. (C.U.)

5–12. A two-wheeled trailer is drawn by a truck at a speed of 30 mph on a level road, but the longitudinal section of the road surface has the form of sinusoidal corrugations whose pitch is 5 ft and depth from crest to hollow is 1 in. The weight of the trailer body and load is 1120 lb, the statical deflection of the springs under this load being 2 in.

a) Neglecting the elasticity of the tires, and assuming that the damping of the springs is proportional to the relative velocity between the body and axle, and that it renders the free vertical oscillations of the load just critically dead-beat, show that the amplitude of the oscillations of the load is about 0.24 in. and that the mean power absorbed by the damping is about 4.13 hp.

b) If the damping is rather less than the critical value, the free motion being oscillatory with a decrement $= e^{\pi}$, find the amplitude of the forced oscillation, and the mean power absorbed by the damping. (C.U.)

5–13. A 24-tooth pinion is mounted on a 12-in. length of $\frac{1}{4}$-in. diam steel shaft. The moment of inertia of the gear is 1.0 lb in.^{2} At the other end of the shaft from the gear is a universal joint, driven by an inclined shaft at speeds ranging from 200 to 1800 rpm. The pinion is engaged to an equal pinion, with which it has 0.002-in. backlash; very little power is transmitted to this. Near the top of the speed range the gears become very noisy. Explain this.

5–14. The auxiliary shaft of an automobile engine governor consists of an 8-in. length of $\frac{3}{8}$-in. diam shaft, on one end of which is a 27-tooth pinion driven at camshaft speed, and at the other end the flyball governor. The moment of inertia of the pinion is 1.0 lb in.^{2}, and of the governor is 1.2 lb in.^{2} at the lowest speeds and 1.4 lb in.^{2} at the highest speed, which is regulated to be 1500 rpm.

When this design has been in production some time, complaints from dealers cite excessive wear on the gear teeth, and occasional breakage of the shaft across the governor keyway. Explain and suggest a remedy.

5–15. A machine contains a high-speed cutter, which it is reckoned may be unbalanced by $\frac{1}{10}$ oz in., while it is to rotate at 12,000 rpm. The cutter, shaft, and motor assembly weighs 50 lb. Determine the stiffness of the springs by which this assembly should be attached to the rest of the machine, if the cutter is not to shake more than 0.0005 in. while running, nor be susceptible to move more than 0.0005 in. if the operator should lean on it with a static force of 50 lb.

5–16. In a die-stamping machine, the upper die moves with approximately simple harmonic motion vertically with a stroke of 2 in. at the speed of 2 cps.

The die weighs 500 lb; the whole machine weighs 4000 lb. Determine suitable springs to place under the four corners of the machine base, if the floor can take a load of 4300 lb maximum, and the machine is not to move more than 0.020 in.

5–17. Elaborate the theory of transmissibility to include damping, as suggested by eq. 5–28, and obtain an expression for the transmissibility. Show then that for all conditions of damping the transmitted force is less than the impressed force if ω is greater than $1.414\omega_n$, but that any damping at all increases the transmitted force. Damping is only useful if ω is less than $1.414\omega_n$, in which case transmissibility is greater than unity.

5–18. A simple pendulum of length 12 in. is attached to a horizontal pin upon the body of a truck. When the truck is given a horizontal simple harmonic motion of frequency 2 cps, the pendulum swings through an angle of 5° with the vertical either way. Find the amplitude of the truck's motion.

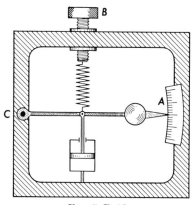

FIG. 5–P–19.

5–19. Figure 5–P–19 shows a spring of stiffness $k = 2$ lb/in., and a damper whose coefficient is 0.6 of critical, attached at radius 2 in. from pivot C, to a simple horizontal pendulum which has a mass of 1 lb at radius 4 in. The pointer A at radius 5 in. reads the motion against the scale, and it is adjusted by thumbscrew B to read zero when stationary. If the box is set upon a machine which has an oscillation of amplitude 0.1 in. and frequency 50 cps, what will be the reading of the pointer A?

5–20. Figure 5–P–19 shows an accelerometer—a device to measure the maximum acceleration in a simple harmonic type of motion. The undamped natural frequency of the needle is 100 cps; the damping is 0.6 of critical. The thumbscrew B is adjusted so that the needle A reads zero, an item which changes as vertical or horizontal motion might be read.

Plot a graph of the accelerometer scale reading against the maximum acceleration of any simple harmonic motion of frequency less than 50 cps, and of any amplitude that does not induce too great an angle of the arm AC to spoil the linear response of the spring.

5-21. The figure shows a face-cam which restrains the motion of mass m to move continuously with simple harmonic motion $x = \frac{1}{2}A(1 - \cos \omega t)$. Attached to the mass m by a stiff spring (constant k) is another mass M, so that k/M is very much greater than ω^2. Investigate whether the motion of M agrees with that of m more closely when a dashpot producing viscous damping (constant c) is added between M and m, or between M and a fixed point (as shown in dotted lines). Determine also and compare the force between m and the cam surface.

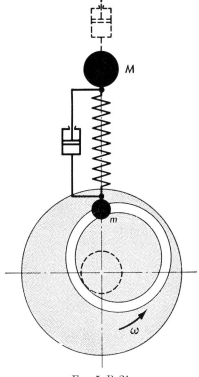

5-22. A weight suspended by a coil spring has a natural period of 0.8 sec for vertical oscillations when the upper end of the spring is fixed. The weight being initially at rest, the upper end of the spring is given a vertical oscillation which continues for 0.5 sec and then stops, the displacement during that time being expressed in inches by $\frac{1}{2}(1 - \cos 2\pi t)$.

Calculate the amplitude of the resulting oscillation of the weight, if the effects of damping during the time considered are negligible.

5-23. A rubber ball is dropped from a height of 10 ft on to a smooth rigid floor, and rebounds to a height of 8 ft.

Fig. 5–P–21.

Determine the damping constant of the rubber; assume the motion of the center of the ball is a damped sine motion for the duration of contact.

5-24. Figure 4–37 (page 172) represents a flywheel fitted with a rope-brake dynamometer; the tension in the rope is controlled by the mass m and spring of stiffness k lb/in. The coefficient of friction is μ. The flywheel is driven by a constant torque at a steady mean speed.

Show that the frequency of the free oscillation of m vertically, and of the flywheel about its mean speed of revolution, is $\dfrac{e^{\pi\mu}}{2\pi}\sqrt{\dfrac{k}{m}}$.

Find also an expression for the ratio of the angular amplitude of oscillation of the flywheel to that of the rope surrounding it. (C.U.)

Chapter 6

THREE-DIMENSIONAL ROTATION

6–1. Introduction — Vector Conventions. Some of the most surprising phenomena that exist in dynamics are the result of rotation. One, we have seen in Chapter 4, is that a body balanced statically may yet wobble violently when revolving. Another example is the gyroscope which always behaves most eccentrically when twisted: everyone knows of the trick that has been played on innocent hotel bellboys of hiding a sizable spinning gyroscope within a suitcase.

The original gyroscope was made to prove that the earth rotates on its own axis, rather than the sun around the earth, whence the name gyroscope. But in achieving an understanding of this, we will also obtain an explanation of the boomerang, and find the reason for the action of a spinning top that seems to prefer an "unstable" position balanced on its end and raises itself against gravity to reach this position.

This chapter is intended to complete, first, the study of rotating balance started in Chapter 4 by introducing two more powerful methods than those given there. These concepts will also explain the gyroscope, which we then turn our attention to. However, an understanding of the simple gyroscope is possible without these preliminaries; so if the reader is interested only in the gyroscope he may turn to Art. 6–15 immediately after Art. 6–2.

Now, throughout mechanics there have occurred certain quantities which were completely specified by their size, and other quantities which have both size and direction. These have been called respectively scalar and vector quantities. Some examples that have occurred are, of scalars: mass, volume, energy; and of vectors: force, velocity, acceleration, momentum.

One of the principal characteristics of vector quantities is that they must obey the parallelogram law of addition rather than the simple algebraic law.

Considering angular motion in three dimensions, it is evident that angular velocity is a vector, for it has a magnitude, a direction, and sense. Just how a vector should be drawn to represent angular velocity is a matter for convention, and the customary representation is to lay the vector along the axis of rotation. To try to define the angular velocity by the linear velocity of some part of the body would lead to all

228

sorts of confusion, so that idea is not followed. The sense of the vector
is defined as the direction of advance if the body were a right-hand screw
rotating in the same manner about the same
axis (Fig. 6–1).

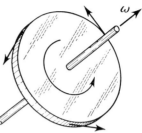

All vectors in angular motion are represented by this convention; other such vectors
are angular acceleration, torque (couples),
and angular momentum.

6–2. Angular Displacement and Velocity.
Angular displacement—that is, the measure
of the turning of any body through various
angles—is a vector, for it has magnitude,
together with sense, clockwise or counterclockwise, and a direction defined in terms of the
axis about which it swings. Yet it is an irregular vector, for it does not
obey the law of vector addition (the parallelogram law). Instead, addi-
tions of this vector must be found by application of spherical trigonom-
etry.

FIG. 6–1.

Den Hartog* gives the simplest illustration of this: take a book lying
face up on the table. Turn it over three times about mutually perpendicular axes, as in Fig. 6–2. First turn it over its open edge, then over
its bottom edge, then rotate it about a vertical axis perpendicular to
the table, and it will be found to be as it started. Three of these improper
vectors have thus been added for zero resultant, instead of the proper
vector resultant in Fig. 6–2e.

On the other hand, angular velocity *is* a properly behaving vector.
But now, because it is composed of the rate of change of the improper
displacement vectors, this fact will have to be demonstrated: it is not
a difficult task when derived from the vector properties of linear velocity.

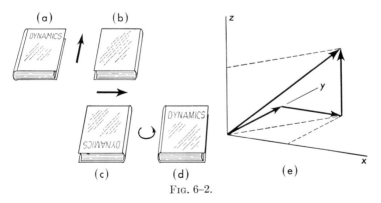

FIG. 6–2.

* J. P. Den Hartog, *Mechanics* (New York: McGraw-Hill Book Co., Inc., 1948),
p. 316.

In Fig. 6–3 the line OP has an angular velocity ω which produces a velocity V at the point P, on the sphere of radius $r = OP$. Thus OP swings toward OQ. This velocity V is resolved into any two components V_1 and V_2; when these are divided by radius r, they are called the angular velocity components ω_1 and ω_2 respectively. Following the convention for drawing these vectors they appear as the parallelogram at the origin, which must be similar to that of vectors V, V_1, V_2, with each side reduced by the factor $1/r$.

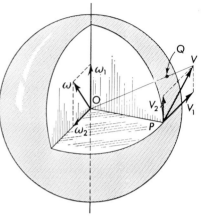

Thus any angular velocity may be resolved into vector components, and any number of angular velocities about a point may be added vectorially.

Example 1. In Fig. 6–4a a circular disk is mounted askew on an axle, which is rotating at speed ω.

Fig. 6–3.

Suppose the mounting is at 30°. Assume x- and y-axes as shown. Then the disk may be said to have two component rotations: ω_x, of magnitude $\omega/2$, in the sense that the far side rises and the near side moves downward, together with ω_y, of magnitude 0.866ω, in the clockwise sense when viewed from below.

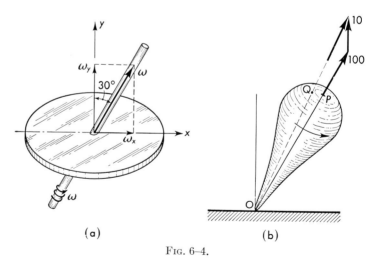

(a)   (b)

Fig. 6–4.

Example 2. A symmetrical top spinning at 100 rpm about its axis, which is inclined at 30° to the vertical in the sense shown, is given also an angular velocity of 10 rpm about the vertical, so that its axis OP describes a cone.

The angular velocity is then approximately 109 rpm about the instantaneous axis of rotation OQ (Fig. 6–4b). The top center point P therefore moves away from you.

Now to conceive of components of angular velocity is to some rather difficult. Yet this is no more the same as saying that a rigid body actually rotates about two different axes simultaneously than, when a body moves northeast and is spoken of as having a component velocity north and a component east, it can be said to mean that the body has a linear motion in two directions at once. A component will always give only a partial representation of the situation. In three-dimensional space, three components in three orthogonal directions may occur.

6–3. Right-Handed Set of Axes. If, in the work that follows, the signs ($\pm$) of various relations between moments, angular velocities, etc., are to appear consistently and correctly, it is necessary to adopt a rule covering the direction of the third axis when two have been chosen.

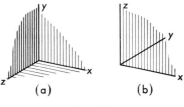

The rule is applied as follows: in Fig. 6–5a it is presumed that the x and y positive directions are chosen, say, in the vertical plane. Then

(a)   (b)

FIG. 6–5.

the z-axis (positive direction) must be forward. Or in Fig. 6–5b if the x and y positive directions are right and backward horizontally, then the positive z must be vertically upward.

The rule is described in this manner: suppose a right-handed screw lies in the z-axis, and the slot in the screw head lies in the x-axis. A 90° turn by a screwdriver from the x over to the y will advance the screw in the positive z direction. It then automatically follows that a turn from y to z would advance a screw laid in the x-axis in the positive x direction; and for a y screw, a turn from z to x will show the positive y-direction.

Three orthogonal axes conforming to this convention are called a right-handed set.

You do not have to use a right-handed set, but if you do not it will be wise to watch out carefully for the signs ($\pm$) in derived equations, and not quote formulas blindly.

6–4. Dynamic Balance. In Fig. 6–6a a rotor is represented as a single weight W, at radius r (in the plane of the paper), and located a distance d along the axis from the point O. It is proposed to find balance weights to be placed in the A and B planes; and this is easily done by the methods of Chapter 4. To find W_B, moments of the centrifugal forces about O are taken, and the equation for solution is

$$Wrd(\omega^2/g) = W_B r_B L(\omega^2/g) \qquad (6\text{--}1)$$

Now instead of this let us superimpose coordinate axes x, y, z, as in Fig. 6–6b with origin at O. We may think of these axes either that the

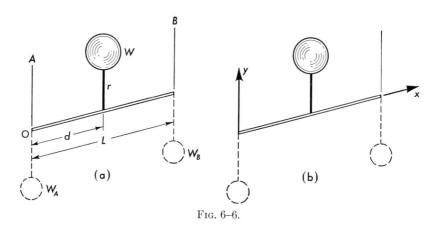

FIG. 6–6.

radius line r of the weight is instantaneously in the x, y plane, or that the axes rotate with the body, being fixed in the body, with r permanently in the x, y plane. The latter is preferable. Then note that the radius r is merely the y dimension of weight W, so that the centrifugal force is $Wy(\omega^2/g)$ and its moment about O is $Wxy(\omega^2/g)$, for distance d is the x dimension of W. Equation 6–1 is replaced by

$$Wxy(\omega^2/g) = W_B r_B L(\omega^2/g)$$

If there are a number of eccentric masses in the x, y plane, the sum of their centrifugal moments which must be balanced is expressed as

$$\left(\sum_{n=1}^{n} W_n x_n y_n \right) (\omega^2/g) \text{ or } \omega^2 \Sigma mxy$$

The term Σmxy has the same dimensions as a moment of inertia and yet it depends upon the product of two coordinates rather than the square of one. It is called a "product of inertia" and designated as I_{xy}. We then write

$$\text{Unbalanced moment} = \omega^2 \Sigma mxy = \omega^2 I_{xy} \qquad (6\text{--}2)$$

and corresponding to eq. 6–1, this unbalance can be eliminated by adding balance weight W_B

$$\omega^2 I_{xy} = W_B r_B L(\omega^2/g) \qquad (6\text{--}3)$$

Now note the sense of this unbalanced moment. With r (Fig. 6–6) and d in the positive y and x directions, I_{xy} will be positive and the moment $I_{xy}\omega^2$ can be represented by a torque vector in the positive z direction, that is, in the figure, straight toward you, or

$$+I_{xy}\omega_x{}^2 = +T_z \qquad (6–4)$$

Observe also that (unlike moment of inertia) a product of inertia is as easily negative as positive. For instance, the radius arm of Fig. 6–6b could be in the negative y direction.

We turn to the case of three-dimensional dynamic unbalance, and here the old method (eqs. 4–11, page 148) gave for the horizontal and vertical components $(W_B r_B)_H$ and $(W_B r_B)_V$ the equations

$$\begin{aligned}
(\omega^2/g)\,\Sigma Wrd\,\cos\,\theta &= -(W_B r_B L)_H (\omega^2/g) \\
(\omega^2/g)\,\Sigma Wrd\,\sin\,\theta &= -(W_B r_B L)_V (\omega^2/g)
\end{aligned} \qquad (6–5)$$

In Fig. 6–7 the configuration of one (say W_1) of the unbalanced masses of Fig. 4–14 (page 147) is shown viewed from the plane B end, and it is plain that $r_1 \cos \theta_1$ is the y dimension and $r_1 \sin \theta_1$ the z dimension of the weight W_1. Thus $W_1 r_1 d_1 \cos \theta_1$ becomes $W_1 y_1 x_1$, and $W_1 r_1 d_1 \sin \theta_1$ becomes $W_1 z_1 x_1$ and eqs. 6–5 transform to

$$\begin{aligned}
(\omega^2/g)\,\Sigma Wyx &= \omega^2 \Sigma mxy = \omega^2 I_{xy} = -(W_B r_B L)_H (\omega^2/g) \\
(\omega^2/g)\,\Sigma Wzx &= \omega^2 \Sigma mzx = \omega^2 I_{zx} = -(W_B r_B L)_V (\omega^2/g)
\end{aligned} \qquad (6–6)$$

Of course, all this has merely introduced a new terminology. The amount of work to find the products of inertia of a system of discrete masses disposed in various directions, which we have so far used to represent one unbalanced rotor, is identically the same as to find the moment sum in eq. 6–5. Yet the method is better, for it can be applied to other types of rotors, as will follow.

An important conclusion from eq. 6–6 is that when any system of masses comprising a rotor has the property that all products of inertia in any plane containing the axis of revolution, with origin anywhere on that axis, are zero, then that system is in dynamic balance; for this is tantamount to saying that there are no centrifugal moments in any direction about any point on the axis. Two origins and two perpendicular planes will determine the matter completely.

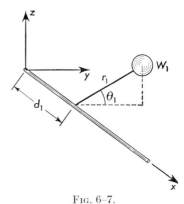

Fig. 6–7.

We also know that if the center of gravity of the whole rotor lies on the axis of revolution, the rotor is in static balance but not necessarily in dynamic balance. Thus $I_{xy}\omega^2$ or $I_{zz}\omega^2$ will give the centrifugal couple unbalance (rather than the moment) when the origin of the coordinates is at the center of mass of the body.

6–5. Dynamic Unbalance of an Inclined Thin Rod. The thin rod of Fig. 6–8 is one of the simplest cases of a solid body which is not balanced.

Let the rod be inclined at an angle θ to the x-axis about which it is revolving with angular velocity ω_x. Choose the y-axis so that the rod is in the xy-plane.

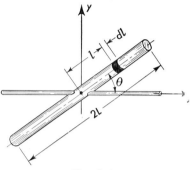

Now with the center of the rod on the x-axis, the unbalance will be a couple. The sense of this couple will be to increase the angle θ and thus it is represented by a vector in the z-direction. The couple must be found by summation of the moments of centrifugal force from

Fig. 6–8.

all such elements as the one shown in the figure: with the radius measured as y and the moment arm of the force measured as x, it is plain that the couple we are seeking can be written in the new notation as

$$T_z = +I_{xy}\omega_x^2 \quad \text{or} \quad (\Sigma xy \cdot \delta m)\omega_x^2$$

But since the x and radius y of every elemental length of rod varies, the sum (Σ) will consist of an infinite number of infinitesimal parts, or, that is, it will be an integral sum:

$$T_z = \omega_x^2 \int xy \cdot dm \tag{6–7}$$

Measure the position of the element by the distance l along the rod from the origin; then the mass of the element is $(M/2L)dl$ when M is the whole mass and $2L$ the total length of the rod. We convert x and y to l by $x = l \cos \theta$ and $y = l \sin \theta$, so that eq. 6–7 becomes

$$T_z = \omega_x^2 \int_{-L}^{+L} (l \cos \theta)(l \sin \theta)(M/2L)dl$$

$$= \frac{M}{2L}\omega_x^2 \sin \theta \cos \theta \left[\frac{l^3}{3}\right]_{-L}^{+L}$$

$$= \tfrac{1}{6}ML^2\omega_x^2 \sin 2\theta$$

Since $ML^2/3$ is recognizable as the moment of inertia of the rod about the z-axis,

$$T_z = \tfrac{1}{2}I_z\omega_x^2 \sin 2\theta \tag{6–8}$$

and comparing eq. 6–7, the product of inertia has been found to be

$$I_{xy} = \tfrac{1}{2}I_z \sin 2\theta \tag{6–9}$$

6-6. To Obtain Products of Inertia. We have now shown that in order to balance various rigid bodies, which cannot be divided (as in Chapter 4) into a finite number of discrete masses, it is necessary to find the products of inertia of the body with respect to the axis of rotation and a perpendicular axis.

The methods available for finding these products of inertia are the same three that are used for finding moments of inertia. They may be found by integration, as in the preceding article; this is sometimes tedious but often unavoidable. They may often be found by using the formula for transfer between parallel axes and the formula for transfer between angularly inclined axes, when the body can be broken down analytically into a number of geometric shapes. These formulae for transfer will be developed in the following articles.

6-7. Products of Inertia of Symmetrical Bodies. The last paragraph in Art. 6-4 reasoned that when a body is balanced, its products of inertia are zero. Take, for instance, the solid of revolution in Fig. 6-9, which revolves about the x-axis and is obviously balanced.

$$I_{xy} = \Sigma xy \cdot \delta m$$

But for every point such as P with position (x', y') there is another point P' at $(x', -y')$, and since the whole body consists of such pairs, the sum will vanish, or that is,

$$I_{xy} = 0$$

Similarly with x and z, the body is the sum of pairs such as $Q(x', z')$ and $Q'(x', -z')$ so that

$$I_{xz} = 0$$

Thus the body would rotate about the x-axis without causing any centrifugal moments about the origin of these coordinates. To show it revolves perfectly in balance, the products of inertia must be zero for a similar set of axes, say X, Y, Z, with origin at a different point along the axis of rotation.

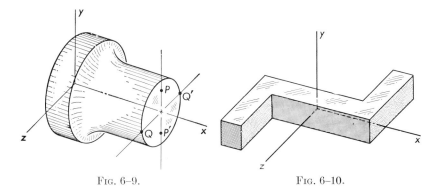

FIG. 6-9.   FIG. 6-10.

For a body having only one plane of symmetry, such as the Z-shaped object of Fig. 6–10, with axes x, y, z as shown, the same type of reasoning shows that I_{xy} and I_{yz} are zero, while I_{zx} is not. The plane of symmetry is the xz plane. To cover this case the theorem must be stated as follows:

> THEOREM: For any body or system of particles that contains a plane of symmetry, the product of inertia, with respect to any axis in the plane and any intersecting normal to the plane, is zero.

This fact is of the greatest use because most bodies encountered in engineering design are symmetrical geometrical shapes or combination of such shapes. Because of this, products of inertia are generally much more easily found than are moments of inertia.

6–8. The Parallel-Axis Transfer Rule.

> THEOREM: If the product of inertia of any body with respect to two rectangular axes x, y through the center of mass is known, the product of inertia with respect to axes X, Y, where X is parallel to or coincident with x, and Y parallel to or coincident with y, is given by

$$I_{XY} = I_{xy} + Mab \qquad (6\text{–}10)$$

where M is the mass of the whole body, a the X dimension and b the Y dimension of the center of mass.

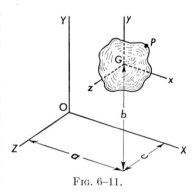

FIG. 6–11.

The proof of this is simple enough. In Fig. 6–11 the location of the origin G of the rectangular set xyz is given in coordinates from O as (a, b, c). Any point P in the body can be located as (x, y, z) or (X, Y, Z), but the latter is synonymous with $(x + a, y + b, z + c)$. Then

$$
\begin{aligned}
I_{XY} &= \Sigma mXY = \Sigma m(x + a)(y + b) \\
&= \Sigma mxy + \Sigma mxb + \Sigma may + \Sigma mab \\
&= \Sigma mxy + b\Sigma mx + a\Sigma my + ab\Sigma m
\end{aligned}
$$

But if G is at the center of mass of the body, Σmx and Σmy vanish by definition. Then

$$I_{XY} = \Sigma mxy + ab\Sigma m = I_{xy} + Mab$$

since $M = \Sigma m$ is the whole mass of the body.

Example 1. Find the product of inertia with respect to the X, Y-axes of the rectangular lamina of Fig. 6–12a, of length $X = a$, height $Y = b$, thickness $Z = t$, and total mass M.

Establish x- and y-axes through the center G of the rectangle, parallel to the sides. Then, because of symmetry,

$$I_{xy} = 0$$

Hence

$$I_{XY} = 0 + M(a/2)(b/2) = \tfrac{1}{4}Mab$$

And for such a body, rotating about the X-axis with angular velocity ω_x, there will be a moment of centrifugal forces about the origin equal to

$$I_Z = I_{XY}\omega_x^2 = \tfrac{1}{4}Mab\omega_x^2$$

which is the moment of the centrifugal force at the center G about O.

Example 2. Find the product of inertia of the same rectangular lamina with respect to the sides meeting in the upper left corner (Fig. 6–12b).

The transfer distances are, for the x-change $a/2$, and for the y-change $-b/2$. Thus

$$I_{XY} = 0 + M(a/2)(-b/2) = -\tfrac{1}{4}Mab$$

6–9. Products of Inertia by Integration. For nonsymmetrical bodies it is necessary to integrate. Mathematical integration is, however, restricted to bodies whose boundaries may be expressed by an equation. Some examples are given.

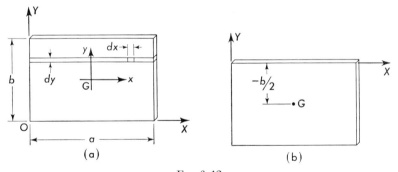

(a)   (b)

FIG. 6–12.

Example 1. Find the product of inertia of the rectangular lamina in Fig. 6–12a about the X, Y-axes. This is the same as Example 1 in the preceding article, and should therefore check the solution.

Let the lamina (of this particular thickness) have a mass of μ per unit area. Then the mass of the elemental area $dx\, dy$ is $dm = \mu dx\, dy$.

The product of inertia of the strip shown with ordinate Y and thickness dy is

$$Y\left[\int_0^a X\mu\,dx\right]dy$$

or for the whole lamina

$$I_{XY} = \int_0^b Y\left[\int_0^a X\mu\,dx\right]dy$$

$$= \mu\int_0^b Y[a^2/2]\,dy$$

$$= \frac{\mu a^2}{2}\cdot\frac{b^2}{2} = \frac{1}{4}Mab$$

since $\mu ab = M$, the mass of the whole lamina.

Example 2. Find the product of inertia of the quarter sphere in Fig. 6–13, about the x, y-axes.

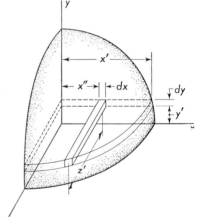

We are interested only in the x and y dimensions of the body, so show first a horizontally cut slice of thickness dy at height y', and then the prismatic bar of thickness dx, and length z' to the surface of the sphere. This prism will be the element having mass $\mu z'dx\,dy$.

Now as we sum all such bars in the horizontal slice, the z' diminishes with increased x''. The equation relating points on the sphere's surface is

$$x^2 + y^2 + z^2 = r^2$$

FIG. 6–13.

Therefore for the horizontal slice with $y = y'$

$$\delta I_{xy} = y'\int_0^{x'} x''\mu z'\,dx''\,dy$$

$$= \mu y'\left[\int_0^{x'} x''\sqrt{(r^2 - x''^2 - y'^2)}dx''\right]dy$$

Then for the whole quarter-sphere the summation of all such slices is made, varying y' from 0 to r, giving

$$I_{xy} = \mu\int_0^r y'\left[\int_0^{x'} x''\sqrt{r^2 - x''^2 - y'^2}\,dx''\right]dy$$

On the inner integral, y' is held constant so

$$I_{xy} = \mu \int_0^r y' \left[-\frac{2}{3} \cdot \frac{1}{2} \cdot (r^2 - x''^2 - y'^2)^{3/2} \right]_{x''=0}^{x''=x'} dy$$

$$= \frac{\mu}{3} \int_0^r y' \{ (r^2 - y'^2)^{3/2} - (r^2 - x'^2 - y'^2)^{3/2} \} \, dy$$

But the points x', y' lie on the circle in the xy plane, or $x'^2 + y'^2 = r^2$, so

$$I_{xy} = \frac{\mu}{3} \int_0^r y'(r^2 - y'^2)^{3/2} \, dy$$

$$= \frac{\mu}{3} \left[-\frac{2}{5} \cdot \frac{1}{2}(r^2 - y'^2)^{5/2} \right]_{y'=0}^{y'=r} = +\frac{\mu}{15}(r^2)^{5/2}$$

$$= \frac{\mu r^5}{15} = Mr^2/(5\pi)$$

since $\qquad M = \frac{1}{4}\mu(4\pi r^3/3)$

6–10. Relation Between Axes at an Angle. If we can find the moments and products of inertia of a body with respect to some axes X, Y, Z, when we know those with respect to some axes x,y,z which have the same origin but are inclined, then in conjunction with the procedures outlined in the preceding articles we may find the inertia of any body most easily.

When the rotation of axes is in two dimensions, that is, when the X- and Y-axes are in the xy plane, the Z- and z-axes being coincident, the relations are given by

$$I_X = I_y \sin^2 \theta + I_z \cos^2 \theta + I_{xy} \sin 2\theta \qquad (6\text{–}11)$$

$$I_Y = I_y \cos^2 \theta + I_z \sin^2 \theta - I_{xy} \sin 2\theta \qquad (6\text{–}12)$$

$$I_{XY} = (I_y - I_z) \sin \theta \cos \theta + I_{xy} \cos 2\theta \qquad (6\text{–}13)$$

if the angle θ is measured as in Fig. 6–14.

The proof of these is simply by substitution. The geometry of the figure shows that for any representative point P its coordinates (X, Y) and (x, y) are related by

$$\left. \begin{array}{l} X = x \cos \theta - y \sin \theta \\ Y = x \sin \theta + y \cos \theta \end{array} \right\} \qquad (6\text{–}14)$$
$$Z = z$$

The moment of inertia I_X is defined as $\Sigma m(Y^2 + Z^2)$ for $(Y^2 + Z^2)$ is the square of the radius from the point to the X-axis.

$$\begin{aligned} I_X &= \Sigma m[(x \sin \theta + y \cos \theta)^2 + z^2] \\ &= \Sigma m[x^2 \sin^2 \theta + y^2 \cos^2 \theta + z^2(\sin^2 \theta + \cos^2 \theta) + 2xy \sin \theta \cos \theta] \\ &= \sin^2 \theta \, \Sigma m(x^2 + z^2) + \cos^2 \theta \, \Sigma m(y^2 + z^2) + \sin 2\theta \, \Sigma mxy \\ &= I_y \sin^2 \theta + I_z \cos^2 \theta + I_{xy} \sin 2\theta \end{aligned}$$

This proves eq. 6–11, and the other proofs are similar.

Example. Find the moments and product of inertia with respect to the X- and Y-axes of the L-shaped laminar body in Fig. 6–15 with the dimensions given and of mass m per square inch.

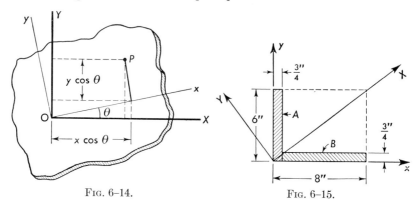

FIG. 6–14.   FIG. 6–15.

Choose axes x, y along the geometrical lines of the body, and having the same origin as X, Y. Then by finding first the inertia about these axes, we may use the formulae for angle-swing. This will be simpler than approaching the problem directly.

Divide the body into two parts A and B. The masses of the two are

$$m_A = m \times 6 \times \tfrac{3}{4} = 4.5m$$
$$m_B = m \times 7\tfrac{1}{4} \times \tfrac{3}{4} = 5.438m$$

For part A:

$$I_x = \tfrac{1}{3}m_A \cdot (6)^2; \quad I_y = \tfrac{1}{3}m_A(\tfrac{3}{4})^2$$
$$I_{xy} = m_A(\tfrac{3}{8} \times 3)$$

For part B:

$$I_x = \tfrac{1}{3}m_B(\tfrac{3}{4})^2; \quad I_y = \tfrac{1}{12}m_B(7\tfrac{1}{4})^2 + m_B(\tfrac{29}{8} + \tfrac{3}{4})^2$$
$$I_{xy} = m_B(\tfrac{29}{8} + \tfrac{3}{4})(\tfrac{3}{8})$$

Thus the sum gives

$$I_x = 12m_A + 3/16m_B = 55.02m$$
$$I_y = 3/16m_A + 23.52m_B = 128.6m$$
$$I_{xy} = 1.125m_A + 1.64m_B = 13.98m$$

Now a comparison between the respective positions of the X, Y and x, y-axes in Figs. 6–15 and 6–14 will show that the angle θ used in eqs. 6–11 through 6–13 is here negative; from the geometry of Fig. 6–15 we have then

$$\sin \theta = -6/10 \quad ; \quad \sin^2 \theta = 0.36$$
$$\cos \theta = +8/10 \quad ; \quad \cos^2 \theta = 0.64$$
$$\sin 2\theta = -0.96 \quad ; \quad \cos 2\theta = 0.28$$

Substitution in the three transfer formulae gives

$$I_X = m(128.6 \times 0.36 + 55.02 \times 0.64 - 13.98 \times 0.96) = 68.1m$$
$$I_Y = m(128.6 \times 0.64 + 55.02 \times 0.36 + 13.98 \times 0.96) = 115.5m$$
$$I_{XY} = -m(128.6 - 55.02)0.48 + m13.98 \times 0.28 \qquad = -31.4m$$

(A digression to consider the *area* moments and product of inertia for the same figure, which is then regarded as the section of a standard structural angle, will disclose that all three results are the same numerically, if for m (mass per unit area) we substitute merely the numeral one. For instance, the area moment of part A about the x-axis is $I_x = \frac{1}{3}a_A(6)^2$ so that for both parts A and B this moment becomes $I_x = 12a_A + (\frac{3}{16})a_B$, where a_A and a_B refer to the areas of parts A and B, respectively, equal to 4.5 and 5.438 sq in.)

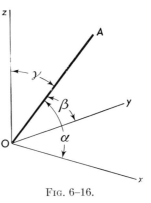

FIG. 6-16.

In the case that all three axes X, Y, Z are at an angle to the original x, y, z-axes, all moments of inertia may be found by means of the formula of eq. 6-15. A line OA (Fig. 6-16) through the origin O of the system x, y, z is drawn, and it is found that this axis makes oblique angles α, β, γ with the x, y, z-axes respectively. This line can then represent the X or Y or Z-axis successively. Thus if for any body using reference space x, y, z the moments of inertia I_x, I_y, I_z and the products of inertia I_{xy}, I_{yz}, I_{zx} are known, then about this axis OA

$$I_{OA} = I_x \cos^2 \alpha + I_y \cos^2 \beta + I_z \cos^2 \gamma$$
$$-2I_{xy} \cos \alpha \cos \beta - 2I_{yz} \cos \beta \cos \gamma - 2I_{zx} \cos \gamma \cos \alpha$$
$$(6\text{-}15)$$

The proof of this will not be undertaken here but may be found in certain of the volumes referred to at the end of this chapter. The style of the proof is similar to that used in proving eq. 6-11.

As an alternative, the formulae 6-11 to 6-13 may be applied twice.

6-11. The Principal Axes of Inertia. Every rigid body has three orthogonal axes with respect to which all products of inertia vanish. These axes are called the principal axes of inertia.

There are three such axes through every point which might be picked as their origin; but the most useful origin is the center of gravity (center of mass) of the body.

The moments of inertia with respect to the principal axes are called the principal moments of inertia.

Three thoughts result from this. First, in connection with symmetrical bodies as discussed in Art. 6–7, since it has been shown certain products of inertia vanish, so one principal axis must be normal to each plane of symmetry, and two be in the plane.

Again, we can immediately deduce that the condition for any rotating body to be in dynamic balance is that the axis of rotation be a principal axis of the body through the center of mass. There are three such axes, mutually perpendicular, for every rigid body.

Thirdly, it is to be seen that the equations for angular-transfer of moments of inertia (eqs. 6–11, 6–12, 6–13) simplify if the reference axes x, y, z are the principal axes as follows: For the rigid body of Fig. 6–14,

$$I_X = I_y \sin^2 \theta + I_x \cos^2 \theta \tag{6-16}$$

$$I_Y = I_y \cos^2 \theta + I_x \sin^2 \theta \tag{6-17}$$

$$I_{XY} = \tfrac{1}{2}(I_y - I_x) \sin 2\theta \tag{6-18}$$

if the axes x, y, z are the principal axes of inertia of the body.

In eq. 6–18 we see a way to prove that these axes about which the products of inertia vanish are orthogonal, for they must satisfy the condition $\sin 2\theta = 0$.

A further property is that the principal moments of inertia are the maximum and minimum moments of inertia of the body. This may be shown as follows: suppose in any rigid body we arbitrarily pick a plane xy. Then from eq. 6–11 we can proceed to find the moment of inertia I_X for any X-axis in the plane, for this involves only variation of the angle θ. For a maximum I_X among all the possible values of θ, we write

$$\frac{d}{d\theta}\left(I_X\right) = 0$$

or by differentiation of eq. 6–11,

$$0 = 2I_y \sin \theta \cos \theta - 2I_x \sin \theta \cos \theta + 2I_{xy} \cos 2\theta$$
$$0 = (I_y - I_x) \sin \theta \cos \theta + I_{xy} \cos 2\theta$$

This is the condition in eq. 6–13 that $I_{XY} = 0$. Hence X is a principal axis of inertia in the xy plane when I_X is a maximum. Now add together eqs. 6–11 and 6–12 to obtain

$$I_X + I_Y = I_x + I_y$$

Thus for all X, Y-axes chosen the sum of the two moments of inertia (with same origin) is a constant; which means that if θ is so chosen that I_X is a maximum, I_Y must be a minimum.

In the three-dimensional case, the same logic can be applied: suppose we proceed to search throughout a given rigid body for the axis about which the moment of inertia is the maximum for the whole body. Let this be called the X-axis. Then normal to this there is the YZ plane, but there are an infinite number of Y-axes possible in the plane. Swing the Y around until we find the Y about which the moment of inertia is the minimum in that YZ plane. Then since it is also at right angles to the X it must give the minimum of all minimums in the body. Since I_Y is minimum in the YZ plane, I_Z must be maximum *in that plane*, and at the same time a minimum in the XZ plane.

Any body may be likened to an ellipsoid with three orthogonal axes (in general, of different lengths), which can be made so that it has moments of inertia equal to that of the body about every axis. Such an ellipsoid is called the "equimomental ellipsoid." It is plain that the ellipsoid would be balanced (i.e., no products of inertia) if revolved about either of its three axes of symmetry. And because of the three different lengths on the three axial sections (all ellipses), the explanation of maximum, minimum, and intermediate moments of inertia becomes plainer. These inertial ellipsoids are dealt with in most books on classical advanced dynamics at quite some length.

Example 1. Find the moments and products of inertia of the cylinder of Fig. 6–17 inclined at an angle θ to the axis of revolution, which passes through its center. Find also the unbalanced couple, when it revolves with speed ω about this axis.

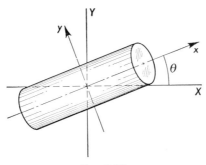

Fig. 6–17.

Let the rotational axis be X, and angle θ be in the XY plane. Then find the principal axes, which are those of symmetry. The x-axis is the centerline of the cylinder; then the y can be anywhere in the midsectional plane, but let the xy and XY planes be coincident, so that Z and z axes are coincident.

The cylinder has radius r and length l, with total mass m, therefore

$$I_x = \tfrac{1}{2}mr^2$$
$$I_y = I_z = \tfrac{1}{4}mr^2 + \tfrac{1}{12}ml^2$$
$$I_{xy} = I_{yz} = I_{zx} = 0$$

From eqs. 6–16 and 6–18

$$I_X = I_x \cos^2 \theta + I_y \sin^2 \theta = \tfrac{1}{4}mr^2(1 + \cos^2 \theta) + \tfrac{1}{12}ml^2 \sin^2 \theta$$
$$I_Y = I_y \cos^2 \theta + I_x \sin^2 \theta = \tfrac{1}{4}mr^2(1 + \sin^2 \theta) + \tfrac{1}{12}ml^2 \cos^2 \theta$$
$$I_Z = I_z$$
$$I_{XY} = \tfrac{1}{2}(\tfrac{1}{12}ml^2 - \tfrac{1}{4}mr^2) \sin 2\theta$$

The unbalanced couple is $I_{XY}\omega^2$. And comparison with the example of the slender rod and its solution given in eqs. 6–8 and 6–9 shows agreement within the approximation that r was negligible.

Suppose the dimensions are $r = 2$ in., $l = 12$ in., and the cylinder is of steel, intended to be axially aligned, but actually with $\theta = 2$ minutes of angle; it revolves at 6000 rpm.

The mass m is found from the volume:

$$m = 0.2816\left(\frac{\pi \times 4 \times 12}{386}\right) = 0.11 \text{ lb sec}^2/\text{in.}$$

The sine of the angle is best reckoned in radian measure:

$$\frac{1}{2}\sin 2\theta = \frac{1}{2}(2\theta) = \frac{2 \times \pi}{60 \times 180} = 5.82 \times 10^{-4}$$

Then unbalanced couple

$$T_z = \left(\frac{12^2}{12} - \frac{2^2}{4}\right)0.11 \times 5.82 \times 10^{-4}\left(\frac{2\pi6000}{60}\right)^2 = 278 \text{ lb in.}$$

This can be corrected by drilling counterbalance holes at the ends of the cylinder.

Example 2. Find the principal axes of inertia through the center of mass of the right triangular wedge of Fig. 6–18. This is the same as finding the axes about which it could rotate in balance.

We will start by using the result of Problem 6–9, which gives the product $I_{xy} = Mab/12$ about the x, y-axes. Then from a handbook, neglecting the thickness,

$$I_x = Mb^2/6$$
$$I_y = Ma^2/6$$

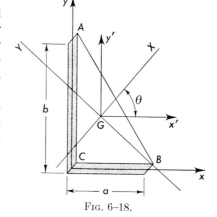

FIG. 6–18.

Through the center of gravity, with axes x', y', z' located at $x = a/3$, $y = b/3$, by parallel transfer:

$$I_{x'} = I_x - Mb^2/9 = Mb^2/18$$
$$I_{y'} = I_y - Ma^2/9 = Ma^2/18$$
$$I_{x'y'} = I_{xy} - Mab/9 = -Mab/36$$

The principal Z-axis by symmetry passes through G normal to the surface of the plane. Take the X-axis as inclined at angle θ from the x'-axis. Then the product of inertia I_{XY} vanishes, or by eq. 6–13

$$0 = -\tfrac{1}{2}(I_{y'} - I_{x'}) \sin 2\theta + I_{x'y'} \cos 2\theta$$

$$\tan 2\theta = -\frac{2I_{x'y'}}{(I_{x'} - I_{y'})} = \frac{ab}{b^2 - a^2}$$

This can be reduced to

$$\tan \theta = [(a^2 - b^2) \pm \sqrt{b^4 - a^2b^2 + a^4}] \div ab$$

For $a = b$ this is at $45°$. In general though, the X-axis does not pass through the corner C, nor is it perpendicular to the side AB.

6–12. Desire for Maximum Moment of Inertia. In Fig. 6–17 it was seen that the sense of the centrifugal couple was such as to try to increase the angle θ. There is no couple when θ is zero or $90°$ (cf. eq. 6–18). However if θ is very small the torque due to I_y is larger than that due to I_z, and θ tends to increase: therefore the equilibrium with $\theta = 0$ is an unstable equilibrium. On the other hand, if θ is just away from $90°$, the torque is such as to try to make the angle $90°$, showing that this is a position of stable equilibrium.

We conclude therefore that if a body is free to turn about any axis, it will try to align itself so that it spins around the axis about which it has maximum moment of inertia.

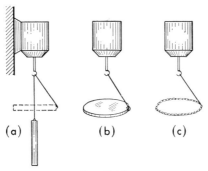

Fig. 6–19.

This is a phenomenon which is easy to demonstrate. For example, Fig. 6–19 shows three experiments which may be performed, using a small electric motor as the driving spindle. In Fig. 6–19a a small rod with an eye in one end is attached by a string to the spindle. Initially hanging vertically down, on rotation it will soon pick itself up to rotate in an almost horizontal plane (dotted lines). In Fig 6–19b a circular disk attached similarly by a string to one edge will act similarly, and in Fig. 6–19c a loop of beaded key ring can be made to do the same, becoming first a vertical then a horizontal circle. This is of course the same as the famous cowboy trick of rope spinning.

6–13. The Equimomental Body. It may have been noticed that no formula was given for product of inertia, along with eq. 6–15 for moment of inertia, when three axes X, Y, Z have relative angular positions to axes x, y, z. This was principally because it is then necessary to define both axes by their direction-cosines, which makes the relations rather cumbersome. Such cases only rarely occur in engineering applications, and the method of approach that is then advocated is the use of the equimomental body.

It has been pointed out that for every rigid body an ellipsoid can be found which is equimomental. The requirements for dynamical equivalence are three: that the total mass of the original and the equivalent are equal, that the positions of their centers of mass (with respect to the axes, etc.) are the same, and that about every axis their moments and products of inertia are equal. Such a pair of bodies will then react to any applied force, or rotation, in exactly the same manner. Now, furthermore, any ellipsoid can be seen to have an equimomental equivalent in a star such as shown in Fig. 6–20 consisting of six light rods, in pairs, directed according to the principal axes of the ellipsoid, and carrying six equal masses,* considered concentrated at a point.

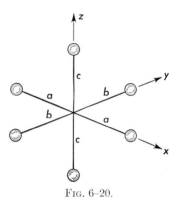

Fig. 6–20.

It is plain that if the masses are equal and the rod lengths equal in pairs, the center of the star must be at the center of mass of the ellipsoid or original body it is intended to replace. Then, so that products of inertia be zero with respect to principal axes, the star rods must be aligned with the principal axes of the original. Thirdly, so that the mass and the moments of inertia about these axes agree, we have the four conditions:

$$6m = M \text{ of original}$$
$$2mb^2 + 2mc^2 = I_x$$
$$2mc^2 + 2ma^2 = I_y$$
$$2ma^2 + 2mb^2 = I_z$$

With these the lengths of the rods a, b, c are easily determined.

* E. J. Routh (*Elementary Rigid Dynamics*, p. 31) shows that theoretically an equimomental equivalent can be found for every rigid body, which consists of only four equal balls, arranged at the corners of a tetrahedron.

Suppose then, for example, it is desired to balance the elliptical cylinder mounted obliquely on the rotor shaft AA as in Fig. 6–21 by means of drilled holes in two balancing disks. The procedure is first to

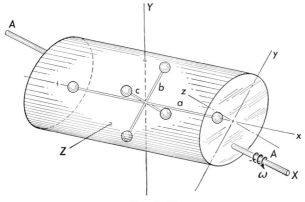

FIG. 6–21.

determine the equimomental star aligned with the principal axes of the cylinder, and to calculate the masses m and lengths a, b, c of this star. This is quite simple, for the principal axes are obvious and a will be found in terms of the length, b the major axis, and c the minor axis of the cylinder. It is then necessary only to figure the balance needed for the star, and the principal difficulty is not more than the manipulation of the compound oblique angles involved with respect to the geometrical axis of rotation.

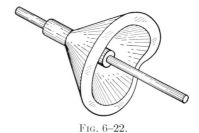

FIG. 6–22.

Actually, as mentioned, calculable problems of this kind rarely occur. Designs are more likely to be too involved for calculation, as for example the conical cam of Fig. 6–22, and recourse is made directly to the automatic balancing machine.

6–14. Angular Momentum. We now turn to a new concept, one which may be used as an alternative to that of products of inertia in discovering unbalance, but which will also explain the gyroscope.

We start with the description of an experiment which may be performed: the Z-shaped rigid bar of Fig. 6–23 passes through a transverse hole in the shaft AA, where it is gripped with some friction, and the ends of the bar BC are parallel to the shaft AA. The whole contraption rotates about the vertical axis with speed ω_A. Now the angular momentum as considered earlier has been thought of as the product $I_{AA}\omega_A$, and it can be changed by application of a torque. If this is the case, then we may expect if we were to raise some such device as the pair of bumpers shown in the figure at the bottom, until they interfere with the rotating arms and so stop the rotation ω_A (we are not bothering with rebound), that by applying such a couple we can destroy all the momentum.

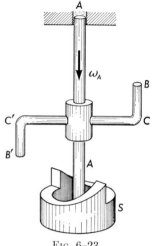

But this is not the case, for when the bumpers are raised, and ω_A reduced suddenly to zero, the end B has a momentum which will carry it forward, and the end B' will continue away from you, with the result that there will now be a rotation about axis CC'. Since this angular momentum cannot have been created by the impact, it must have been there all the time! Originally the momentum was more than $I_{AA}\omega_A$.

It may be noted that the object we have considered is not balanced, for this is the basis for the difference. For a balanced

Fig. 6–23.

object, that is, one spinning about a fixed axis coincident with a principal axis of inertia, the angular momentum of the body is correctly and wholly expressed as the product $I_{AA}\omega_A$.

The basic definition of angular momentum, it will be recalled, is not in terms of angular velocity and moment of inertia, but rather, being more appropriately described as moment of momentum, it is the sum of moments of the linear momentum of each particle of which the body is comprised.

Thus in Fig. 6–23, though there is no angular velocity about axis CC' while ω_A continues, yet the points along BC and $B'C'$ have their momentum, and, being at a distance from axis CC', these momenta have their moment about axis CC'.

In other words, angular momentum is better written Σmvr, and only when $v = r\omega$ does this become $\Sigma mr^2\omega$ or $I\omega$. Thus a body rotating about any fixed axis may have three component vectors about the three orthogonal axes which together constitute its moment of momentum.

It may then be proved that these three possible components are most easily reckoned when the axes chosen are the principal axes of the body. The total angular momentum H of any body then appears as the vector sum of these three components in the principal axes, or

$$H = I_x\omega_x \nleftrightarrow I_y\omega_y \nleftrightarrow I_z\omega_z \qquad (6\text{–}19)$$

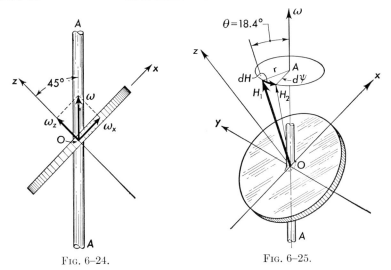

FIG. 6–24.   FIG. 6–25.

where ω_x, ω_y, ω_z are the vector components of the actual angular velocity ω referred to the principal axes x, y, z.

Because of the transverse component of moment of momentum as seen in the illustration of Fig. 6–23, it follows that the direction of the resultant vector H will not coincide with the direction of the spin-axis whenever the rotating body is unbalanced.

Example. The circular disk of Fig. 6–24 is mounted at 45° to its axis AA of rotation. Find its angular momentum.

The principal axes of the disk are normal to its plane and in any two directions in its plane. We choose for the xz plane that containing the axis of rotation. Then the components of ω are

$$\omega_x = 0.707\omega; \quad \omega_z = 0.707\omega; \quad \omega_y = 0$$

since the angle $AOz = 45°$. The moments of inertia are $I_x = I_y = \frac{1}{4}Mr^2$ and $I_z = \frac{1}{2}Mr^2$. The components of angular momentum are therefore

$$H_x = 0.707I_x\omega = 0.707Mr^2\frac{\omega}{4}$$

$$H_z = 0.707I_z\omega = 0.707Mr^2\frac{\omega}{2}$$

The z component is twice that of the x component and the resultant H_1 shown in Fig. 6–25 will make an angle (arctan 2) of 63.4° with the x-axis, or $\theta = 18.4°$ with the axis of rotation AA. The magnitude of the total angular momentum is

$$H = \sqrt{5}H_x = 0.707\sqrt{5}Mr^2\frac{\omega}{4} \tag{6–20}$$

As the body rotates, this angular momentum vector H will describe a cone around the axis AA, moving from position H_1 to H_2.

Now we have met once before a vector that continually changed direction—the vector of the tangential velocity of a point moving around a circle. In that case we found the change in direction was the cause of centripetal acceleration, while any change in magnitude was caused by tangential acceleration.

Therefore we shall expect the rate of change of *direction* of an angular momentum vector H to cause a torque just as much as the rate of change of its *magnitude* ($I\alpha$) was caused by a torque.

In Fig. 6–25 suppose the vector H moves from position H_1 to H_2 in an infinitesimal time dt, without changing magnitude. The vector change dH lies on the base of the cone, being of magnitude $H \sin \theta \, d\psi$ as appears from the geometry, and where θ in this example happens to be 18.4°. The rate of change of H is therefore perpendicular to its instantaneous position H_1, which is the $-y$ direction, and needs for its accomplishment the application of a torque. The inertia reaction of the rotating skew disk is thus reversed from this, in the $+y$ direction, and

$$T_y = +H \sin \theta \frac{d\psi}{dt} = H\omega \sin \theta$$

From the example used and eq. 6–20 this is

$$T_y = \sqrt{5/2} \, I_x \omega^2 \sin \theta$$

and this may readily be shown to be the same as the unbalanced couple obtained by the product of inertia method, although the exercise is left to the reader.

6–15. The Gyroscope and Precession. Although the explanation of the principle of the gyroscope is entirely contained in the preceding article, we will again start by observations of a physical experiment.

Many people think of a gyroscope as a special symmetrical rotor mounted in gimbal rings (alternatively called a Cardan suspension after a scientist of the sixteenth century) which allow it up to three degrees of rotational freedom, after the manner of Fig. 6–26. However, this is a very special case, as any disk, wheel, flywheel, turbine rotor, or any solid of revolution when revolving exhibits gyroscopic effects.

We take then a bicycle wheel, free to rotate about a fixed axle which has been made a little longer than is usual in a bicycle in order to provide handles; but a toy gyroscope within a single gimbal ring will do equally well. Support this wheel to one side by a post, as in Fig. 6–27, with its axle horizontal. The weight of the wheel, of course, will cause it to fall off, unless the wheel is set spinning rapidly. But then, when spinning, the axis surprisingly remains horizontal, or very nearly so, while it rotates slowly around the post, just as if the top of the wheel were rubbing slightly against some invisible ceiling. Reverse the direction of spin of the wheel, and the slow turning also reverses. This rotation of the axis is called precession.

(Model, Courtesy Sperry Gyroscope Co.)
FIG. 6–26.

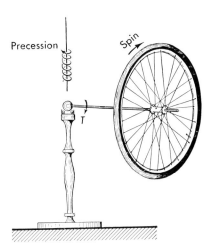

FIG. 6–27.

Now we wish to demonstrate that if the precessing axis falls at all, this is due to friction at the pivot on the post. Set the wheel as before, spinning and precessing; and then simulate an increased frictional moment by holding a vertical pencil against the free end of the axle to slow down the rate of precession. The result observed is that the axle yields to gravity, slowly dropping. As an alternative, an increasing torque in the same sense as friction may be achieved by hanging the pivot end of the axle by a wire, instead of supporting it on a post. The increasing torque due to twist in the wire will increasingly cause the free end of the axle to drop.

A third experiment can be made to emphasize the effect of torque about the vertical axis. With the wheel spinning and precessing about the post or on the wire, try hurrying the precession. The axle will be observed to rise.

For a final observation, note that as the spin velocity of the wheel gradually diminishes, the precessional velocity accelerates.

The explanation of these phenomena can be accomplished in several ways—three are given here.

In all these tests there was a strong couple applied to the axle of the spinning wheel, due to the off-center support of the wheel's own weight. The other smaller torque of friction or external force slowing or hurrying precession was changeable. Let us consider the effect of a single torque applied to the axis of a spinning wheel.

First, imagine that the four quadrant points of the wheel A,B,C,D (Fig. 6–28) are marked with white spots and that while it is spinning with angular velocity ω_s as shown, the couple of forces F is applied: thus there is a torque about the horizontal axis. At the instant considered, the four points are in the location shown and have velocities in

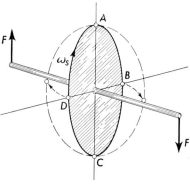

Fig. 6–28.

the plane of the wheel. But now the effect of the couple is to push C backward and A forward, and such applied forces will produce accelerations. Therefore A and C will gain new components of velocity while B and D are unaffected. After, say, one quarter of a turn, B and D with their old velocities will arrive at locations C and A, but A will arrive at a point somewhere nearer than B was, and C will arrive at a point behind the earlier position of D. The wheel therefore will be caused to turn its axis in a clockwise direction viewed from above.

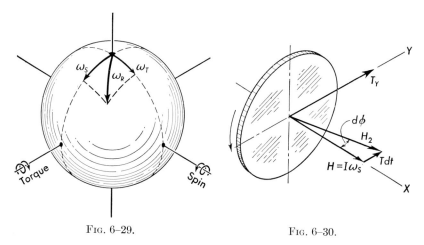

Fig. 6–29.   Fig. 6–30.

The wheel is not unyielding to the effect of the couple, but the result occurs after a 90° lag. To show this again, consider a sphere (Fig. 6–29) instead of the wheel. The original spin velocity shown as ω_s is about a horizontal axis. The applied torque about a perpendicular axis will after a short time add a new *component* of rotation ω_T. The resultant angular velocity, the vector sum $\omega_s + \omega_T$, will be ω_R. Thus the rotation will shift from the path given by ω_s over to ω_R, which is a counterclockwise turn of the spin axis when viewed from above.

To find a quantitative value for the precession, we use the vector diagram of angular momentum. It is plain that since the gyro wheel is rotating about an axis about which it is very carefully balanced, this is a principal axis of inertia; the angular momentum is thus given by $H = I\omega_s$, and H and ω_s are vectors in the same sense and direction. Now the application of a constant torque T throughout a short time interval dt will add a new component of momentum equal to the angular impulse $T\,dt$ in the same sense as the angular velocity component ω_T of Fig. 6–29. We can consider no longer an interval than the infinitesimal dt because the torque T is continually changing its direction. So, in Fig. 6–30, the vector resultant of the original $H = I\omega_s$ and the infinitesimal $T\,dt$ is a new H_2. The magnitude of H_2 is unchanged from H, for $T\,dt$ is perpendicular. Yet the direction has changed by the infinitesimal angle $d\phi$ during time dt. This points to a counterclockwise angular velocity of the axis of spin (when viewed from above) given by $d\phi/dt$. The geometry of the triangle shows

$$\tan d\phi (= d\phi) = \frac{T\,dt}{I\omega_s}$$

$$I\omega_s \cdot \frac{d\phi}{dt} = T \qquad\qquad (6\text{–}21)$$

Thus the magnitude of the angular velocity of precession is found. We have shown that without frictional effects at the post support, the wheel should precess in the direction demonstrated, maintaining its axis in a horizontal plane. Moreover, we have explained the last observation of the experiments, that the precession accelerates as the spin slowly diminishes with time due to axle friction; for in eq. 6–21 with constant T and I the product of spin and precessional velocities is constant.

The other observations of our experiment must now be explained. It is clear that a constant torque acting (as did the weight of the wheel in the experiment) always 90° ahead of the spin axis will maintain a constant precessional velocity (except as the spin diminishes). Or stated in reverse, the freely precessing gyroscope acts as an automatic counterbalance to any applied external torque. Writing the precessional velocity $d\phi/dt$ as ω_p eq. 6–21 will give the inertia (reversed effective) gyro reaction torque as

$$-T = I\omega_s\omega_p \qquad\qquad (6\text{–}22)$$

Therefore if ω_p is prevented either by friction or a pencil on the free end of the axle, the reaction is less than the weight torque, and the axle begins to fall. On the other hand, if precession is hurried, the gyro reaction is greater than required, and will raise the axle.

Example. Determine the precession of a bicycle wheel as in Fig. 6–27, neglecting friction at the support. The wheel has a radius of gyration of 11 in., and spins at 200 rpm. The support is 3 in. from the center of the wheel.

$$T = W \times 3 \text{ lb in.}$$
$$I = W \times (11)^2/386 \text{ lb in. sec}^2$$
$$\omega_s = 2\pi \times 200/60 \text{ rad/sec}$$

Then from eq. 6–21

$$\frac{d\phi}{dt} = \omega_p = T/I\omega_s = 0.456 \text{ rad/sec}$$
$$= 4.36 \text{ rpm}$$

Note that this is independent of the weight of the wheel.

6–16. Two Laws of Gyrodynamics. The equation 6–21 already derived is the basis for the two principal theorems or laws of action of a gyroscope. They are stated as follows:

> THEOREM: A state of equilibrium exists when any symmetrical body, spinning about its axis of symmetry and constrained by not more than one point on this axis, precesses while a torque T is applied about an axis perpendicular to the spin axis, the precession being a constant angular velocity ω_p of a magnitude given by $T/I\omega_s$, about an axis mutually perpendicular to the other two, and in the sense that tends to make the spin axis coincide with the torque axis;

and the other is the corollary of this—

> THEOREM: When no external torque is applied to any symmetrical body, spinning about its axis of symmetry, the spin axis will remain fixed in space.

The second law can be demonstrated by a gyroscope mounted in three gimbal rings as in Fig. 6–26. Provided that the bearings are well adjusted for minimum friction, the base can be moved around in the hand and twisted any way without affecting the original alignment of the spin axis. The slight variations that may arise due to the unavoidable presence of friction are minimized by using the largest available gyro rotor running at the highest possible speed.

The gyro remains fixed in space, and by this is meant astronomical space. Thus if a gyro could be driven indefinitely in a free suspension, it would form on the earth a 24-hour clock, due to the relative rotation of the earth once a day. Torque about the spin axis of the gyro will not affect the direction of the axis, but merely the spin velocity.

Many applications of the first law are found in ordinary machines; and it is well to remember that any rotating wheel will exhibit gyroscopic action. For instance, consider the action of the crankshaft and flywheel of an automobile as you drive around a corner. These usually revolve clockwise when viewed from the front, so that on turning a corner to the right, the torque applied to the shaft through its bearings will cause it to attempt to precess by raising its forward end and depressing its rear end. Thus some weight will be lifted off the front wheels of the car. On an icy road it is easier to start a front-wheel skid on a right turn and a back-wheel skid on a left turn.

For another automobile example, note the cause of front-wheel shimmy. One wheel runs over a stone or a hole in the road. To prevent the rise or drop (which involves an angular change in the wheel axle) the wheel will precess right or left, so that if the bearings are worn, vibration is set up from the initial twist and subsequent caster action.

Very serious problems arose in an early design of airplanes, from the use of a rotary engine. In this the crank remained stationary while the ring of cylinders rotated, driving the propeller: an example was the Gnome-Rhône engine with seven cylinders. Of course this engine acted as a very sizable gyroscope and the pilot felt himself as if seated on the innermost gimbal ring of Fig. 6–26. When he applied rudder, the plane would precess up or downward; in trying to flatten out of a dive many pilots crashed because they went into a spin. The modern plane with propeller or turbine suffers from the same effects but to a much lesser extent.

In calculating the magnitude and direction of gyroscopic torques, care must be exercised to distinguish between action and reaction, especially when precession is forced. In the following example, two approaches will be shown.

Example. Determine the gyro effect on a pair of wheels and axle of a locomotive as it rounds a corner. We take the pair of driving wheels to be 6 ft in diameter, with radius of gyration 2 ft, weighing as a unit with the axle 2 tons. Suppose the speed is 60 mph around a curve of radius 1500 ft to the right. Then

$$I = 4000 \times (2)^2/32.2 \quad \text{lb ft sec}^2$$
$$\omega_s = 88/3 \quad \text{rad/sec}$$
$$\omega_p = 88/1500 \quad \text{rad/sec}$$

since 60 mph = 88 ft/sec. Thus the gyroscopic torque will have magnitude

$$T = I\omega_s\omega_p = 855 \text{ lb ft}$$

Now for the directions involved:

a) Suppose we regard the turning as caused by a steering couple pushing the left wheel forward and holding back the right. Thus in Fig. 6–31 at (b) with the applied torque vertically down, the angular momentum vector $I\omega_s$ tries to precess downward, into the axis shown

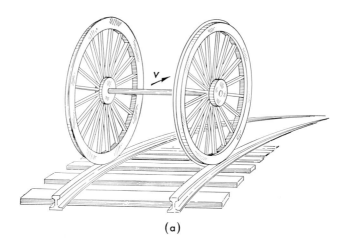

(a)

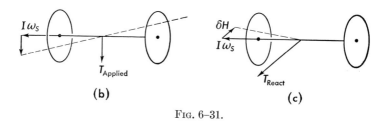

(b)   (c)

Fig. 6–31.

by the dotted line. The unit therefore will press more strongly on the left rail and relieve some pressure on the right rail. The change in pressure is the torque divided by the rail center distance (4 ft $8\frac{1}{2}$ in.), or 182 lb.

b) Suppose we regard the turning as a forced precession. Then for the original vector $I\omega_s$ (Fig. 6–31c) to be moved around, there must be added a vector δH. This can only be caused by an external torque in the same sense. The gyro inertia reaction torque opposes this, and is therefore as shown by the vector T_{react} horizontally backward. The conclusion is then the same.

The gyroscopic torque from any pair of rolling wheels rounding a corner is therefore shown to augment the usual centrifugal effect. However, in laying out a railroad track, it is generally reckoned to be so much less than centrifugal effects that it is ignored in figuring the superelevation at curves.

6–17. Applications of the Fixed-Axis Gyroscope. Whereas in many machines gyroscopic torques have to be reckoned with, in others they are used as the basis of control. The property of maintaining the direction of its spin axis over a long period of time, provided it is free from external torque, is used in navigational instruments, in automatic pilots, and in naval gun control.

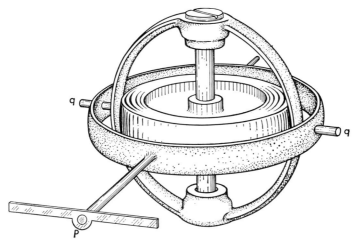

Fɪɢ. 6–32.

The artificial horizon is an instrument used in aircraft which enables the pilot to know his attitude whenever flying blind, as at night. Essentially, it is a gyroscope mounted in two gimbal rings, as in Fig. 6–32, with the spin axis vertical. The second gimbal ring, which is free to turn about a fore-and-aft axis, carries an indicator P which is parallel to the axis qq between the gimbal rings. If when the ship is in level flight the assembly is set in the position shown, any subsequent banking angle will show as a relative angle between the level pointer P and the frame of the instrument. But in any climb the gyroscope can move about axis qq without other effect. The instrument needs resetting at regular intervals, for friction and the earth's rotation will both cause wandering. Some instruments are supplied with a special pendulous device to help prolong this interval. The rotor is driven either electrically or by compressed air entering through the hollow rings.

In naval gun control, gyroscopes are used to maintain the directional angles of fire while the ship rolls, pitches, or yaws.

The action of an automatic pilot for a ship depends upon a gyroscope which actuates electric switches for control of the rudder. Suppose in

Fig. 6–33a the direction N is set for the gyroscope, which must be mounted so that it is unaffected by rolling and pitching. The rudder is straight at the start. Then suppose the ship yaws to the east as at (b). The gyro axis carries an electric contact which on turning touches either of two surfaces L and R, and now, since the gyro direction still points north as set, contact is made through L. This starts the steering mechanism to give it left rudder and correct the yaw, and at the same time turns the disk on which the contacts L and R are mounted, so that the steering mechanism stops itself. The condition at (c) results and

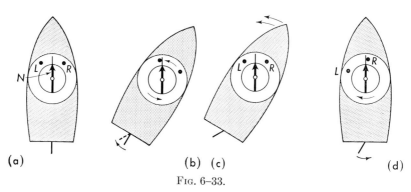

(a)   (b) (c)   (d)

FIG. 6–33.

the ship swings back into course. As it returns to proper setting (as at d) the gyro electric contact touches plate R and the steering mechanism returns both the rudder and the L-R disk to their original straight position.

Adjustment of the interval between L and R contacts, and of the relative motion of the rudder and L-R disk, is needed to suit the device to a particular ship. Maladjustment may produce serious yawing oscillation, for the inertia of the ship will cause overcorrection. Some such oscillation is unavoidable, however, and indeed is always present when steering by hand. The automatic pilot is able to reduce yawing to within half a degree.

6–18. The Ship Stabilizer. Some people object to the rolling of a ship, and a gyroscope of large size within the hull is able to remedy this. The limitations of size, however, make the incorporation of any device to counteract pitching impossible, and pitching produces in unhappy sailors a much worse internal sensation.

In the design and loading of a ship the metacentric height is of great importance. This height is the distance h on the hull centerline between the center of gravity and the vertical through the center of buoyancy (Fig. 6–34). It determines the period of roll of the ship as the length of a pendulum, and it is generally adjusted, by the disposition of cargo, to a very few feet. But in connection with a gyroscopic stabilizer, it is this height which acts as the moment arm for the gyro couple to counteract rolling. In contrast, the moment arm on which any gyroscope would have to act to counteract pitching might be half the length of the ship, and this explains the very much greater torques that would be needed.

Gyroscopic stabilizers are of two sorts—active and passive. The passive variety is no more than a large rotor spinning about a vertical axis fixed in the hull. It will therefore resist both rolling and pitching,

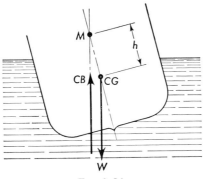

Fig. 6–34.

principally the former, by converting each into the other. But its chief action is that, in resisting any tendency to roll, it adds strong damping to the rolling oscillation.

For in Fig. 6–34 suppose the ship rolls at an angle θ: the inertia couple of the ship about the metacenter M will give the equation of motion:

$$I_M\ddot{\theta} + I_{\text{gyro}}\omega_s\dot{\theta} + Wh \sin \theta = \text{Moment of wave force}$$

and as h is usually sensibly constant through small angles of roll, this represents a damped forced harmonic motion. The moment of inertia I_M may be written $(W/g)(h^2 + k_g^2)$ in which k_g is the radius of gyration of the ship about the fore-and-aft axis, a dimension which may reach 50 ft on a large liner.

In the active variety, the large rotor is mounted, with its axis normally vertical, in a gimbal ring held between athwartship trunnion bearings. The gimbal or frame carries a gear segment which is in mesh with a pinion driven by an electric motor, called the precession motor. Figure 6–35 shows a view from the rear. Suppose the angular momentum vector is vertically upward and the ship starts to roll to starboard (right-hand side in the figure): the upper end of the axis will try to precess forward. Now if the precession motor is used to start this same sense of precession earlier, a strong countertorque can be applied to the hull preventing the roll of the ship almost before it begins. The pre-

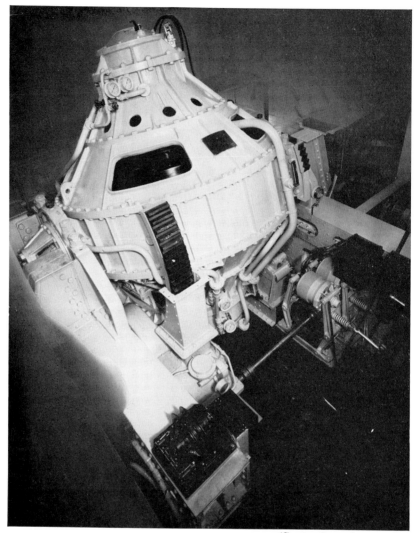

(Courtesy Sperry Gyroscope Co.)

FIG. 6–35.

cession motor is switched on by a very small "pilot" gyroscope along-side the large one, which carries electric contacts.

These stabilizers have been installed in a number of small yachts and medium-sized vessels. The largest installation was made by the Sperry Gyroscope Company for the Italian liner "Conte di Savoia": in this three rotors were used, each of 13 ft in diameter and weighing 108 tons apiece, with normal spin velocity 800 rpm (maximum 920 rpm). The three rotors were a compromise of necessity, for it was not possible to fabricate a single rotor of sufficient size. A precession up to 60° on either side of the vertical was allowed for, though at higher angles the stabilizing torque (varying with the cosine of the angle) is seriously reduced. The initial maximum stabilizing torque, based on the ship's natural period of roll of 24 sec, was 2150 ton ft; the precession motors needed were each of 100 hp output. It is significant though that on this ship the entire installation weighed 660 tons, or $1\frac{1}{2}$ per cent of the ship's displacement, so that when she unfortunately was sunk during the second World War, no similar installations have since been contemplated.

6-19. The Gyroscopic Compass. The ship's compass is probably the most valuable of all adaptations of the gyroscope. This has great advantages over the magnetic compass, for it will seek true north and is also unaffected by the steel hull of a ship.

The essential part of this instrument is a gyroscope mounted within gimbal rings with three degrees of freedom, and a pendulous weight

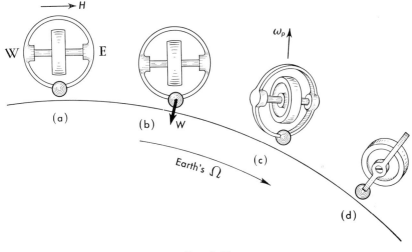

Fig. 6–36.

attached to the innermost ring. Figure 6–36 shows just this ring. We will show first that this gyro will oscillate about a position in the vertical plane containing true north, and secondly that there is an equilibrium position in which the gyro might be set that it will maintain constantly.

The gyro in Fig. 6–36 is presumed held within gimbal rings (not shown) at a fixed point on the earth at the equator, and the figure represents a south-side view of the equatorial section. It is supposed that the gyro is started, as at (a), horizontally with its axis east-west, which is as far off from the desired direction as possible; its momentum vector is then H. If we ignore temporarily the pendulous weight, it is plain that, due to the fixity of its axis, after a certain interval of time the gyro would reach the configuration (b); however, this involves an inclination to the horizontal, and the weight therefore will cause a torque. This torque is represented by a vector directed to the north horizontally, that is, into the paper, and therefore the momentum vector H will turn that way. The diagram (c) shows the east end of the gyro axis turning north. This precession will continue until the axis reaches the north-south plane, as at (d). But since there is only precession when there is torque, and there is only torque when there is an inclination of the axis to any hori-

zontal plane, the east end of the gyro axis will arrive in the meridian inclined slightly upward. The torque will not cease then on arrival in the meridian but will continue the precession of what was the east end of the spin axis toward the west. Furthermore, the gyroscope and its support will have acquired a kinetic energy of precession: the result is that the axis will swing as far to the other side as that from which it started, before the precession ceases. It follows that the axis will sweep out an elliptical cone (Fig. 6–37) of which the horizontal meridian ON is the centerline.

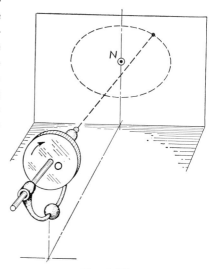

Fig. 6–37.

This is on the equator; but at other latitudes a similar situation holds, although the line ON (Fig. 6–37) is not horizontal. The pendulous gyroscope will seek the north but will never reach it.

Now secondly, let us suppose on the basis of this periodic vibration about the meridian, that if the gyro axle is placed in the meridian (at any latitude) it will remain there. Obviously this is so at every point on the equator, for with the axle in the horizontal meridian no torque will be exerted by the pendulous mass to cause deviation. At any latitude λ, however, with the spin axis parallel to the axis of the earth, the pendulum will exert a torque which in northern latitudes will cause *the north end to turn west*, and in southern latitudes east. On the other hand, if the spin axis is horizontal, it must be made to precess at the same rate that the earth rotates in order to preserve its position on the meridian; or if left free without a pendulous weight in northern latitudes *the north end will wander east*, in southern latitudes west (Fig. 6–38).

This motion is relative to an observer on the earth, for the gyro strives to maintain its direction relative to the fixed stars while the earth turns under it.

In between these two attitudes (i.e., between elevations λ and zero) we may expect to find an elevation where the torque from the pendulum is sufficient to produce the correct precession. Let the elevation be an angle α (Fig. 6–39); then the pendulum torque will be $wl \sin \alpha$. And the desired rate of change of momentum* must be $I\omega_s\Omega \sin (\lambda - \alpha)$, where

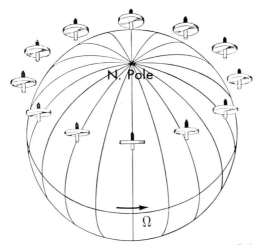

(Redrawn by permission of Sperry Gyroscope Co.)

Fig. 6–38.

Ω is the angular velocity of the earth (cf. Fig. 6–25, page 249). Equating these to find α at any latitude we obtain

$$wl \sin \alpha = I\omega_s\Omega(\sin \lambda \cos \alpha - \cos \lambda \sin \alpha)$$
$$(wl + I\omega_s\Omega \cos \lambda) \sin \alpha = (I\omega_s\Omega \sin \lambda) \cos \alpha$$
$$\tan \alpha = \frac{I\omega_s\Omega \sin \lambda}{wl + I\omega_s\Omega \cos \lambda} \qquad (6\text{–}23)$$

The existence of an equilibrium position is therefore shown, and moreover since it has also been shown that if the gyroscope spin axis is started from anywhere near that position the axis direction will not wander very much further from it, this position, with inclination α less than λ, must be one of stable equilibrium. Furthermore, by making wl very large in comparison with $I\omega_s\Omega$ (note Ω is small) the inclination α can be made so small as hardly to be noticeable: in actual designs it is about one-tenth of a degree.

---

* Assuming the spin velocity is high so that the instantaneous value of angular momentum H is closely $I\omega_s$, in the direction of the axis, neglecting precessional momentum.

Since the meridional position given by eq. 6–23 is one of stable equilibrium, it follows that when damping is introduced to act upon any initial oscillation, as in Fig. 6–37, the amplitudes will diminish each swing, until the axis is sensibly in the desired configuration. In starting a ship's compass, the axis is placed as nearly true as is convenient, and the compass will settle in between four and eight hours. But before describing further the methods for introducing damping, an alternative to the pendulum on the inner gimbal ring is important.

This alternative is the mercury ballistic, whose action is similar to an inverted pendulum. We compare its action with that of the pendulous weight in Fig. 6–36: suppose again that the gyroscope is set

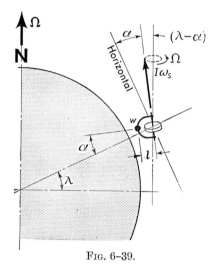

Fig. 6–39.

on the equator with its axis east and west, horizontally. The mercury ballistic is a U-tube partially filled with mercury and having a larger reservoir at either side (Fig. 6–40). Its height may be so arranged that when horizontal its center of gravity coincides with the center of the gyro rotor, and then it is called nonpendulous. In any case after starting as at (a) in the figure, and with no moment from the mercury, the east end starts to rise relative to the earth (as at b). Now some mercury runs

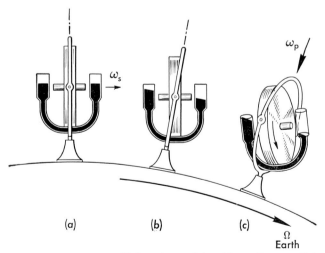

(a)   (b)   (c)

Ω
Earth

(Redrawn by permission of Sperry Gyroscope Co.)
Fig. 6–40.

over to the west end, producing a torque of the opposite sense to that with a pendulum weight, with the result that the east end precesses toward the south, and this continues until the gyro axis arrives in the meridian with the south end inclined upward. We see therefore that the axis traces an elliptical cone exactly as with the pendulous mass (Fig. 6–37), the only difference being that the gyro axis in trying to align itself with that of the earth prefers a rotation counter to the earth's.

This mercury pendulum is called ballistic because its response is small to quick vibrations: this is an essential characteristic when the compass is to be mounted on shipboard. For no matter how the gimbals or other supports are devised, some effects from the motion of the ship must reach the pendulum. With the mercury ballistic, however, the small bore of the tubes prevents any significant shifting of the mercury under rapidly changing forces, while presenting little or no resistance to slow changes from the earth's motion.

In the actual design of a gyroscopic compass the following problems must be overcome: (a) the provision of frictionless three-dimensional or gimbal mounting, (b) the provision of damping to reduce the elliptical oscillation about the north, (c) the elimination of avoidable inherent errors, (d) compensation for unavoidable inherent errors.

The reduction of friction is accomplished by means of an electrical follow-up system. The gyroscope's rotor and the inner gimbal ring are separated from the outer rings as nearly as possible—the rotor part is named the "sensitive element," and the outer support system the "phantom element." For instance, the rotor and its cage may be supported by a circular horizontal ring floating in an annular bath of mercury; the latter is supported within a gimbal system and carries the compass card. As the gyro precesses it has merely to move itself and overcome very slight resistance from the mercury. But any slight movement of this sensitive element relative to the phantom actuates a switch starting an electric motor, the "azimuth motor," which makes the phantom follow the sensitive element. The switch is usually electrical, but one make of compass uses an air jet (pumped by the rotor) which blows upon a seesaw electrical switch, and any rotation will then direct the jet to depress one side or the other. The phantom is designed to follow the sensitive element within at most one-quarter of a degree, and the job of overcoming the friction in gimbal rings and compass card is laid upon the azimuth motor. Since the relative motion of sensitive element and phantom is restricted to such a small amount, other makers are satisfied to use a vertical axle in ball bearings in place of the mercury ring, but one maker (Anschütz) has the whole sensitive element encased in a sphere floating in a spherical shell of mercury. The electric current for the drive of the rotor has to be carried over the interval by flexible strips or by induction.

The second problem of introducing damping to diminish the oscillations about the meridian is overcome by either of two methods. The method easier to understand consists of placing an extra mercury U-tube alongside the governing mercury or pendulum: in this tube baffles are included, so that turbulence and fluid friction prevent the free flow of this mercury even under the slow influence of the earth, with the result that its oscillation lags in phase with the gyro precession; ideally the phase lag is 90°. Or this damping mercury is contained within a circular tube (Fig. 6–41) called a Frahm damper, so that any movement of the

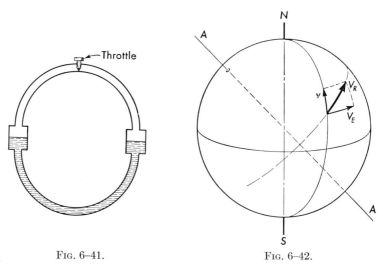

FIG. 6–41.   FIG. 6–42.

mercury involves a passage of air over the top of the loop, and this passage is restricted by a throttle valve to the same effect. The alternative method of damping, as used in the Sperry compass, is to mount the mercury ballistic on the innermost ring of the phantom rather than the sensitive element, and then to connect the two by a pin that is not on the vertical axis. For the explanation of this the reader is referred to the publications of the Sperry Company.

The principal inherent error of any gyroscopic compass is called the meridional velocity error. Suppose a ship in northern latitudes is steaming north with velocity v. Then in Fig. 6–42 the ship and compass will have two components of velocity: V_E, the velocity of the earth eastward, and v. The compass is then fooled into believing the rotation of the earth is about axis AA, which is perpendicular to the resultant V_R, and will so align itself. This error arises whenever the ship has any *component* of velocity in the meridian; it is more serious in the far north and far south, for there the velocity V_E is less. No automatic correction of the error is possible; some compasses carry a mechanical device by which the lubber line is moved relative to the compass card, on the adjustment of control knobs for speed, course, and latitude: other designs rely merely on looking up the error in tables provided. This error, of course, becomes very serious whenever the north component of velocity v can approach V_E in magnitude, and is the principal reason that gyroscopic compasses are not very satisfactory when used in aircraft.

Another error arises due to a north component of acceleration, which is called the ballistic error. For each north component of velocity there is a specific velocity error: with changing northern velocity, this error will then change say from δ_1 to δ_2. The tendency of the compass, however, is to change too quickly and overshoot the new desired deflection δ_2, reaching say δ_3. The difference ($\delta_3 - \delta_2$) is the ballistic error. It can be shown that the movement is "dead-beat," and no error exists in a compass when designed so that the period of the undamped oscillation about the meridian (Fig. 6–37) is about $84\frac{1}{2}$ minutes. This is the period of a simple pendulum whose length is equal to the radius of the earth. A complication of this is due to the fact that this period is not constant all over the earth; as a result some gyro compasses are designed for no ballistic error only at (say) latitude 40° N, where most sailing is done, while other compasses are adjustable for any latitude by changing the speed of their rotor.

The elimination of this inherent error reflects upon the earlier design problem of damping. For if the compass is to settle within a reasonable length of time after starting up, say in four hours, and the period of each swing is $84\frac{1}{2}$ minutes, damping must be strong enough to suppress the initial amplitude in two swings.

6–20. Motion of the Spinning Top.

Why is it that a child's spinning top when started at any angle brings its axis of spin into the vertical?

The answer lies in the shape of the axle at the base, which should be rounded rather than pointed.

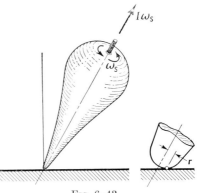

Fig. 6–43.

Suppose that the top spins about an inclined axis as in Fig. 6–43, in a counterclockwise sense viewed from above. Precession will be slow in comparison with spin, so that the angular momentum is sensibly only about the axis of symmetry, as shown by the vector $I\omega_s$. The weight, through the center of gravity, and the reaction from the ground form a couple which causes the precession of the spin axis in a cone around the vertical, counterclockwise viewed from above. An enlarged view of the rounded base is shown in the inset to the figure, and because the spin is about the axis there tends to be slipping at the point of contact. With the directions taken in this illustration, the result is a frictional force toward you out of the paper, and this is the cause of secondary couples, one about the spin axis merely slowing down the spin, the other about the center of mass causing the precession of the axis upward, or decreasing the slant angle. The top is therefore soon vertical, in which position it settles for some while and is called a "sleeping" top.

6–21. Nutation and Natural Frequency. There is another motion of the precessing spinning top, which is not so easily observed. It is easier to see with the bicycle wheel described in Art. 6–11. And the bicycle wheel is just another form of top, for it is supported from a single point on its axle.

When the spinning bicycle wheel is first set on its support (Fig. 6–27) it is observed to drop slightly until the precession gets going. This is natural, for it was pointed out before that only a freely precessing gyroscope acts as an "automatic counterbalance" to the applied torque. To get the precessional velocity, the inertia of the gyro against motion about this diameter must be overcome.

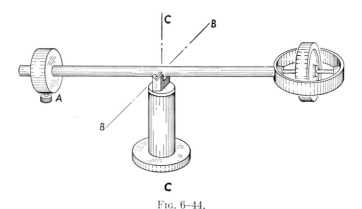

Fig. 6–44.

But now another effect enters the picture. When the wheel axis is set horizontally on the post, and then on being released starts to drop, it acquires a kinetic energy of dropping: and thus when the weight-torque has had time to produce the correct precession, the gyro reaction torque is enough to balance the weight but not enough to counteract this downward inertia. The free end of the axle thus overshoots the mark. The principle of energy then explains that as much further potential energy as is lost in dropping will be converted into excess precession. The greater torque from the extra precession then stops the falling and starts the free end rising. Again, a kinetic energy of rising is acquired as the precession slows to its proper value, but the free end again over-shoots the mark.

A typical oscillation is thus started with the free end of the wheel axle rising and falling as it precesses around the pivot point. This is called nutation, or nodding. An instrument which demonstrates the phenome-non particularly well is Fessel's gyroscope, which is shown in Fig. 6–44. It consists of a gyroscope mounted in a single ring attached to one end of a balanced arm, with its spin axis aligned with the arm. This arm is supported at the center on a horizontal knife-edge bearing enabling it to move about axis BB, and the whole support with the arm is free to rotate about the vertical central axis CC. Now the balance of the arm may be adjusted by moving the counterweight A. With the gyroscope on the heavy end, when released, the spinning gyro will drop and start precessing. With the gyro on the light end, on release it will rise as it starts precessing. The free end, when released from rest, will trace a path as in Fig. 6–45a; if the gyro is started with some precession, in the right direction though of improper quantity, the free end will trace the path shown in Fig. 6–45b. Or if the gyro is given initially a velocity opposing precession it will fall much more, as it has to overcome this negative amount before it produces the proper amount and the path will be of the type shown in Fig. 6–45c.

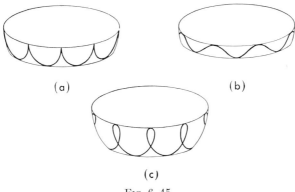

(a)

(b)

(c)

Fig. 6–45.

The frequency of small nutational oscillations can be found as follows. Suppose in Fig. 6–44 that the angular momentum of the gyroscope is $I\omega_s$, that the precessional velocity is ω_p around the vertical axis CC about which the whole moving assembly has moment of inertia I_C, and that the dipping about axis BB is with angular velocity Ω, and the moment of inertia about this axis is I_B for the arm, gyro, and counter-weight. Now ω_p and Ω are variables, although ω_s is constant. We pre-sume that the arm is out of balance by the small amount Wh on the gyro side so that the gyro starts dropping. This small torque must overcome inertia about axis BB as well as overcome the gyro reaction due to precession about CC. Therefore

$$Wh - I\omega_s\omega_p = I_B(d\Omega/dt) \tag{6-24}$$

Now about axis CC, there will be a gyro inertia torque from the precession Ω, hastening precession ω_p, so

$$I\omega_s\Omega = I_C(d\omega_p/dt) \tag{6-25}$$

By differentiating the second for substitution of $d\Omega/dt$ in the first, we obtain

$$\frac{I_B I_C}{I\omega_s} \frac{d^2\omega_p}{dt^2} + (I\omega_s)\omega_p = Wh \tag{6-26}$$

which is a simple harmonic motion of frequency

$$f = \frac{I\omega_s}{2\pi\sqrt{I_B I_C}} \tag{6-27}$$

which is of course unaffected by the amount of the unbalance Wh. The frequency of oscillation of Ω is also the same.

In Fessel's gyroscope this frequency is slow because of the large moments of inertia I_B and I_C in comparison to that of the gyro itself. But in a simple gyroscope mounted in gimbal rings (as Fig. 6-26) the nutational frequency is exceedingly rapid. Depending on the design of the gimbals, it may be over 50 per cent higher than the speed of spin. This trembling can be seen in such a gyro by applying a sudden tap to the bearing at one end of the spin axle.

6-22. Gyroscopic Effect on Critical Whirling Speeds. As the last application in this chapter we will turn to what is known as a gyroscopic effect on the critical speeds of turbines, as this forms an interesting example not only of angular momentum theory, but also of a method of analysis wherein two results are interdependent, and two relations must be found for their solution.

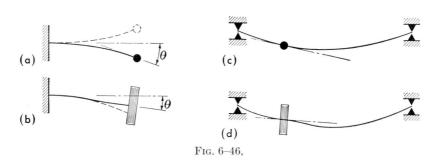

Fig. 6-46.

It has been shown that when a shaft carrying one or more disks rotates, it suffers bending due to the unavoidable presence of any slightest unbalance. Fig. 6–46a, for instance, shows a mass on the end of an overhung shaft which when whirling has a maximum slope θ. If the mass were, however, a disk (Fig. 6–46b), the disk would show a reluctance to submit to the wobble; it will try instead to maintain itself in a plane, after the manner of the figure, so that the shaft is forced into a much stiffer shape and may even have double curvature.

A similar situation is shown in Fig. 6–46d where the disk again reduces the slope of the shaft from that that would occur with a concentrated mass only (Fig. 6–46c). Of course if the disk were at midspan here, no difference would be seen.

These effects are called gyroscopic because they are likened to the property of the gyroscope to maintain its directional axis, but they are not to be confused with gyroscopic precession. As an example of the analysis, we will take the case of Fig. 6–46d.

Evidently the shaft when whirling suffers from two effects of the disk. First there is the centrifugal force from the disk since its center is deflected; secondly there is the centrifugal or gyroscopic couple. Note that any force F (Fig. 6–47a) in producing a deflection y_F cannot avoid also causing an angular change (slope) θ_F; similarly any couple C produces as in Fig. 6–47b both a θ_c and a y_c. These resultants can be found in a structural handbook, and are

$$\left.\begin{aligned}
y_F &= \left(\frac{a^2b^2}{3EIl}\right)F = \alpha F \\[4pt]
\theta_F &= \left[\frac{ab(b-a)}{3EIl}\right]F = \beta F \\[4pt]
y_c &= \left[\frac{ab(b-a)}{3EIl}\right]C = \beta C \\[4pt]
\theta_c &= \left[\frac{a^2-ab+b^2}{3EIl}\right]C = \gamma C
\end{aligned}\right\} \tag{6–28}$$

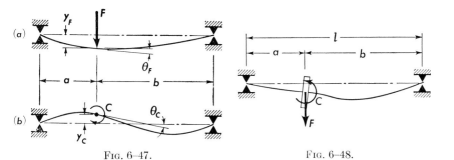

FIG. 6–47.   FIG. 6–48.

where as in Fig. 6–48 the disk is a distance a from one end, b from the other, so that the span is $a + b = l$ between simply supporting bearings. Note the example of Maxwell's reciprocal theorem that $\theta_F = y_c$ above for $F = C = 1$. The symbols α, β, γ are introduced merely for a short-hand notation.

In the case in point, we do not have two y and θ values. Rather, the actual deflection y and slope θ are the difference of the two effects above, since we have a centrifugal force trying to increase and a gyroscopic couple trying to decrease both deflection and slope. Hence

$$y = y_F - y_c = \alpha F - \beta C$$
$$\theta = \theta_F - \theta_c = \beta F - \gamma C \qquad (6\text{–}29)$$

The magnitude of force and couple must now be found, and of course they depend on y and θ, which makes the problem interesting. In Fig. 6–48 we presume the disk is mounted slightly eccentric by an amount e and that (as in Art. 4–12) the heavy side maintains its position radially outward on the disk, damping be-ing excluded; this means then that the rotations of the disk around the shaft and of the bent shaft around its whirl are syn-chronous. The centrifugal force, acting at the center of mass of the disk, is then

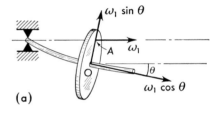

(a)

$$F = M(y + e)\omega_1^2$$

More precisely it should of course be written $M(y + e \cos \theta)\omega_1^2$ be-cause e is measured on the in-clined disk; but the assumption is made, and is in fact inherent in eqs. 6–28 if they are linear re-lations as given, that θ is a small angle and y a small deflection.

The centrifugal couple acting may be found either by the meth-od of products of inertia, or by analysis of changing momentum. We choose the latter,[*] and show in Fig. 6–49a the disk rotating with speed ω_1 about the axis between the bearings. But this is not a principal axis of the slant disk, and therefore we resolve ω_1 into a rotation $\omega_1 \cos \theta$ about the tangent to the shaft and a rotation $\omega_1 \sin \theta$ about a diameter of the disk. Thus the components of angular momentum are $H_p = I_p\omega_1 \cos \theta$ about the polar axis and $H_d = I_d\omega_1 \sin \theta$ about the diametral axis of inertia.

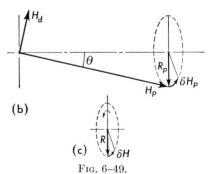

(b)

(c)

FIG. 6–49.

---

[*] For the former, see J. P. Den Hartog, *Mechanical Vibrations* (3d ed.; New York: McGraw-Hill Book Co., Inc., 1947), pp. 317–20.

We look at the vector H_p first, and note that it is by far the larger. The end of this vector (drawn from a pole) traces the circular base of a cone (Fig. 6–49b) of radius $R_p = H_p \sin \theta$, and it is around this circle that the change-in-momentum vector δH_p appears, being the difference between later and earlier positions of vector H_p. But δH_p is equally the change in R_p, i.e., the change in the radial component of H_p (and we observe that parallel motion of any momentum vector does not involve couples).

Now the smaller vector H_d also has a radial component, this time upward, of magnitude $H_d \cos \theta$, and so both together produce the radial R of Fig. 6–49c given by

$$\begin{aligned} R &= H_p \sin \theta - H_d \cos \theta \\ &= (I_p \omega_1 \cos \theta) \sin \theta - (I_d \omega_1 \sin \theta) \cos \theta \\ &= \tfrac{1}{2}(I_p - I_d)\omega_1 \sin 2\theta \end{aligned}$$

or for small θ

$$R = (I_p - I_d)\omega_1 \theta$$

This vector R rotates with speed ω_1 and thus in time δt there is a change $\delta H = R\omega_1 \delta t$, or an inertia couple reaction

$$C = \frac{\delta H}{\delta t} = (I_p - I_d)\omega_1^2 \theta \tag{6–30}$$

in the sense opposite to δH.

For a disk the polar moment of inertia I_p is twice the diametral, so that

$$C = I_d \omega_1^2 \theta$$

We can apply these results for F and C to eqs. 6–29:

$$\begin{aligned} 3EIly &= a^2 b^2 M(y + e)\omega_1^2 - ab(b - a)I_d\omega_1^2\theta \\ 3EIl\theta &= ab(b - a)M(y + e)\omega_1^2 - (a^2 - ab + b^2)I_d\omega_1^2\theta \end{aligned}$$

Upon gathering terms in θ and y, these appear neater:

$$\begin{aligned} y(1 - \alpha M\omega_1^2) + \theta(\beta I_d\omega_1^2) &= \alpha Me\omega_1^2 \\ -y(\beta M\omega_1^2) + \theta(1 + \gamma I_d\omega_1^2) &= \beta Me\omega_1^2 \end{aligned}$$

These can then be solved simultaneously for y or θ: for instance

$$y = \frac{[\alpha(1 + \gamma I_d\omega_1^2) - \beta^2 I_d\omega_1^2]Me\omega_1^2}{(1 - \alpha M\omega_1^2)(1 + \gamma I_d\omega_1^2) + (\beta I_d\omega_1^2)(\beta M\omega_1^2)}$$

We are interested, however, in *critical* speeds, which occur with indeterminately large values of y, when the denominator above becomes zero. (The denominator is of course the determinant of the two equations.) Hence ω_1 has the critical speed value ω_c if

$$(1 - \alpha M\omega_c^2)(1 + \gamma I_d\omega_c^2) + (\beta I_d\omega_c^2)(\beta M\omega_c^2) = 0$$

or, upon grouping ω_c's,

$$MI_d(\alpha\gamma - \beta^2)\omega_c^4 + (\alpha M - \gamma I_d)\omega_c^2 - 1 = 0 \qquad (6\text{-}31)$$

This is a bi-quadratic soluble for ω_c, but actually when α, β, M, and I are substituted for a particular shaft, it produces only one positive root.

Example. A turbine wheel of weight 160 lb and moment of inertia 6000 lb in.^{2} is mounted on a $2\frac{1}{2}$ in. diam shaft. The two bearings are 26 in. apart, and the wheel is $9\frac{1}{2}$ in. from one. Find the critical speed.

In eqs. 6–28

$$\alpha = 5.483 \times 10^{-6} \text{ in./lb}$$
$$\beta = 0.2449 \times 10^{-6} \text{ rad/lb (in./lb in.)}$$
$$\gamma = 4.591 \times 10^{-8} \text{ rad/lb in.}$$

assuming $E = 30 \times 10^6$ psi. Now without considering the gyroscopic couple, the critical speed would be

$$\omega_c = \sqrt{\frac{kg}{W}} = \sqrt{\frac{1}{\alpha M}} = 663 \text{ rad/sec}$$

Including the gyro effect, however, eq. 6–31 gives

$$\left(\frac{1840.7}{386 \times 10^4}\right)\omega_c^4 + 601.82\omega_c^2 - 386 \times 10^6 = 0$$

yielding

$$\omega_c^2 = 46.785 \times 10^4$$
$$\omega_c = 684 \text{ rad/sec}$$

which shows that the gyroscopic effect here has raised the critical speed 3 per cent and this with the turbine disk quite near midspan.

Many further problems exist within this field. For example, Stodola,* to whom the above treatment is largely due, presents also the case of a disk with precessional velocity equal and opposite to the spin velocity of the shaft, possible when the disk is loose on the shaft. This condition, which Dr. Stodola has managed to produce experimentally, produces a critical speed lower (instead of higher) than that without gyro effect. Jasper† states that cases have been investigated by the U. S. Navy, in which even slow-speed (100 rpm) marine propellers exhibited sufficient gyro effects to change the critical speeds significantly.

The graphical method of finding deflections of Arts. 4–21 and 4–22 may also be adapted to include gyroscopic couples. The procedure is a modification of Stodola's method: after a first approximate solution without gyro effects, the slope and approximate speed then found are

---

* A. Stodola, *Steam and Gas Turbines*, trans. by L. C. Loewenstein (New York: McGraw-Hill Book Co., Inc., 1927), Vol. I, pp. 430–36; Vol. II, pp. 1113–22.

† N. H. Jasper, "Critical Whirling Speeds of Shaft-Disk Systems," *Paper 52-F-33* of the A.S.M.E. (1952).

used for a second graphical solution, in which the gyroscopic couples appear as steps in the bending moment diagram.

BIBLIOGRAPHY

Of comparable difficulty:

BROWN, F. L. *Engineering Mechanics.* 2d ed. New York: John Wiley & Sons, Inc., 1942, Chap. 16 on products of inertia.

CRABTREE, H. *Elementary Treatment of the Theory of Spinning Tops, and Gyroscopic Motion.* London: Longmans, Green & Co., Ltd., 1909.

DEN HARTOG, J. P. *Mechanics.* New York: McGraw-Hill Book Co., Inc., 1948, Chaps. 12 and 17.

FERRY, E. S. *Applied Gyrodynamics.* New York: John Wiley & Sons, Inc., 1933.

INGLIS, SIR CHARLES. *Applied Mechanics for Engineers.* Cambridge: University Press, 1951, Chap. 20.

WORTHINGTON, A. M. *Dynamics of Rotation.* London: Longmans, Green & Co., Ltd., 1920.

Publications of The Sperry Gyroscope Corp., Great Neck, N. Y.

Mathematically inclined (approach through Euler's equations, etc.):

DIEMEL, R. F. *Mechanics of the Gyroscope.* New York: The Macmillan Co., 1929.

GRAY, A. *Treatise on Gyrostatics and Rotational Motion.* London: Macmillan & Co., Ltd., 1918.

JEANS, J. H. *Theoretical Mechanics.* Boston: Ginn & Co., 1907, Chap. 11.

KLEIN, F., and SOMMERFELD, A. *Theorie des Kreisels* (in four vols.). 4th ed. Leipzig: Teubner, 1910.

LANZA, G. *Dynamics of Machinery.* New York: John Wiley & Sons, Inc., 1911, Chap. 5.

RAWLINGS, A. L. *Theory of the Gyroscopic Compass and Its Deviations.* 2d ed. New York: The Macmillan Co., 1944.

ROUTH, E. J. *Elementary Rigid Dynamics.* (Vol. I of "Dynamics of a System of Rigid Bodies.") 5th ed. London: Macmillan & Co., Ltd., 1891, Chaps. 1 and 5.

———. *Advanced Rigid Dynamics.* (*Ibid.*, Vol. II) Chaps. 1, 3, and 4.

TIMOSHENKO, S., and YOUNG, D. H. *Advanced Dynamics.* New York: McGraw-Hill Book Co., Inc., 1948, Chap. 5.

WEBSTER, A. G. *The Dynamics of Particles, and of Rigid, Elastic, and Fluid Bodies.* 2d ed., reprint. New York: Stechert & Co., 1922, Chaps. 6 and 7.

WHITTAKER, E. T. *Analytic Dynamics.* 4th ed., reprint. New York: Dover Publications, 1944, Chaps. 5 and 6.

PROBLEMS

6-1. The figure shows an electric rotor which has an angular velocity $\omega_x = +300$ rad/sec together with a turning velocity $\omega_z = -40$ rad/sec while point O on the axis is fixed. Find the linear velocity of point C, at a radius of 2 in.

6-2. Tests on an electric rotor (Fig. 6-P-1) show that about the two bearings there is an out-of-balance given, in terms of its products of inertia, by:
about O

$$I_{xy} = -0.15 \quad \text{oz in. sec}^2$$
$$I_{xz} = +0.20 \quad \text{oz in. sec}^2$$

about P

$$I_{x'y'} = +0.15 \quad \text{oz in. sec}^2$$
$$I_{z'x'} = -0.30 \quad \text{oz in. sec}^2$$

Balancing holes are to be drilled in the slip-rings A and B, at radius 2 in. Find the weight to be removed and its location in each ring, necessary for dynamic balance.

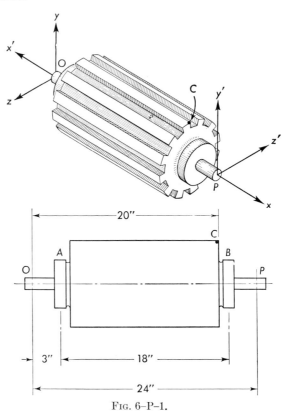

FIG. 6–P–1.

6–3. Another rotor, as in Problem 6–2, needs to be balanced because

about O:
$$I_{xy} = +3.6 \quad \text{oz in.}^2$$
$$I_{zx} = +1.8 \quad \text{oz in.}^2$$

about P:
$$I_{x'y'} = +3.6 \quad \text{oz in.}^2$$
$$I_{z'x'} = -12.6 \quad \text{oz in.}^2$$

Find the weight and location of drilled holes to be made at 2 in. radius in the rings A and B.

6–4. An 18-in. diameter turbine disk, of weight 100 lb and moment of inertia 4000 lb in.^{2}, when mounted on its shaft, is found to have peripheral run-out (axial displacement) of 0.010 in. Find the unbalanced couple if this is run at 12,500 rpm. The thickness of the wheel is negligible in comparison with the radius.

6–5. A cylindrical rotor, solid steel, of 6-in. diameter and 15-in. length is bored for a shaft. But whereas the hole at one end is central, the hole at the other end is found to be 0.015 in. eccentric. Find the position and weight of metal to be removed by drilling axially into the ends at radius 2.5 in.

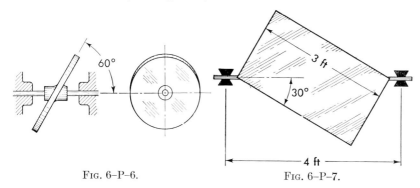

FIG. 6–P–6.   FIG. 6–P–7.

6–6. A wobble-plate (swash-plate) hydraulic motor involves use of an elliptical thin flat plate set with its major axis at 60° to the axis of revolution. The ellipse is such that the projected axial view is a circle of diameter 4 in.; the plate weighs 2 lb, and it revolves at 3600 rpm about a vertical shaft held in bearings 3 in. apart. Find the bearing loads.

6–7. Find the vertical and horizontal bearing loads, with their maxima, when the flat plate in the figure, weighing 10 lb, rotates at 600 rpm about a diagonal axis. (Den Hartog)

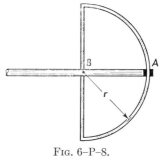

FIG. 6–P–8.

6–8. Integrate to find the product of inertia of a wire formed to a quadrant arc of a circle, radius r, weight w per unit length. Hence write the expression, in terms of angular velocity ω, for the bending moment at point A in the mechanical mixer (Fig. 6–P–8) if the weld at point B should become broken.

6–9. Prove by integration that the product of inertia of the right triangular prism (Fig. 6–18) of thickness t, and total mass M, in which angle C is 90° and $BC = a$ and $AC = b$ in length, is given by $Mab/12$ with respect to the two rectangular sides.

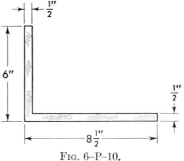

6–10. Find the principal axes of inertia through the center of gravity of the

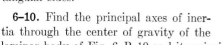

FIG. 6–P–10.

laminar body of Fig. 6–P–10 and its principal moments of inertia, if it weighs 7 oz.

6–11. Find I_{xy}, the direction of the principal axes XYZ and the magnitude of the principal moments of inertia of the Z-section body, which weighs $\frac{1}{4}$ lb per cu in. The thickness of the body is 1 in.

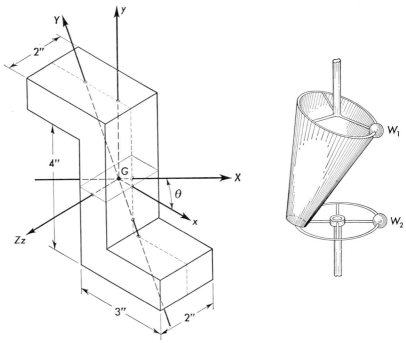

Fig. 6–P–11.

Fig. 6–P–12.

6–12. A sorting machine uses for a distributor a sheet-metal frustrum of a right cone. The upper circle of 9 in. diameter is central with the axis of rotation. The center of the lower circle, of diameter 1.5 in., is at a radius of 9 in. and the cone centerline is 12 in. long. Weights W_1, W_2 are added to the frame to produce static balance. Find the unbalanced couple at 30 rpm. The weight of the frame may be neglected and the weight of the cone is 5 lb.

6–13. Show by the method of the changing moment of momentum vector that the couple unbalanced when any plane lamina rotates about any axis X in its plane XY through its center of mass, is equal to $I_{XY}\omega^2$.

6–14. Two eccentrics are mounted on a $\frac{1}{2}$-in. shaft at 90° to each other and 6 in. apart, as in the figure. Each eccentric is

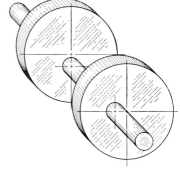

Fig. 6–P–14.

a circular steel disk, of 4-in. diameter, $\frac{1}{2}$ in. in thickness, and eccentric $\frac{1}{2}$ in. Find the direction and magnitude of the total angular momentum (of the eccentrics without shaft), when the shaft rotates at 600 rpm.

6–15. As for Problem 6–14, but the eccentrics of Fig. 6–P–14 differ by 180° around the shaft.

6–16. A bent crank as in Fig. 6–P–16 is rotating around the x-axis.

a) Find the dimension a which will bring the whole into static balance about the x-axis.

b) Find the bending moment in the weld W at the shaft when rotating at 1000 rpm.

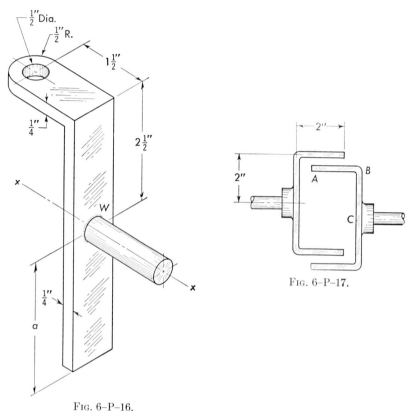

Fig. 6–P–16.

Fig. 6–P–17.

6–17. Assuming that the geometrical shape remains unchanged and neglecting fluid friction, etc., determine suitable sections for the round bars AB and BC, of the pair of beaters in the figure that are to revolve at 10,000 rpm. The material is to be stainless steel, and working stress from dynamic sources is not to exceed 10,000 psi.

6–18. The cast-iron feed screw (auger) shown is to undergo a corrosion test in which it will be run with a rim velocity of 30 ft/sec in sea water. The screw is mounted on the end of a shaft that projects from two bearings 24 in. apart, with the near side of the screw 3 in. from the nearer bearing centerline. Find the radial loads to be expected on these bearings. It may be assumed that the helix is of rectangular section as shown, and that the helix perimeter subtends exactly 360°.

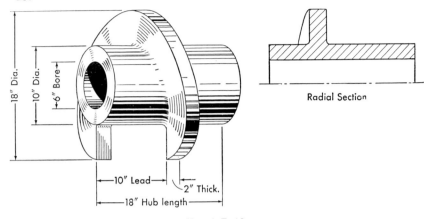

Radial Section

←—10" Lead—→ ⌐⌐2" Thick.
←————18" Hub length————→

Fig. 6-P-18.

6-19. If a dive bomber, which is coming down head-on at a steep angle, changes direction by a short curve into the horizontal, in which sense will be the gyroscopic action if the turbine rotor is rotating clockwise when viewed from aft?

6-20. a) If an ordinary top is rotating clockwise, viewed from above, and the upper end of the axis is pushed horizontally north, which way will it really lean? Explain.

b) When the top has got into a leaning position, describe its subsequent action due to its own weight.

6-21. Describe the effects on the bearings of a turbine-rotor in a ship, rotating about a longitudinal axis, when the ship is (a) rolling, (b) pitching.

6-22. A gyro rotor is mounted in a monorail car with axis of spin fixed in the body of the car. In what direction should the axis be mounted, and in which sense the gyro rotate, so that when rounding a corner in either direction it will cause the car to lean inward, counteracting centrifugal force?

6-23. The flywheel of an engine on a ship weighs 6000 lb and has a radius of gyration of 3.55 ft. It is mounted on a horizontal axle which is parallel to the longitudinal axis of the ship and has a speed of 420 rpm clockwise when viewed from the stern. Find the gyroscopic couple when the ship is turning to the left with an angular velocity of 0.10 rad/sec. What are the axle reactions if the distance between the centers of bearings is 4.4 ft?

6-24. The rotor of an electric locomotive motor weighs 9000 lb, and its radius of gyration is 1.63 ft. The axis of rotation is the centerline of the wheel axle and the bearings are 4 ft 0 in. apart, center to center. Neglecting the effect due to elevation of the outer rail, find the vertical reactions of the bearings when the locomotive goes around a right-hand curve of 1000 ft radius at 65 mph. The wheels are of 63" diameter.

6-25. In spite of admonitions, a boy is riding a bicycle with his hands off the handlebars. He causes the bicycle to lean over to the right at the speed of $\frac{1}{2}$ radian per second.

a) What is the gyro effect of the front wheel, and how does it affect the caster action?

b) If the front wheel and tire weigh 5 lb and have an effective radius (both of rolling and of gyration) of 13 in., and the bicycle is traveling at 10 mph, calculate the gyroscopic torque on either wheel.

6–26. An airplane has a gas turbine whose rotor weighs 500 lb, with radius of gyration 6 in., and rotates at 12,000 rpm in bearings 6 ft apart.

Show that even when the plane pulls out of a 450-mph dive with an acceleration of 9 g's into the horizontal, the gyroscopic loads on the bearings are insignificant when compared to the other causes of loading.

6–27. A little air compressor in a high-speed plane consists of 6-in. diameter turbine and impeller, together weighing 2 lb, with WR^2 about its axis 8 lb in.², mounted in bearings 5 in. apart, with its axis fore-and-aft in the plane. The rotor turns at 120,000 rpm. Find the forces on the bearings when the plane levels off from a dive at 700 mph, producing a centrifugal load on the pilot of 6 g's.

6–28. The flywheel in an automobile weighs 50 lb and has a radius of gyration of 5 in. It is mounted at the end of a 3-in. diameter shaft, with its center 2 in. behind the rear main bearing, from which the shaft projects as a cantilever.

Allowing for both inertia and gyroscopic effects, find the maximum bending moment in the shaft when the car is rounding a 200-ft radius curve to the left at 60 mph at which speed the shaft rotates at 2500 rpm, clockwise when viewed from the front.

6–29. A turbine rotor of a steamship rotates about an axis along the ship at 300 rpm and has a moment of inertia 200 ton ft sec². The ship pitches 7° above and below horizontal and has a period of oscillation of 10 sec. Find the maximum added loads on the bearings of the turbine, if they are 16 ft apart. Assume the pitching to be in simple harmonic motion.

6–30. A machine weighing 2 tons is carried by a rotating turntable, 3 ft in diameter, but is not fastened to it. The machine has a flywheel revolving about a horizontal axis at 100 rpm. If the flywheel has a moment of inertia of 150 lb ft sec², at what speed of rotation of the turntable will the machine overturn? The center of gravity of the machine is in the axis of rotation.

6–31. A motorcycle weighing 300 lb has two wheels, each of 15 lb, radius of gyration 12 in., and outside diameter 28 in. The engine has a disk-shaped flywheel weighing 20 lb, of diameter 10 in., rotating at 3000 rpm in the same direction as the wheels when the machine is traveling 60 mph. The center of gravity of the machine is 16 in. above the ground, and that of the rider is 36 in. above the ground. The rider weighs 170 lb.

Find the angle from the vertical at which the machine and rider together must lean inward when rounding a corner of 300-ft radius, to maintain equilibrium against both centrifugal and gyroscopic effects.

6–32. The drawing shows a model made* to demonstrate the stability of the Brennan Mono-rail car. The framework $ABCD$, balanced in unstable manner on two peg legs, carries a gyro spinning about the horizontal axis OX and

* H. Crabtree, *Spinning Tops*, p. 72.

mounted in a single gimbal ring, free to rotate about the vertical axis EZ in the frame. To the upper end of this axle of the ring is attached the crank H; a spring is stretched from this crank to the projection S of the frame.

If a gust of wind disturbs the equilibrium of the frame, describe the subsequent motion.

6-33. A light rod of length $2l$ has a small mass m fixed at each end: it is hinged at its middle point to the forked upper end of a vertical shaft so that it can swing relative to the shaft in a vertical plane. The shaft is caused to rotate with uniform angular velocity ω about its axis, and the rod, rotating with the shaft, is set at a small angle α to the horizontal and released. Show that the rod will oscillate with frequency $\omega/2\pi$ and that the torque on the shaft will fluctuate twice in every revolution between the values $\pm 2ml^2\omega^2\alpha^2$.   (C.U.)

6-34. Prove that the period of small oscillations of a gyroscopic compass is given approximately by

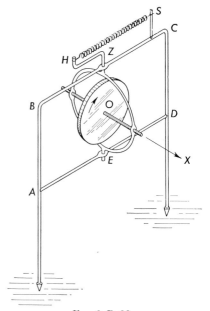

Fig. 6–P–32.

$$T = 2\pi\sqrt{\frac{I\omega_s}{Mgl\Omega\cos\lambda}}$$

when I = polar moment of inertia of the gyroscope
ω_s, Ω = angular velocities of gyro spin, and of the earth
λ = latitude at the compass

and the gravity control is equivalent to a mass M at a distance l from the gyroscope center.   (C.U.)

6-35. A vessel in latitude 50°N is traveling south at 25 mph. Find the compass correction that must be made for this motion. Take the radius of the earth to be 4000 miles.

6-36. A Schlick stabilizer for reducing the rolling of a ship consists of a balanced flywheel maintained in rapid rotation and carried in a frame which swings about a transverse axis athwart the ship. The two axes intersect at right angles, and when the ship is at rest the axis of the flywheel is vertical, the frame being weighted for this purpose. Its swinging motion about the transverse axis is resisted by a couple proportional to the angular velocity of swing.

The moment of inertia of the flywheel about its axis is C and its angular velocity of spin is n. The free undamped period of swinging of the frame when the flywheel is at rest is $2\pi/q$.

When the ship is rolling steadily through a small angle with period $2\pi/s$, find an expression for the ratio of the mean energy dissipated by the apparatus to the mean kinetic energy of the rolling ship, and show that when $q \neq s$ this ratio has a maximum value for variation of the damping resistance given by $\dfrac{C^2 n^2 s}{IJ(s^2 - q^2)}$ where I is the moment of inertia of the whole ship about its longitudinal axis, and J that of the flywheel and frame about the transverse axis. It is to be assumed that the angular motion of the frame is small. (C.U.)

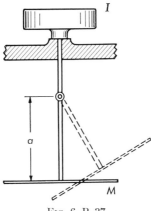

Fig. 6–P–37.

6–37. A heavy flywheel, with moment of inertia I, is mounted at the upper end of a light shaft which is free to rotate in a vertical bearing as shown in the figure. Below the bearing the shaft has a hinge joint and at its lower end it carries another flywheel in the form of a thin uniform disk of radius r. The mass of the disk is M and the distance from its center of gravity to the hinge is a. The shaft is given an initial angular velocity Ω while in the vertical position.

Show that if $r > 2a$ the shaft will be stable in this position for all values of Ω; while if $r < 2a$ it will be unstable if

$$\Omega^2 > \frac{4ga}{4a^2 - r^2}$$

Show also that in the latter case, if

$$\Omega^2 = \frac{8ga}{4a^2 - r^2}$$

and the shaft is displaced slightly from the vertical, its swing will stop momentarily at an angle θ to the vertical given by

$$\cos \theta = \sqrt{c^2 + 1} - c$$

where

$$c = \frac{Mr^2 + 2I}{M(4a^2 - r^2)} \tag{C.U.}$$

6–38. On an automatic machine a 2-in. milling cutter A rotates at 10,800 rpm on the horizontal axis y-y being driven through belting by the $\frac{1}{4}$ hp electric motor B, which turns at 3600 rpm. The whole assembly is mounted on the vertical shaft C. In operation a cam mechanism (not shown) turns the assembly

10° about the axis x-x, bringing the cutter into contact with the work for a short time, and returns it, the whole work cycle taking one-quarter second. The timing of this work cycle, the cutting loads, etc., are very particular; yet it works well.

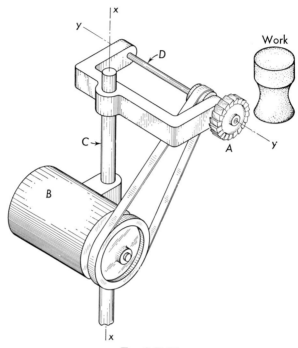

Fig. 6–P–38.

Now a designer wishes to make a change: the motor B and belt-drive are to be replaced by a small 10,800 rpm electric motor mounted at D. You are asked to express an immediate opinion whether this change will jeopardize the successful operation of the machine.

Would your opinion be the same, had the belt-drive shown in the figure been crossed?

Chapter 7

STATIC AND DYNAMIC FORCES IN MACHINES (RIGID)

7-1. Outline. When the parts of a machine are in motion, they are subjected to two types of force: first, of course, there is the force which is transmitted from the driver through to the working member to produce the work desired and to overcome incidental friction. Then also there are the inertia forces and couples, and these must be overcome by a further force from the driver.

The study of kinematics of mechanisms will have shown to the reader that in many machines—for example, in the simple four-link chain or the slider-crank—the uniform speed of a driving member does not usually dispense with accelerations in sequel members. However it was shown in Chapter 1 that when d'Alembert's principle is applied there is an extended meaning to the term equilibrium: by the addition of "reversed effective forces" and couples to the real forces and couples acting upon any body or group of bodies in motion, those bodies will be found still to obey the rules of static equilibrium, that the vector sum of all forces acting upon each body must vanish, and the vector sum of moments about any point must also vanish.

Thus the solution of a problem of forces in a moving machine will follow the pattern found best for static frameworks: the machine is "separated" into "free bodies." Each free body will exert or react to forces and/or couples at the points of contact with its neighbors, and there will also be acting the resultant inertia effect. These forces may be found by a graphical or analytical study (though the former predominates). Most of the problems encountered in machine design will be found to be two-dimensional.

And now it will be well to undertake some sample problems. First some examples in static force analysis are given; the examples in dynamic force analysis which follow show that the method of attack is essentially the same. In the application of the laws of equilibrium, several approaches are nearly always possible, so that technique for either the simplest and fastest solution or the most accurate solution is the essence.

7-2. Two-Force Body. When a rigid body is subjected to only two forces, it is evident that those two forces must be collinear, equal and opposite: for if moments be taken about any point on the line of action of one, the moment of the other must be zero. Thus being collinear, they must be equal and opposite. Any such body will then be either in compression or in tension.

7–3. Three-Force Body. When just three external forces act upon a body, they must be concurrent, in order that the moments about the point of intersection of the lines of action of two of them may be zero for the third.

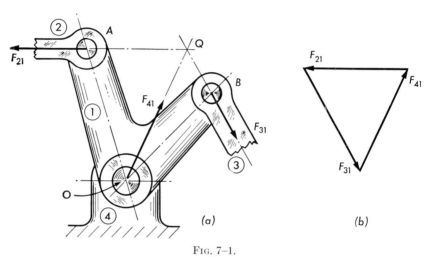

Fig. 7–1.

Examples of such a planar system are very common. In the bell-crank of which the plan view is shown in Fig. 7–1 the lines of action of the two forces from the neighboring tensile rods 2 and 3, are known, and the magnitude of one, F_{21}, is given. It is desired to find all forces.

By the symbol F_{21} is meant the force exerted *by* link 2 *on* link 1. This nomenclature has been suggested by previous authors and will be used consistently. It is plain that if F_{21} is as stated, F_{12} will be the reaction by member 1 on link 2, and thus must be equal and opposite to F_{21}. Always then $F_{xy} = -F_{yx}$.

In Fig. 7–1 consider the forces acting on the bell-crank (member 1) as a "free body" in static equilibrium. Its weight has no effect for it acts along a line perpendicular to the page. The lines of action of F_{21} and F_{31} meet at point Q. Hence OQ is the direction of F_{41}. From the vector triangle of forces, in the figure at (b), by first drawing F_{21} as given to scale, the magnitudes of the others are found.

This is one method. On the other hand if only F_{31} were of interest, it might be desirable by measurement of dimensions, to find it directly by its moment about point O. From these F_{41} could subsequently be found.

The preferred technique is in most cases so to arrange the analysis that the taking of moments is obviated.

When the system acting on a body consists of parallel forces, use of the moment relation is a necessity.

7–4. Three Forces and a Torque. Suppose in the preceding problem of the bell-crank, the known force F_{21} has to overcome a known torque resistance in the shaft O, and the remaining effort is to be passed on through link 3. The method of moments might be used, or alternatively

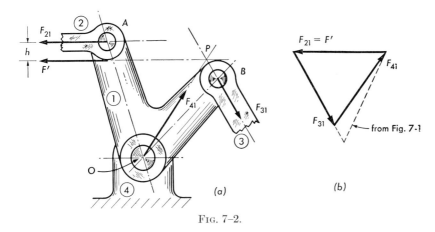

Fig. 7–2.

the known force and torque may be united (refer to page 19). Suppose $F_{21} = 100$ lb and the torque $T = 250$ lb in. The line of action of the resultant F' (still being of magnitude $F_{21} = 100$ lb) is transposed to a parallel axis distant an amount h (Fig. 7–2), where

$$h = T/F_{21} = 2.5 \text{ in.}$$

Then the three forces F', F_{31}, and F_{41} are concurrent in point P, and their analysis proceeds as before.

7–5. More Than Three Forces. The problem just explained would become that of a member on which four forces act if the effect of the weight of the link were considered, the axis O being horizontal. This, however, is relegated to a place among the problems at the end of this chapter.

The "Industrial Brownhoist" bucket forms another illustration. It is desired to find the reactions at the principal joints, when the bucket is being closed, and has reached the configuration shown in Fig. 7–3. The bucket is suspended by four cables: two form the loop passing the pulley A; the other two pass over three sheaves at B and two at A. When taking a bite, the action of this second cable is thus to pull down on the frame with force $4T$, and up on the three-sheave drum 2 with force $6T$, for cable tension T. There is no need of any lift on the first cables until the load is to be carried. Suppose then that T is equal to one-eighth the weight W of the whole bucket assembly.

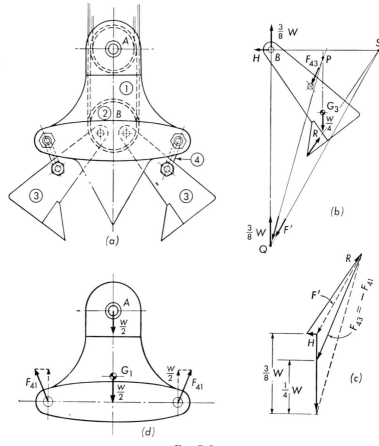

Fig. 7–3.

First consider the main frame. Suppose its weight is half the weight W. From sheaves A there is a further downward load of $W/2$ and thus links 4 will be in compression, carrying such a load that the vertical component in each is $W/2$. This appears on the figure.

Now in the free-body diagram of the jaw, the force upward by sheave B is $3/8\ W$. The horizontal force H at this pin is unknown, as is also the reaction R from the ground. The weight $W/4$ of the jaw, acting at G_3, and the force F_{43} are known completely.

It is possible to take moments about the point of ground contact and hence find H, which will solve the problem directly. But it is not necessary to take moments, proceeding instead as follows:

F_{43} and the weight have a resultant along the line PQ, found by vector sum through P. Q is vertically below pin B and hence on the line of action of that vertical force $3/8\ W$. The sum of the three known forces is therefore F' on line of action SQ. S is the point of concurrency of F' and H and must therefore be on the line of action of the ground reaction R. From these directions the vector polygon at (c) in the figure may therefore be completed.

7–6. Three or More Forces with Inertia. If a body is accelerating under the influence of forces, the reversed effective forces and couples must be added to the external forces on the "free body" diagram.

Example 1. A ladder leaning against a vertical wall is subjected to a pull from a rope tied to its base. It is desired to find what pull will give this lowest point an acceleration outward of 20 ft/sec², reaching a velocity of 10 ft/sec when the ladder makes an angle of 60° with the horizontal.

The ladder is 12 ft long, weighing 40 lb, with the center of gravity assumed midway in its length.

Figure 7–4 shows the instantaneous position. In order that the inertia forces may be added to the "free body" diagram, it is necessary first to reckon the accelerations by the usual methods of kinematics. At (b) therefore in the figure a velocity vector diagram shows that when the base point A has a velocity of 10 ft/sec, the top B must have a downward velocity of 5.774 ft/sec and the relative velocity $V_{B/A} = 11.55$ ft/sec.

Then at (c) the acceleration of A, given as 20 ft/sec² horizontally, is the vector that starts the acceleration vector diagram. To it is added the normal acceleration of B toward A, $a^n_{B/A}$, found from the relative velocity $= (11.55)^2/12 = 11.11$ ft/sec². With the tangential relative acceleration, $a^t_{B/A}$, these produce the vertical acceleration of B shown by ob. The acceleration of G and angular acceleration of the ladder are then given by

$$a_G = 15.766 \text{ ft/sec}^2$$
$$\alpha = 2.459 \text{ rad/sec}^2 \text{ clockwise}$$

Calculation of the inertia force f and couple q gives

$$f = ma_G = \frac{40}{32.2}(15.766) = 19.6 \text{ lb}$$

$$I_G = \frac{1}{12} \cdot mL^2 = \frac{40}{32.2} \cdot (12) \text{ lb ft sec}^2$$

$$q = I_G \alpha = \frac{480}{32.2}(2.459) = 36.65 \text{ lb ft}$$

These are shown on the "free body" in Fig. 7–4a in dotted lines. Now it is easier to combine both the forces and couple acting at and around

G into one. f and q combine to give f, displaced by an amount $h = q/f = 1.87$ ft to act through point K; then this unites with $W = 40$, giving the force F along KQ.

In the figure at (d) a force diagram is started: $ma(= f)$ and W unite to form F, and it is plain that the three other unknown forces will close this vector polygon.

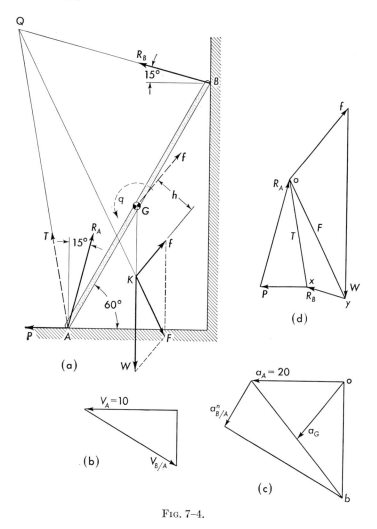

Fig. 7–4.

The reaction R_B at B may be found by taking moments about point A. It is assumed that the coefficient of friction at A and B gives a friction angle θ of $15°$ in each case. By measuring on the figure the perpendiculars to F and R_B from A, we obtain $R_B = 8.6$ lb.

Now in the vector polygon at (d) enter R_B, and thus from the known directions of R_A and P, close the polygon and by measurement find

$$R_A = 23.4 \text{ lb}$$
$$P = 10.1 \text{ lb}$$

As an alternative to the last step, the taking of moments may be avoided as follows. The lines of action of the known resultant F and the unknown quantity R_B intersect in Q. Thus the resultant of R_A and P, which we will call T, must be in the direction AQ. In the vector diagram at (d) draw line ox parallel to QA, and yx from the end of vector F parallel to BQ. Then yx represents R_B and xo represents T which may be resolved into R_A and P, with the results given above.

Example 2. Elliptical Lathe Headstock. If the preceding problem seems outside the realm of machines, consider the same mechanism used in the design of a lathe chuck for turning elliptical cylinders: both are

(Courtesy Monarch Machine Tool Co.)

Fig. 7–5.

examples of the kinematic trammels mechanism. Fig. 7–5 shows the Monarch oval chuck viewed from the rear of their lathe. The principle upon which the chuck works will be found described in two or three kinematics texts*; it consists of the driving shaft A of the headstock spindle, integral with which is a slide, forming a tee-piece with the spindle and pointed out by the arrow on Fig. 7–5. This slide fits into ways ACD (Fig. 7–6a) cut in the face-plate P; and at right angles to this in the face-plate there is another slot BCE, which is the ways for

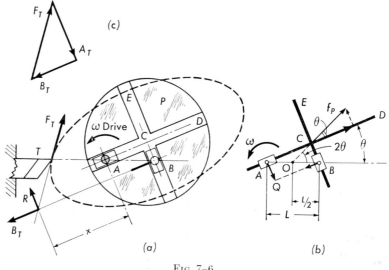

FIG. 7–6.

slide B. For a given setting, the centerline B is fixed, although for different ratios of the axes for the ellipse the distance AB is adjustable within limits. Now the work to be machined to an ellipse is fastened to the face-plate, and cut by the fixed tool T.

In this problem a careful study of the geometry of the figure yields much help. It is plain that point C, at the cross of the ways, is the center of mass for both the face-plate and the work. But the point C moves in a circle about point O (Fig. 7–6b) midway between A and B fixed centers: if the distance AB is set to be L, then C moves at radius $L/2$ around O with constant angular velocity 2ω relative to O. This fact is proved by the observation that the angle ACB is a right angle, and the locus of C is thus a circle on AB as diameter.

As a result, the inertia force of face-plate and work-piece together is a simple centrifugal force $f_p = (W/g)(L/2)(2\omega)^2$ in the direction OC, that is, it makes an angle θ with the line ACD where angle CAB is also θ (Fig. 7–6b).

Now, neglecting friction, the slide A can carry no force in the direc-

* J. H. Billings, *Applied Kinematics* (3d ed.; New York: D. Van Nostrand Co., 1953), p. 48; V. L. Doughtie and W. H. James, *Elements of Mechanism* (New York: John Wiley & Sons, Inc., 1954), p. 145

tion ACD, nor can slide B carry any in direction BCE. Resolution of f_p in these directions shows a load $f_p \sin \theta$ on the bearing of shaft A and a load $f_p \cos \theta$ on the bearing of shaft B. Both have the same maximum.

For example, the weight W of face-plate and work-piece might be 25 lb and the distance $L = \frac{1}{2}$ in., while driving speed $\omega = 24$ rad/sec (or 229 rpm). Then the bearing loads from this source are 37.5 lb maximum. These figures are based on a 6×5 in. ellipse and a (vertical component) cutting speed of 300 fpm.

But there is also the force from the cutting tool which causes independent reactions at the two bearings. The force F_T acts tangentially, and we call the reactions at A and B, A_T and B_T. Again, because of the ability of the slides to bear only normal loads, the forces A_T and B_T must be equal and opposite to the components of F_T in those directions (Fig. 7–6c). The maximum that either reaction can be is thus equal to F_T, and by a lucky coincidence this maximum on one bearing occurs when the other is zero, and vice versa. For instance, when C is over B (angle $\theta = 0$) A carries all of F_T and B carries all of f_p.

Turning to consider the torque requirements for driveshaft A, it appears that there is no inertia effect. For the line of action of f_p (Fig. 7–6b) passes through point Q which is the point of concurrence of the other two reaction forces, and there is no change in the angular velocity while the center C moves around. To overcome the cutting tool force F_T, torque is necessary of course: in Fig. 7–6a the forces F_T and B_T are shown combined to produce resultant R (equal and opposite to A_T) so that the torque to be produced by the driveshaft is Rx. Now R (or A_T) is a minimum when $\theta = 0$, when B carries no load and $R = F_T$: thus the minimum torque required of the drive through A is $F_T AT$. For the 6×5 ellipse used in illustration, this is $(5/2)F_T$ lb in. The maximum torque of A occurs when $\theta = 90°$, when $B_T = F_T$ and $A_T = 0$, so that the couple is $F_T \cdot BT$ or $3 F_T$ lb in.

The value of F_T depends upon the material being cut and the depth of the cut, and may be estimated from published horsepower figures for various cuts on ordinary lathes. It will vary a little, for the cutting speed is not constant in the direction tangent to the ellipse: the component of the speed perpendicular to line AT is constant.

7–7. Different Systems of Force Treated Separately. Sometimes it is advantageous to break down the forces acting on a mechanism, finding the reactions due to each imposed force separately and adding the effects later. The example just given of the elliptic chuck is a case in point; for another, when balancing a number of eccentric loads (centrifugal forces) on a rotor (Art. 4–6) it was found easier to find a balance for each load separately and then add the balancing forces vectorially.

The advantages lie either in the fact that fewer forces may be considered at one time, or else that the two systems are independent. For an example a toggle clamp is considered. First the forces due to an applied pressure are found, and then those due to the weight of the links. The two systems are independent, for the applied pressure might be changed without affecting the weights or the reactions therefrom.

Example. In a toggle-clamp mechanism (Fig. 7–7a) two equal forces F are applied, thereby clamping the object D. Find the clamping force on D due to F, and the static reactions at the pin joints, neglecting friction.

a) First system of forces, those due to F only. All weights of members ignored.

In link 1, considered as a free body since the only forces are those externally applied through the pins at the ends, these forces must be collinear. The force exerted by link 1 on the pin at B is in direction AB. This will be called F_{1B}. Similarly the force on B from link 2 is F_{2B} and is in the direction CB.

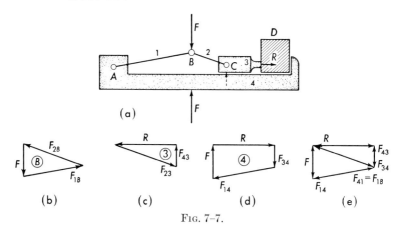

Fig. 7–7.

Considering the pin at B as a free body, the triangle of the three concurrent forces must form the closed vector triangle shown in Fig. 7–7b. The magnitudes are thus found.

Considering block C as a free body, the force from 2 (F_{23}) is equal and opposite to F_{2B}. The clamping reaction R is horizontal; and without friction the reaction F_{43} must be vertical. The line of action of F_{43} must pass through pin C because those of the other two forces do. If the length of F_{23} is thus taken from that of F_{2B}, the triangle of Fig. 7–7c can be completed. Thus the clamping force R is found by measurement to equal 96 lb, if F is 50 lb.

Figure 7–7d shows the closed polygon of the four forces acting on the frame. The solution may then be checked by placing these four on the original figure of the mechanism, in their correct lines of action, whereupon their moments about any point will be found to vanish.

Since in the three vector figures (b, c, and d) it is seen that every line was drawn twice, it is preferable and more economical to use the one diagram of Fig. 7–7e which is the composite form.

The pin-joint reactions due to $F = 50$ lb are:

at A, $F_{14} = -F_{1B} = 98$ lb
at C, $F_{23} = -F_{2B} = 102$ lb

b) Second system of forces, those due to weights of the members— clamping force F ignored.

If the weights of the members are taken into account, it is plain that their centers of gravity must be located. Furthermore there must be a supporting external force from below equal to the total weight, and there will be some clamping force on the body D without application of any force F.

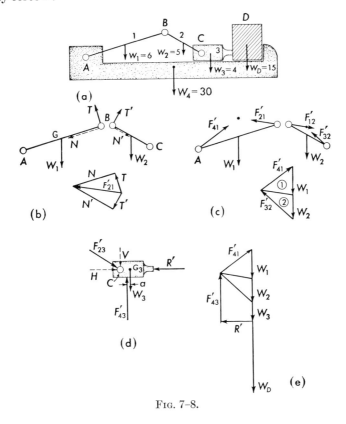

Fig. 7–8.

In Fig. 7–8 then, the weights and centers of gravity of the members are shown; F is omitted. The support upward on the base must total 60 lb, and the position of its resultant could be found by taking moments;

however, the clamp is probably to be set on a table so that the support will be a distributed force; thus its particular position is immaterial.

Members 1 and 2 each have three forces acting upon them. The reaction at pin B cannot be vertical; it can be found by taking moments. In Fig. 7–8b these two members are shown as free bodies: the three forces acting on member 1 are applied at points A, G, and B. By taking moments about A, the tangential component T of the unknown reaction F'_{21} through B may be found, but the other component N remains undetermined, for it has no effect on the moment about A. Turn then to attend to link 2, and by the moments about point C of W_2 find the tangential component T'. Then the reaction F'_{21} through B is determinable by the vector sum shown: the component T' is reversed to find F'_{21}. Note that F'_{21} is not the resultant of T and $-T'$.

Now in part (c) of the figure the three forces on link 1 are found because they will be concurrent and because they form a closed vector triangle. Similarly the three forces on link 2 are found.

In part (d) of Fig. 7–8 the four forces on link 3 are shown. For equilibrium the horizontal clamping force R' must balance the horizontal component H of F'_{23}. The vertical reaction F'_{43} will be equal and opposite to the sum of W_3 and the vertical component V of F'_{23}, and its line of action is shown. The dimension a is given by

$$a = \frac{V}{V + W_3} \cdot \overline{CG_3}$$

c) Summation of the two systems. If it is desired to find the forces through the joints, or the clamping force, when a grip F is applied as in Fig. 7–7 but taking the weights of the members also into account, then the results shown in Figs. 7–7 and 7–8 are added, for the two systems of forces are independent and additive.

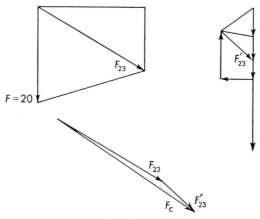

FIG. 7–9.

Thus, for an example, if the grip F is 20 lb, the force acting upon the pin joint C is the vector sum of the force F_{23} due to this F, and the force F'_{23} due to the weights of the members. The force diagram which is similar to that in Fig. 7-7e, except for $F = 20$ lb and for the configuration of the clamp of Fig. 7-8a, is shown in Fig. 7-9 alongside of and to the same scale as the weight-force diagram of Fig. 7-8e. The sum of the two appropriate vectors appears below and gives the total force F_c acting upon C; it measures approximately 35.6 lb.

7-8. Journal Friction and the Friction Circle. Within machines the significance of friction depends mostly on the type of lubrication. In slow-moving and static linkages the lubrication is usually poor, and the coefficient of friction is approximately determinable from data based on dry-friction coefficients to be found in handbooks. In higher-speed machines the friction depends on the lubricant—its viscosity and film thickness—and is usually a very small quantity.

In the former case, friction will arise in all contacts. Between sliding surfaces the frictional force is the product of the coefficient of friction (regarded as a constant) and the normal force, and is in the direction opposing possible or actual relative velocity. Besides a few examples of its occurrence included here, it is of importance in many mechanisms, notably the power screw and the action of gear teeth and in power transmissions by belt drive and clutch action. But for these the reader is referred to many texts in elementary mechanics and in the design of machine elements. Friction between rolling surfaces will not be developed here either.

But sliding friction as it applies to journals and pin-connected links is directly of interest. In Fig. 7-10 a shaft is turning slowly clockwise with indifferent lubrication within a fixed journal. Presuming the load is vertically downward, contact initially or statically would be directly below the center, but due to rotation the shaft "climbs up" the inside surface of the journal until limiting friction allows slippage. In the

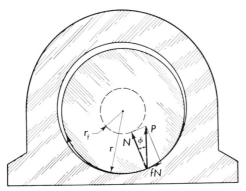

Fig. 7-10.

figure the difference in diameters of the two bodies is greatly exaggerated for the sake of clearness.

Now there will be some normal force N of reaction between the two surfaces, and due to N a tangential frictional force fN where f is the coefficient of friction. Their sum will be vertical P which will be equal and opposite to the load. The friction angle ϕ ($=$ arc tan f) is independent of the size of P, and therefore the line of action of P will always be tangent to the small circle of radius r_f. This circle is then called the *friction circle*.

The radius r_f is $r \sin \phi$ where r is the shaft radius, but it is always taken as $r \tan \phi = fr$ because f is not a precise quantity anyway.

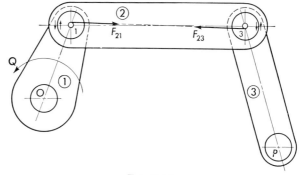

FIG. 7–11.

An application of the friction circle to a linkage is shown in Fig. 7–11. Two cranks 1 and 3 are joined by a connecting link 2. The mechanism is moving slowly due to a torque Q applied to crank 1, which is transmitted to crank 3. Connecting link 2 is a two-force member; the pins are taken to be integral with the cranks. Relative motion imposes the frictional forces shown by the small arrows, and these determine the side of the friction circles to which the reaction is tangent. But it is easier to note that the effect will always be to hinder motion, and thus the moment of reaction F_{21} on the driver 1 must be increased, while the force F_{23} driving the follower 3 will have a diminished moment.

7–9. Variation of Forces with Motion. In most mechanisms during the cycle of their motion, the members suffer accelerations that vary continually, depending on their relative disposition. For instance, in the example of the sliding ladder of Art. 7–6, the solution found is correct only for the instant considered in which the ladder's inclination was 60° from the horizontal. A moment later, a different pull would be needed. And in the example of the elliptical chuck, the variation of forces was considered.

Thus for the full analysis of a machine, a large number of successive calculations of the type illustrated are generally needed. The results are often presented in the form of some graph. We give first a very simple example.

Example. A trapdoor initially horizontal is released and falls under the influence of gravity. Find the successive variations of the reaction at its hinges until it reaches the vertical. Neglect friction.

It is assumed that the trapdoor is a homogeneous thin flat plate, hinged along one edge. The starting acceleration of such a door was investigated earlier (page 23). Initially then there is an angular acceleration, and the reaction at the hinge is vertical as shown by vector Oa in Fig. 7–12.

After dropping any angle θ, the inertia forces consist of a radial centrifugal force $(W/g)r\omega^2$, where $r = OG$, acting at the center of gravity G, and of a tangential force $(W/g)r\alpha$ acting at the center of percussion E. The distance $GE = k_G{}^2/r$ (refer to page 21), which in a flat plate equals $r/3$.

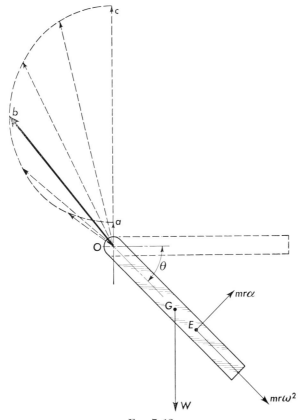

Fig. 7–12.

At the position illustrated the support reaction is the vector Ob.

When the door reaches the vertical, the centrifugal is the only inertia force, so that the support reaction reaches its maximum value of $W + (W/g)r\omega_{max}^2$.

The variation of this reaction force is thus shown by the curve abc, which is a *polar force diagram*, being plotted from the pole O.

The force may be found theoretically as follows, friction being neglected:

By energy change, the angular velocity at θ is given by

$$\tfrac{1}{2}I_0\omega^2 = Wr \sin \theta$$
$$I_0 = (4/3)(W/g)r^2$$

Therefore $(W/g)r\omega^2 = (3/2)W \sin \theta$

By differentiation, or by taking moments about O,

$$(W/g)r\alpha = (3/4)W \cos \theta$$

By moments about G the component R_T of reaction R perpendicular to the door through O is

$$R_T = (1/3)(W/g)r\alpha = (W/4) \cos \theta$$

And the component in direction GO is

$$R_N = (W/g)r\omega^2 + W \sin \theta = (5/2)W \sin \theta$$

Thus the magnitude of the force of bearing reaction is

$$R = \sqrt{R_N^2 + R_T^2} = (5/2)W\sqrt{1 - 0.99 \cos^2 \theta} \qquad (7\text{-}1)$$

and the direction it makes with the horizontal is

$$\theta + \tan^{-1}(R_T/R_N) = \theta + \tan^{-1}(0.1 \cot \theta)$$

At $\theta = 90°$ R is ten times what it was at $\theta = 0°$

7–10. The Assumption of Rigid Bodies. At this point we want to draw attention to the approximations entailed in assuming that the various members in a machine are rigid.

All members actually are elastic to a greater or less degree. It is impossible to transmit forces without incurring stress, whence follows strain. Now if in a linkage the members are not of the shape and size assumed, error is introduced in the computation of the velocities and accelerations and hence of the forces.

It is therefore plain that any assumption of rigid bodies is tantamount to the assumption that strains will cause a negligible distortion of the geometry of the mechanism. This is the assumption throughout this chapter.

The analysis in Chapter 4 on the whirling and critical speeds of shafting showed cases in which flexibility was included and was found to be of great significance.

On the other hand, in the problem to be taken up next, the compressive forces on the connecting rod of an engine are not (in the usual design) sufficiently large to cause a significant shortening of the rod or change in the position of the piston relative to a crank position. Therefore the assumption of rigidity is justified.

Further investigation of stress and strain due to motion will however be undertaken in Chapter 9.

7-11. Shaking Forces. A man cannot pull himself up by his bootstraps, yet a Mexican jumping bean can careen all over the place. In a machine, if a number of parts are in motion within the frame, the frame is going to be shaken. This is the basis of the problem of vibration isolation.

On the other hand, the forces other than inertia forces—those forces between members that are transmitting the work—are not transmitted to the mounting in a self-contained machine. For instance, a drilling machine produces a torque on the part being drilled, and takes the counter-torque on the tool holder, but if the part is held by the same frame as holds the motor, this torque acts through the frame but is not transmitted to the floor. The machine is self-contained.

As a consequence, the *shaking force* upon a machine considered as a unit comes to mean the vector sum effect of all inertia forces within the unit.

It has already been pointed out that the inertia forces form an independent system of forces within a machine. A very important mechanism is the slider-crank in a simple engine. We take up then the determination of the inertia effects alone in this mechanism, and consider one cylinder of a size common in automobiles.

Example. A single-cylinder engine with the dimensions given below runs at 2500 rpm. Find the shaking force on the frame, treating the whole as a unit, and then show that this is identical with the sum of the forces due to inertia at the contact surfaces of the moving parts with the frame, for the particular position shown in Fig. 7-13, where the crank angle is 45° after inner dead center.

Wt of piston, wrist pin, and rings assembly = W_p = 1 lb 9 oz.
  Center of gravity G_p $\frac{1}{4}$ in. from wrist pin toward head.
Wt of connecting-rod assembly, with bearing inserts, bolts, etc. =
  W_R = 3 lb 1 oz.
  Length between centers = L = 11.0 in.
  Center of gravity G_R 8.3 in. from small-end centerline.
  Radius of gyration about center of gravity k_G = $\sqrt{16.36}$ in.
Crankshaft center of gravity is at journal bearing center (i.e., it is balanced).
  Crank radius = R = 2.5 in.

As with the previous inertia problem, accelerations must be found first. Those required are the accelerations of the centers of gravity of the piston and of the connecting rod, and the angular acceleration of the rod. In Fig. 7–13 Rittershaus' construction* yields the quadrilateral

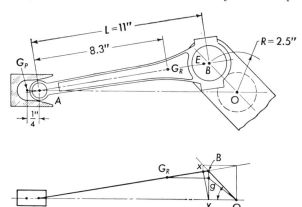

Fig. 7–13.

$OBxy$, which is similar to the acceleration vector diagram. The scale is established by the fact that $\overline{BO}$ represents the acceleration of pin B.

$$\text{Acceleration of } B = R\omega^2 = \frac{2.5}{12}\left(\frac{2500\pi}{30}\right)^2 = 14{,}260 \text{ ft/sec}^2$$

Then it follows that

$\overline{yO}$ = acceleration of A and $G_p = \left(\dfrac{yO}{BO} \cdot 14{,}260\right) = 10{,}150 \text{ ft/sec}^2$

$\overline{gO}$ = acceleration of G_R = 12,660 ft/sec²

$\overline{xy}$ = tangential component of acceleration of B relative to A, so that

$\overline{xy}/\overline{BA}$ = angular acceleration of connecting rod, $\alpha_R = 9950/\frac{11}{12} =$ 10,860 rad/sec² (clockwise)

The inertia forces that are acting on the linkage at the instant under consideration will be the product of the mass and the respective acceleration. Thus

$$f_p = m_p a_{Gp} = 1.562 \times 10{,}150/32.2 = 493 \text{ lb}$$
$$f_R = m_R a_{GR} = 3.063 \times 12{,}660/32.2 = 1210 \text{ lb}$$

where m_p and m_R are the masses of the piston and rod respectively. There is no inertia force on the crank, for its center of gravity has no acceleration.

* Klein's construction, or the regular acceleration vector analysis, could be used equally well.

The only inertia couple acts upon the connecting rod, for neither crank nor piston have angular acceleration. The moment of inertia of the connecting rod about G_R is found from the radius of gyration k_G in the data:

$$I_G = M_R k_G^2 = 0.130 \text{ lb in. sec}^2$$

so

$$q_R = I_G \alpha_R = 1410 \text{ lb in.}$$

Now in Fig. 7–14 these two inertia forces are placed upon a scale drawing together with the inertia couple q_R of the rod. The directions are those of the accelerations in reverse. It is obvious, by considering these as real forces, that there is need of an inertia torque $-Q_i$ (clockwise) to hold the linkage in equilibrium.

The total inertia effect on this mechanism in this position is therefore wholly represented by these two forces and two couples. We proceed to combine these to a single resultant—which is the total inertia effect, the total shaking force.

As shown in the figure at (b) the torque q_R is best first combined with force f_R. The result is a force, still of magnitude f_R and parallel to f_R, but transposed a perpendicular distance h from G_R, given by

$$f_R h = q_R$$

or

$$h = 1.17 \text{ in.}$$

Now this new f_R and f_p are combined to give F_i, for which the line of action passes through point d. Then since Q_i is a couple, and cannot contribute to any force, F_i alone must be the total shaking force on the engine that we desired to find, although (because of Q_i) it is not yet shown along its true resultant line of action.

For the case of the engine with the dimensions of this example, we measure from the scale drawing

$$F_i = 1625 \text{ lb}$$

Now the second part of this example is to show what is not always plain: that as a result of these two forces and couples (which resolve into F_i and Q_i) certain forces act upon the *frame* of the engine, and that the sum of these actual forces getting through to the frame is still the same F_i and Q_i.

Consider the connecting rod and the piston together as a "free body" (Fig. 7–14c): the forces f_p and f_R with couple q_R are the same as F_i which is taken from the figure at (b). Now the reactions of the neighbors to this free body are only a force f_{CR} by the crank on the rod through pin B, and a side-wall reaction $-S$ by the cylinder wall on the piston. If friction is a negligible quantity (which in a well-lubricated engine it usually is) this side-wall force will be normal to the path of the piston; furthermore

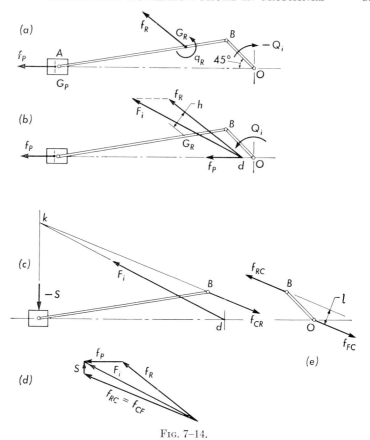

FIG. 7–14.

if the forces on the piston alone as a "free body" are considered, it is plain that the line of action of S passes through the center of pin A. Thus the force F_i, with line of action kd, is balanced by $-S$ and f_{CR}, whose lines of action must meet in point k.

Transferring these to the force polygon at (d), the magnitudes of S and of f_{RC}, the force by the rod on the crank, are found.

Now the "free body" representation of the crank at (e) shows f_{RC} and f_{FC} as the only forces, balanced by torque Q_i. Thus $Q_i = f_{RC} \cdot l$, and f_{CF}, the force on the frame by the crank, is equal to f_{RC}. And so it is proved that the resultant of the two forces on the frame—the forces f_{CF} and S—is equal to F_i. It remains to be shown that the line of action of this resultant is the same as that of F_i (Fig. 7–14b) when combined with Q_i. And this is easy, for F_i has now been shown to be the sum of S and f_{RC} (Fig. 7–14c), while Q_i is the product $f_{RC} \cdot l$. To add Q_i to F_i we therefore shift f_{RC} through the perpendicular distance l (Fig. 7–14e), and combine this with S.

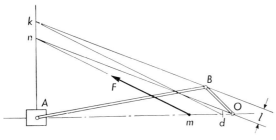

FIG. 7–15.

The resultant appears in Fig. 7–15 as force F (line mn) equal in magnitude to F_i (parallel line dk); it is the sum of F_i and Q_i, or the sum of S (line An) and f_{CF} (line On).

7–12. Minimal Shaking of a Single Engine. The shaking of an engine in its supports is obviously not desirable, but the only way that is open for reducing it is by the addition of some extra counterweight to the crankshaft.

Now if in Fig. 7–14 an extra counterweight is arranged so that the centrifugal force due from it is exactly equal and opposite to the resultant shaking force F_i, then the force (for this particular configuration of the mechanism) will vanish, and there will remain only the couple Q_i. However, unfortunately this is not likely to be the best counterweight for the whole revolution.

The analysis of forces for the whole cycle must first be made in the manner suggested in the last article, and then, with the shaking forces F_i plotted in a polar diagram,* as in Fig. 7–16, the best compromise can be made.

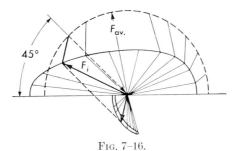

FIG. 7–16.

Figure 7–16 is plotted only for 180° of crank rotation, because the lower half is symmetrical with the upper. The force F_i, already found for the 45° position and consisting of the sum of f_R and f_P, is shown. Now the average radius of this figure is found; it is shown by the dotted-line circle.

* Refer to Art. 7–9, page 298, and Fig. 7–12.

Usually, if a counterweight sufficient to produce a force F_{av} is placed on the crankshaft opposite the crankpin, the shaking forces are regarded as having been reduced to their minimum practicable amount. The remaining force also is shown on the polar diagram as the smaller irregular curve. The point on this curve corresponding to the 45° crank position becomes apparent by subtracting F_{av} at exactly 45° from $F_{i(45°)}$ vectorially.

This whole question of the reduction to a minimum of the total shaking effect of inertia is generally referred to as engine balancing. It is taken up at much greater length in the following chapter, where it is shown that in certain designs of multiple-cylinder engines it is possible to eliminate all but the rocking motion from the couple.

7–13. Dynamically Equivalent Systems. The connecting rod in the simple engine mechanism is an example of what is called a "floating link": that is, it is a member in which there is no fixed point; all points upon it have differing motions.

It was noticed in the determination of the inertia forces acting upon this link that it was necessary to find both the inertia force f_R acting at its center of gravity and the inertia couple q_R. But then it was convenient to combine these to find a single force f_R (Fig. 7–14b) displaced by an amount h from the center of gravity G_R.

In the analysis of most linkages it is not sufficient to compute the forces for one position of the linkage, but the process must be repeated for many succeeding configurations throughout the cycle as mentioned before. For example, a full analysis of an engine requires the analysis to be made for every (say) 10° increment of crank angle; and for every different configuration, the dimension h will vary.

To avoid this item of calculation, the use of a "dynamically equivalent" member is advocated. The advantage is slight, but it involves finding the linear acceleration of two points rather than the linear acceleration of one point and the angular acceleration.

A member is defined as dynamically equivalent to an actual member of a machine, and can hypothetically be regarded as replacing that actual member (for the purposes of dynamic analysis), if it will exhibit exactly the same response to given forces, and the same reactions to given accelerations, as the original. The reactions of the original that we are considering are the force f_R and the couple q_R, which have both position and sense. Now two distinct masses will produce two forces which will have a resultant and a moment. Therefore any rigid body moving in a plane may be replaced hypothetically by a stiff weightless frame carrying two masses upon it; these masses are specific and calculable. (Note the qualification "rigid" body; flexible bodies cannot be so replaced analytically, for they have an infinite number of degrees of freedom.)

Figure 7–17 shows any floating link, having distributed mass, of total value M. It has an acceleration a_G of its center of gravity G and an angular acceleration α, and thus inertia reactions $f = Ma_G$ and $q = I_G\alpha$. At (b) in the figure is a rigid frame of exactly the same shape, but weightless, except for the fact that it is carrying two masses m_1 and m_2 distant

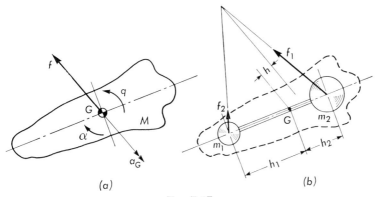

Fig. 7–17.

h_1, h_2 from the point where G would be if it were superimposed on the original. Now the latter will be equivalent to the former dynamically, if the vector sum of the two inertia forces f_1 and f_2 is f, both in direction and magnitude, and if the moment of f_1 and f_2 about G is q.

This will be accomplished if

1. The center of gravity of m_1 and m_2 is G,
2. The sum of m_1 and m_2 is still M,
3. The moment of inertia of m_1 and m_2 about G is I_G.

These expressed mathematically are

$$m_1 h_1 = m_2 h_2 \tag{7–2}$$

$$m_1 + m_2 = M \tag{7–3}$$

$$m_1 h_1^2 + m_2 h_2^2 = I_G = M k_G^2 \tag{7–4}$$

The third may be transformed as follows

$$(m_1 h_1) h_1 + (m_2 h_2) h_2 = M k_G^2$$

using eq. 7–2:

$$(m_2 h_2) h_1 + (m_1 h_1) h_2 = M k_G^2$$
$$(m_1 + m_2) h_1 h_2 = M k_G^2$$

using eq. 7–3:

$$h_1 h_2 = k_G^2 \tag{7–4a}$$

Equivalence therefore demands the satisfaction of the three conditions of eqs. 7–2, 7–3 and 7–4a. Three equations for four unknowns allow one item to be chosen arbitrarily.

The reader may be interested to turn back to page 112 to examine Kater's reversible pendulum in the light of this equivalent system.

The two-mass equivalent system applies (as shown) to any plane motion. When *three-dimensional* motion of a rigid body is to be analyzed, enough equivalent masses must be incorporated to produce the correct components of force and of couple in all senses. It has been shown that a six-mass equivalent system is then most easily reckoned, although a four-mass equivalent may always be found (refer to Art. 6–13).

For the sake of comparison we now apply the equivalent system to the same engine mechanism treated in Art. 7–11.

Example. Solve for the shaking force F_i and the inertia torque Q_i of the engine in the position and with the data given on page 301.

First let us establish the dynamically equivalent connecting rod. This is the only member suffering angular acceleration and thus the only one for which an equivalent is desirable.

The equations, above, allow one item (position or size) of the two equivalent masses to be chosen arbitrarily. Since in the force analysis the acceleration of the wrist pin has to be found, suppose the mass m_1 is assumed to be located at this pin. Then, in Fig. 7–17, if m_1 is at A, the position of m_2 is given by eq. 7–4a, as at point E:

$$\overline{GE} = h_2 = k_G^2/\overline{AG}$$

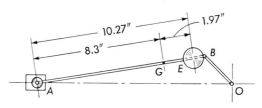

Fig. 7–18.

(This point E is then the center of percussion of the connecting rod with respect to point A, if the rod were removed from the mechanism and suspended as a free pendulum pivoted at A.) But then the weights of two equivalent masses will be (by eqs. 7–2 and 7–3)

$$W_1 = m_1 g = \left(\frac{\overline{GE}}{\overline{AE}}\right)W \qquad (7\text{–}5)$$

$$W_2 = m_2 g = \left(\frac{\overline{AG}}{\overline{AE}}\right)W \qquad (7\text{–}6)$$

Since

$GE = 16.36/8.3 = 1.97$ in.
$AE = 8.3 + 1.97 = 10.27$ in.
$W_1 = (1.97/10.27)3.063 = 0.589$ lb
$W_2 = 3.063 - 0.589 = 2.474$ lb

These appear in Fig. 7–18. Now Fig. 7–19a shows the adaptation of Fig. 7–13 made in order to find the acceleration of point E instead of point G. In the 45° position given for this problem, a_E is proportional to the length of line eO and is therefore of magnitude 13,800 ft/sec². The acceleration of the wrist pin is still $a_A = 10{,}150$ ft/sec². Thus the two inertia forces acting on the connecting rod are

$$f_{R(E)} = \left(\frac{2.474}{32.2}\right)13{,}800 = 1060 \text{ lb (direction } -a_E)$$

$$f_{R(A)} = \left(\frac{0.589}{32.2}\right)10{,}150 = 186 \text{ lb (direction } -a_A)$$

No couple q is involved any longer, so that the angular acceleration of the rod is of no interest. Point E is a fixed point in the rod for all positions of the mechanism, and yet the vector sum of $f_{R(E)}$ and $f_p + f_{R(A)}$ will give the shaking force F_i passing through the same point d (Fig. 7–19b), as shown in Fig. 7–14b.

Now to proceed to find Q_i, the reaction f_{CR} must again be found exactly as it was shown in Fig. 7–14, and there is no need to repeat this explanation.

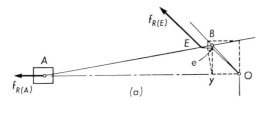

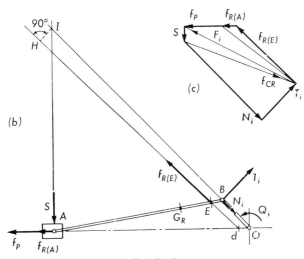

Fig 7–19.

But for interest let another method be used—one that involves taking moments once, instead of using only the principle of concurrence of forces. Let this unknown force f_{CR} which acts through the crankpin be resolved into its components T_i and N_i respectively tangent and normal to the path of pin B. Now considering all forces acting upon the rod and piston to be treated together as a free body, take moments about I (the instantaneous center of velocity of the connecting rod):

$$T_i \times \overline{IB} = (f_p + f_{R(A)}) \times \overline{IA} + f_{R(E)} \times \overline{IH}$$

$\overline{IH}$ must be measured; $\overline{IA}$ and $\overline{IB}$ can be measured or calculated; and for the given position, with the data as taken:

$$T_i = 633 \text{ lb}$$

Now the six forces acting on the free body are f_p, $f_{R(A)}$, $f_{R(E)}$, T_i, N_i, and S, and these must form a closed polygon of forces, as appears around the periphery of diagram (c) in Fig. 7–19. N_i and S are thus found. Note that f_{CR} appears as the sum of N_i and T_i, and that the shaking force F_i also is there. Hence the torque Q_i can be found from f_{CR}, or more easily, from the moment of the tangential force T_i.

$$Q_i = T_i \times R = 1583 \text{ lb in. counterclockwise}$$

7–14. Total Forces in the Engine Mechanism. The torque Q_i investigated above is the torque that must be overcome by some outside source to keep the engine running at the assumed speed. Except for the omission of friction, it would therefore be the instantaneous torque (varying with changing crank angle) to idle an air compressor or pump, if the valves were open or the cylinder head removed.

Now when an engine is working, or a pump is being driven, one more force is active in addition to those considered already: the force due to the cylinder pressure. But the inclusion of this force involves no change in the method of analysis as shown in Fig. 7–19 or Fig. 7–14; it is necessary only to have the additional data provided by a P–V (pressure-volume) indicator diagram of the engine in operation. And then the transmitted torque Q may be found, and also, if required, the forces caused at all joints.

As an example, a general case is solved graphically in Fig. 7–20. The general proportion of the forces follows those of the engine already studied. First the connecting rod is hypothetically replaced by an equivalent rod with masses at the wrist pin A and the center of percussion E; and the acceleration of these two points found. The center of gravity of the crank is at G_C, to provide a counterbalance for the connecting rod (see Art. 7–12). Thus inertia forces f_p, $f_{R(A)}$, $f_{R(E)}$, and f_C are found, the last acting at G_C.

Now the P–V diagram may be used to find the effective gas pressure

P that corresponds to the displacement of the piston from head-end dead center, as shown in the figure at (b); a pressure–crank-angle diagram will serve the same purpose. The effective pressure is the gauge pressure in the case of a single-acting engine, but for a double-acting

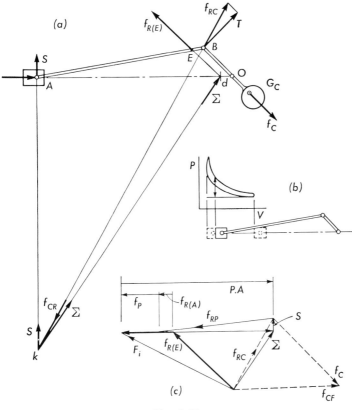

Fig. 7–20.

engine it is the difference in the pressures on the head and crank sides of the piston, of course. Multiplication by the piston area will give the gas force PA, and from this is subtracted f_p and $f_{R(A)}$ to give the "net effective force" on the piston.

The sum of all the known forces except f_C is then Σ which must act through point d, and in the direction shown in the force polygon at (c). Σ and S therefore act through point k, and hence f_{CR} must also. From their directions they can be found on the force polygon. f_{RC} (the opposite to f_{CR}) is then the driving force on the crank, and if it is resolved as shown, the tangential component T is called the *crank effort*, and its moment about O (which is also the moment of f_{RC} about O) is the *turning moment* Q of the engine.

The forces of reaction at the three pins are as follows: the force on the crankpin f_{RC} is already found; the force f_{CF} on the main journal at O by the crank is the sum of f_{RC} and f_C. The force on the wrist pin is found by considering the equilibrium of forces on the piston alone as a free body; in the vector polygon those known are f_p, PA, and S, and thus f_{RP} must close this minor polygon. In general, f_{RP} is not parallel to the connecting rod, as it would be in the case of a static force analysis.

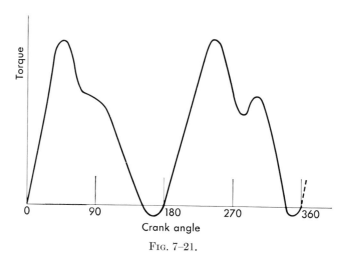

Fig. 7–21.

7–15. The Net Torque Diagram. The net torque Q, found as described above, may be plotted as a graph as is shown in Fig. 7–21. Sometimes this is called the "net crank effort" diagram: the effort of a crank is the

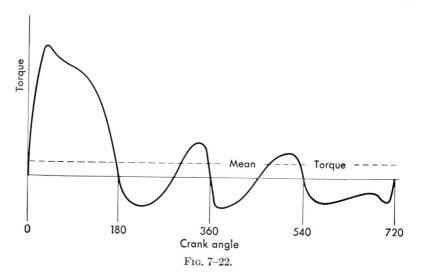

Fig. 7–22.

tangential force on the crankpin, or the net torque divided by the crank radius, so that this is proportional to the torque.

For a double-acting steam engine the diagram of Fig. 7–21 shows a typical form. For a four-stroke cycle engine, such as a diesel or gasoline engine, the curve will not repeat until 720° of crank angle have elapsed, and the typical torque diagram of one cylinder appears as in Fig. 7–22.

Note that in both curves the zeros of torque appear at each 180°, for then, of course, the connecting rod can transmit no moment to the crank. Further use of these torque diagrams will be made in Chapter 8.

7–16. Bearing Reaction Diagrams. To the designer of an engine, a knowledge of the magnitude and direction of the forces to be withstood by his bearings is of major importance in determining the size of the bearing surface, the location of oil holes, and the characteristics of the lubrication necessary. A polar force diagram such as was described in Art. 7–9 will give this information most satisfactorily.

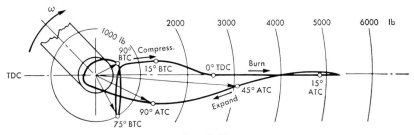

FIG. 7–23.

The same series of force analyses of an engine that was required to produce a torque diagram can be used to plot these bearing force diagrams. The resulting diagram (for the illustrative example that has been used through these engine problems) for the main crankshaft journal bearing is given in Fig. 7–23, for the one revolution that includes compression, ignition, and expansion. This diagram may be derived by successive application of the vector diagrams of Fig. 7–20. For the second revolution in a four-stroke cycle engine, a further double loop will appear almost identical with that in Fig. 7–16, as the gas pressures will have small effect. The magnitude of the forces shown is that of f_{CF}; half will be borne by the main bearing on each side of the crank.

Where one half of any bearing does not rotate as in the main bearing and in the wrist-pin bearing, the vector is shown successively in its absolute position. But, for example, in the crankpin bearing, when both surfaces rotate, the polar force diagram should be constructed to show the position of the force vector *relative* to the crankpin surface.

7–17. Engine Friction. Two items have been neglected in the force analysis presented for a typical engine. The first is the matter of the weights of the various members. An independent analysis of the forces, torque, and reactions due to weight might be made, and the results added vectorially to the previous results, but especially in a high-speed engine the magnitude of these static forces is so small compared to the inertia forces involved that their neglect is justified.

The other item is friction. The difference between the indicated horsepower and the brake (or net transmitted) horsepower in an engine is due principally to the necessary driving auxiliaries such as the fan, an electric generator, the oil and water pumps, and the valve mechanism. Within the engine mechanism (slider crank) itself, the frictional loss rarely amounts to as much as 5 per cent of the power developed. The coefficients of friction applicable to the three bearings, and to the sliding of piston skirt and rings on the cylinder walls, will be in the order of 0.001 to 0.002, depending as it does on the viscosity of the lubricant, the clearance ratio in the bearings, and the relative speeds. An exact value is never determinable; it varies in the same engine under various running conditions. Ordinary dry-friction theory does not apply, as metal-to-metal contact does not occur except sometimes between the top piston ring and cylinder at the top of the stroke, due to burning off the lubricant, and here the velocity is small.

Therefore since the force analysis depends on graphical work, friction will be insignificant.

An interesting reference to the relative amounts of friction power lost in each of various places, such as the several rings, the piston skirt, the wrist-pin bearing, etc., is to be found in papers quoted by Professor L. C. Lichty,* and is there shown by a graph.

7–18. Inertia with Coriolis' Acceleration. In the motion of certain mechanisms the Coriolis component of acceleration and radial acceleration may be present. Though this situation involves a rather more difficult problem in the kinematic analysis, it does not alter the procedure for determining forces, once the true accelerations have been found.

A simple example is to be found in a sort of slingshot. And another example is the drive mechanism of a shaper, which is given in the next article.

In Fig. 7–24 a crank, rotating about a vertical axis, carries a radial slot in which slides a ball of mass m. Friction will be ignored, and it is desired to find the torque necessary to keep the disk at a constant speed ω. The problem can be solved analytically.

Suppose the sliding mass is at radius r at time t. Then the centrifugal force causes a radial acceleration.

* L. C. Lichty, *Internal Combustion Engines* (6th ed.; New York: McGraw-Hill Book Co., Inc., 1951), pp. 401–6, 453.

$$r\omega^2 = \frac{d^2r}{dt^2}$$

With ω a constant, this is the hyperbolic-type differential equation

$$\ddot{r} - \omega^2 r = 0$$
$$r = A \sinh \omega t + B \cosh \omega t$$

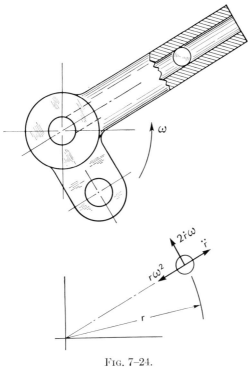

FIG. 7–24.

Presuming the ball was released from rest at radius r_0 at $t = 0$, we have $A = 0$ and $B = r_0$, or

$$r = r_0 \cosh \omega t$$

and the radial velocity, by differentiating, is

$$\dot{r} = r_0\omega \sinh \omega t$$

Now after time t, at radius r, the ball needs a tangential acceleration $2\dot{r}\omega$ (the Coriolis component) only, since there is no angular acceleration producing an $r\alpha$ term. This push from behind by the crank on the sliding body may be regarded as the push that is necessary to increase its tangential velocity to correspond to the increase in radius.

Thus a force $m(2\dot{r}\omega)$ is required at radius r; the driving torque on the crank required to maintain constant speed must be

$$T = 2mr\dot{r}\omega$$
$$= 2mr_0{}^2\omega^2 \sinh \omega t \cosh \omega t$$
$$= m(r_0\omega)^2 \sinh 2\omega t$$

7–19. Shaper Mechanism. The driving mechanism of a typical shaper machine is shown in Figs. 7–25 and 7–26. The bull gear 2 rotating about axis O and driven by the pinion 1 carries a crankpin B on which the rectangular block 3 is free to turn. This block slides in the radial slot cut in the oscillating arm 4. The arm moves therefore with a quick return motion. At the end of this arm 4 is a short connecting link 5,

(Courtesy Hendey Machine Co.)

Fig. 7–25.

which is attached to the sliding ram 6 of the machine. The ram carries the cutting tool, usually in a clapper box, and has a reciprocating motion within its horizontal ways.

It is to be assumed that the driving pinion rotates at constant speed. This is not a very accurate assumption, but until the inertia effects are found, no other seems to be available—a typical dilemma.

The force analysis will be made for a position in which the ram nears the end of its return stroke, as the acceleration will be high; this is the most interesting condition. Also, only inertia and friction forces will be acting. The journals and sliding surfaces are lubricated with grease, so that the coefficient of sliding friction will be assumed as 0.05 throughout.

The velocity and acceleration analyses are shown in Fig. 7–27. To start the velocity vector polygon, a cutting stroke frequency of 130 strokes per minute is assumed, so that the angular velocity of the bull gear is $\omega_1 = 13.6$ rad/sec. The velocity of the pin B in block 3 is calculated from the dimensions; with radius $OB = 5.0$ in., this is $V_B = 68.0$ in./sec. The component of this velocity perpendicular to the oscillating

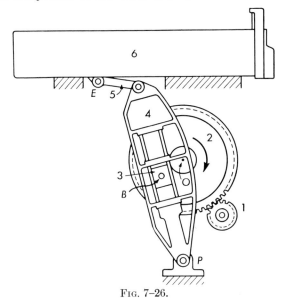

FIG. 7–26.

arm 4 is the tangential velocity of a point C in the member 4, which is instantaneously coincident with B, but maintains a fixed radius PC from the pivot P. From this the velocities of points D and E are found; and the angular velocity of the arm 4 may be found as $\omega_4 = V_C/\overline{PC} = 2.87$ rad/sec. The first acceleration to be ascertained is that of point B, normal to O; it is $V_B^2/\overline{OB} = 925$ in./sec². The acceleration of the same point regarded from pivot P has four components, including a Coriolis component; two are calculable: the normal $a^n{}_{B/P} = V_C^2/\overline{PC} = 110.5$ in./sec², and the Coriolis $a^c{}_{B/P} = 2V_{rad}\omega_4 = 324$ in./sec²; and the directions of the other two, tangential and radial, are known. Since the four still must yield the same acceleration for point B, they are determined graphically as in Fig. 7–27c. The normal and tangential components of B and of C (the point of fixed radius PC) are the same. Thence by proportion the accelerations of G_4 and D are found, and after calculating the normal component of E relative to D, the acceleration of E is obtained; it measures about 2430 in./sec².

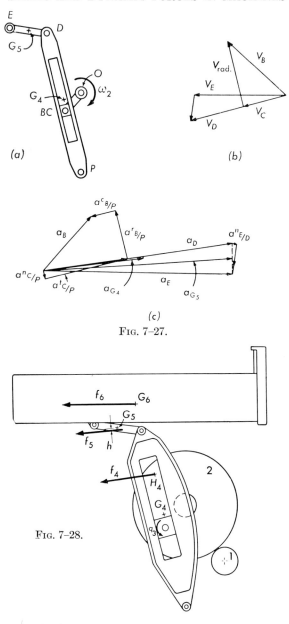

FIG. 7-27.

(a)

(b)

(c)

FIG. 7-28.

The attention is then turned toward the inertia forces and couples. Two methods are open: either we find the acceleration of the centers of gravity and the angular acceleration of each link, or we substitute a two-mass equivalent system for each link having angular acceleration (refer to Art. 7-13). Here, because we are investigating forces at one position only, the former will be simpler. Therefore the accelerations of the centers of gravity G_4 and G_5 and the angular accelerations α_4 and α_5 are determined.

Multiplication of the whole mass of each link by the acceleration of its G will then give its inertia force f; and multiplication of the moment of inertia about that G by the angular acceleration will give the inertia couple q for each. The values of these forces for the case being studied are as follows:

Member	Weight lb	a_G in./sec^2	f lb	Wk^2 lb in.^{2}	α rad/sec^2	q lb in.
3	10			30.5	81.3	6.4
4	95	1290	317.5			
5	8.75	2440	55.3	89.5	47.5	11.0
6	340	2430	2140			

There is no need to reckon q_4 because, since the arm 4 moves about a fixed pivot, it is known that the addition of q_4 to the force f_4 will move its line of action to pass through the center of percussion H_4. With member 5 the addition of f_5 and q_5 will shift the line of f_5 a distance $h = q_5/f_5 = 0.2$ in. The development at this stage is shown in Fig. 7–28.

Now the force analysis of a mechanism always begins at the end furthest from the drive—in this case the sliding ram 6. The first aim is to find f_{56} through the pin E. In Fig. 7–29a of the "free body" 6, the reaction N from the ways is unknown in magnitude and location. As a result of N, there is a frictional force μN ($\mu = 0.05$), with which N is combined to give N', of which only the angle of inclination is known. The two known forces—the weight W_6 and the inertia f_6—are used to start the polygon of forces, as at (b) in the figure. But without the direction of f_{56} or the location of N', one can go no further; a situation which is logically explained by the fact that the forces, such as f_5 and W_5, in the neighboring link are partial causes of f_{56}, and thereby affect N. So we leave this analysis unfinished and turn to the link 5. First the weight and inertia, W_5 and f_5, are easily combined to give F_5 (Fig. 7–29, parts (c) and (e)); this combination reduces it to a three-force member. Something may be found out about f_{56} by taking moments about the end D, but only if it can be assumed that f_{45} passes through a known point. The inclusion of friction circles makes the problem almost insuperable; and so, with the usual facility for self-persuasion, we note that the radius of these friction circles is negligibly small ($0.05 \times$ pin radius). The moment of F_5 about the center of D must then balance the moment of f_{65} alone, and measurement from the figure then yields the magnitude of the tangential component T of the force f_{65}, or

$$F_5 \cdot a = T \cdot \overline{DE}$$

The reaction to T (i.e., $-T$) is then added to the forces on the ram 6; this enables the vector polygon at (b) to be completed as in (d). It is seen that T is very small and that the magnitudes of N' and f_{56} are found by the intersection of the lines N' and $-R$. Then the forces in

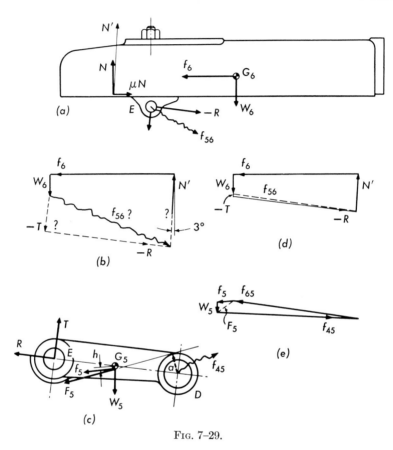

FIG. 7–29.

link 5 are all found by the polygon (e), since $f_{65} = -f_{56}$. This polygon (e) is here reproduced out of scale somewhat, because f_{65} and f_{45} lie very close together—too close for good visibility.

The forces on the next member, the oscillating arm 4, appear in Fig. 7–30a; f_{54}, f_4, and W_4 are known, and these may be combined. First the lines of action of f_4 and W_4 pass through point b, and the direction of their resultant F_4, found in the figure part (c), gives the line cb passing through point c. Now F_4 combined with f_{54} produces the line of action cd. The reactions with the sliding block 3 will be a normal side force S, friction μS which may be combined with S to give the line of action S', and also the inertia torque $-q_3$. Since S' is not yet known, q_3 cannot be combined with it, and it is best to combine q_3 with f_4; however, here q_3 is negligibly small, and the displacement of f_4 is not visible. So the intersection of line S' with the line cd, which has been already found, will give the direction Pd of the force f_{74} through the fixed pivot P; thus all forces are found in the figure at (c).

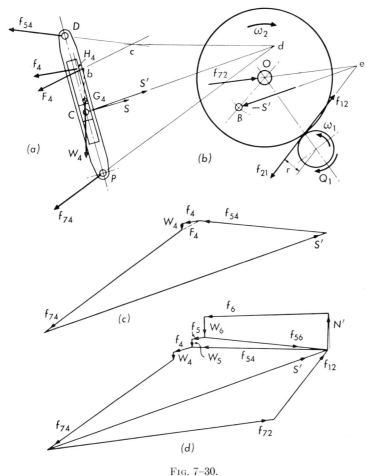

Fig. 7–30.

Passing on to the gear 2 and pinion 1, the directions of the forces appear in Fig. 7–30b if the weights of the two gears are ignored and if it is presumed that gear 2 is balanced with the block 3 upon it. The actual force on the pin B would then be the sum of S' and the centrifugal force f_3. The forces on gear 2 are concurrent at point e, which is found from the line of action of the contact force f_{12}, being along the line of contact of the teeth ($14\frac{1}{2}°$, unless we consider the friction angle to be added).

Finally, Fig. 7–30d shows that all these vector polygons of the various members may be superimposed without duplication to form one figure. The diagram here reproduced is slightly out of scale to improve clarity. Certain magnitudes of forces are of interest, for instance, S' is approximately 5090 lb. And it is to be noted that the machine is over-running the drive, so that to preserve constant speed of the pinion 1, it will have to be held back by a torque $Q_1 = f_{21} \cdot r = 1480 \times 2.2 = 3260$ lb in. $= 272$ lb ft.

7–20. Use of the Energy Principle—Virtual Work. The method of virtual work is in many cases an excellent and powerful method that is an alternative to the method of equilibrium of forces, which has so far been the approach in this chapter.

There are two types of forces acting in machines, those that transmit and do the work for which the machine is required, and those of inertia, including those that overcome inertia.

Suppose we consider the first type only: a certain force P is applied that does work, and overcomes certain resistances $F_A, F_B, F_C, \cdots$. Let P move an infinitesimal distance dx; then F_A will be moved backward ds_A, F_B moved backward ds_B, etc. These distances might be found by the geometry; they are related by the principle "work in = work out" or

$$P \, dx = F_A \, ds_A + F_B \, ds_B + \cdots \qquad (7\text{–}7)$$

Now divide all these by time dt and obtain

$$P v_P = F_A v_A + F_B v_B + \cdots \qquad (7\text{–}8)$$

It is apparent then that we can determine the magnitude of P if we obtain the velocities of the points of interest by kinematic analysis.

Example. In the slider crank a force F of 1000 lb is exerted upon the piston (Fig. 7–31). Find the tangential effort T for the configuration shown.

For the link AB the instantaneous center of rotation is I. If Ω is its angular velocity, then $v_A = IA \cdot \Omega$ and $v_B = IB \cdot \Omega$. By eq. 7–8

$$T = \frac{v_A}{v_B} \cdot F = \frac{IA}{IB} \cdot F$$

By measurement of the scale drawing, $T = \dfrac{5.50}{6.29} \cdot 1000 = 875$ lb.

When inertia forces are to be reckoned with, these must be treated in the same manner as further resistances absorbing some of the work input. Thus eq. 7–7 becomes

$$P \, dx = F_A \, ds_A + F_B \, ds_B + \cdots + (m_1 a_1) ds_1 + (m_2 a_2) ds_2 \qquad (7\text{–}9)$$

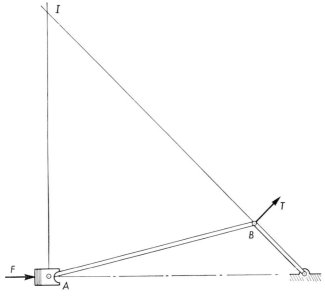

Fig. 7–31.

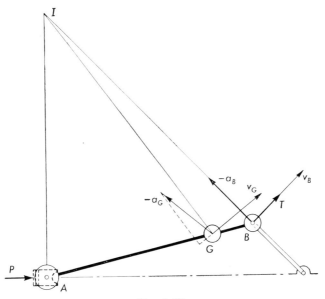

Fig. 7–32.

For angular effects, there may be terms such as $T\,d\theta$ for real work and $(I\alpha)d\theta$ for work against inertia; but the latter type may be eliminated by the use of the two or three masses of the equivalent system (Art. 7–13).

An important qualification of this equation must also be emphasized: work is only the product of force and the distance through which the point of application of the force has moved when the force and the displacement are taken in the same direction. Otherwise the component of the force must be used. Thus after dividing by the time elapsed, eq. 7–8 is more fully expressed as

$$Pv_P = F_A v_A \cos \theta_A + F_B v_B \cos \theta_B + \cdots + m_1 a_1 v_1 \cos \theta_1 + \cdots$$

$$(7\text{–}10)$$

Example. In the slider crank again, suppose the connecting rod were equivalent to three masses at A, G, and B, of weight 3, 2, and 2 lb respectively, and the piston weighs 2.5 lb. Then in Fig. 7–32, by the instant center I the velocities of A, G, and B are found, and by Rittershaus' construction (refer to Fig. 7–13) the accelerations of these same points

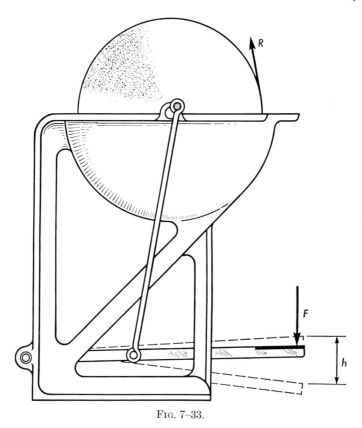

Fig. 7–33.

are also found. Taking the crank radius to be $1\frac{1}{2}$ in., its speed 2500 rpm, and the gas force on the piston $P = 2000$ lb, then the following table shows the information gleaned from scaling the figure:

Force on Linkage	Mass	Accel. ft/sec²	Component Force, lb, in Direction of Velocity	Velocity, ft/sec	Rate of Work Input
$P = 2000$			2000	28.6	57,240
	$m_A = \dfrac{3 + 2.5}{32.2}$	6010	-1027	28.6	$-29,400$
	$m_G = \dfrac{2}{32.2}$	7710	-114	30.5	$-3,470$
	$m_B = \dfrac{2}{32.2}$	8550	0	32.7	0
$-T$			$-T$	32.7	$-32.7\,T$

So transmitted tangential effort $T = (572.4 - 294 - 34.7)100/32.7$
$$= 745 \text{ lb}$$

A different type of application of the energy principle follows:

Example. A treadle grindwheel is turned by a constant vertical force F applied by the foot, and rotation is opposed by the friction force R at radius r (Fig. 7–33). On the upward stroke F is removed. Find the value of F to maintain a constant mean speed.

Measure the vertical distance h between the high and low positions of the point of application of force F. The work input per complete cycle is Fh. Work output is due to one rotation against friction R, or $2\pi rR$. Thus

$$F = 2\pi(r/h)R \text{ lb}$$

To have to solve this by inertia forces, considering the fluctuation of speed, would be a fearful task.

BIBLIOGRAPHY

ANGUS, R. W. *Theory of Machines.* 2d ed. New York: McGraw-Hill Book Co., Inc., 1917, Chaps. 9, 10, 11, and 15.

BEVAN, T. *Theory of Machines.* 2d ed. London: Longmans, Green & Co., 1943, Chap. 12.

COUSINS, F. M. *Analytical Design of High Speed Internal Combustion Engines.* New York: Pitman Publishing Corp., 1941, Chaps. 5–8.

DENT, J. A., and HARPER, A. C. *Kinematics and Kinetics of Machinery.* New York: John Wiley & Sons, Inc., 1921, Chap. 5 and Appendix.

EKSERGIAN, R. "Dynamical Analysis of Machines," *Journal of the Franklin Institute,* Vols. 209–211 (1930–31).

HAM, C. W., and CRANE, E. J. *Mechanics of Machinery.* 3d ed. New York: McGraw-Hill Book Co., Inc., 1948, Chaps. 12, 13, and 15.

HECK, R. C. H. *Mechanics of Machinery.* (Vol. II, "Kinematics and Dynamics.") New York: McGraw-Hill Book Co., Inc., 1925, Chaps. 3, 4, and 5.

TOFT, L., and KERSEY, A. T. J. *Theory of Machines.* 6th ed. London: Sir Isaac Pitman & Sons, 1949, Chap. 2 and elsewhere.

PROBLEMS

7–1. In the epicyclic gear pump shown in Fig. 7–P–1, the internal ring gear of $2\frac{1}{2}$ in. pitch diameter is fixed to the frame. The pinion, of half this diameter,

turns freely on a crankpin P. The crankshaft, with which this crankpin is integral, rotates about axis O.

Mounted upon the pinion with axis at
the pitch radius of the pinion, somewhat
forward of the teeth, is a pin Q to which
is attached the piston rod. The nature
of the mechanism provides linear motion for Q on the vertical diameter of the
ring gear.

When the crank OP makes an angle
of 30° with the vertical the suction of the
piston being moved up causes a downward load of 50 lb. Find the static equilibrium forces at all contacts for this position, together with the torque on the
crankshaft; neglect all friction.

The gear teeth are of 20° pressure
angle, and contact is on the pitch line.

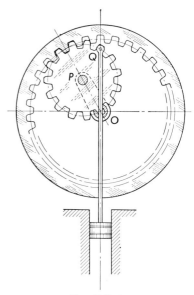

FIG. 7–P–1.

7–2. The bell crank in Fig. 7–1 is in
static equilibrium under the action of its
own weight of 10 lb, of force $F_{21} = 25$ lb, and of a resisting force F_{31}. The crank
moves about the horizontal axis O; it has the arm OA at 30° counterclockwise
from the vertical, and the link 2 is horizontal. The angle AOB is a right angle
and link 3 is parallel to AO. The arm
AO is 12 in. long between centers and
of 3 in. uniform width, while arm BO
is 18 in. long and the same width, from
which dimensions the center of gravity
should be determined. Find the static
load on the bearing O.

7–3. Prove that the torque that
must be exerted by the drive shaft to
overcome the cutting tool force F_T in
the elliptical lathe chuck described in
Art. 7–6 and Fig. 7–6 is given by

$$T = F_T \sqrt{a^2 \sin^2 \theta + b^2 \cos^2 \theta}$$

7–4. The outline diagram shows
the linkwork for a moulding press.
The crank PA rotates about the fixed
center P at 100 rpm, and by means
of the rod AB, gives the lever QB an
oscillatory motion about the fixed center Q. The ram C is operated by the
connecting rod BC.

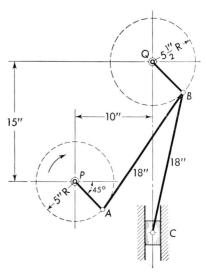

FIG. 7–P–4.

Determine the force exerted by the ram in the position shown when the torque
on the crank PA is 5000 lb in., the efficiency being 80 per cent.   (U.L.)

7–5. The figure shows the elevation and plan views of a three-dimensional mechanism used for a tipping gear, the control being through the vertical shaft at A.

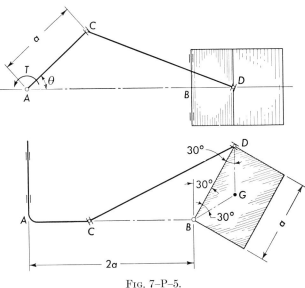

Fig. 7–P–5.

Using the principle of virtual work (or otherwise), show that for the position in which $\theta = \sin^{-1}\frac{3}{5}$, the static torque T which will just prevent tipping is

$$\frac{1}{8\sqrt{3}}[5mga + 10Mga - 8q(2\sqrt{3} + 5)]$$

M is the mass of the parts tipping about the horizontal axis through B, which is centered at G, as shown; m is the mass of the uniform rod CD; and a frictional couple q acts at each axis of rotation.   (C.U.)

7–6. The connecting rod for an internal combustion engine has a length between centers of 9 in. and a total weight of $3\frac{1}{4}$ lb. Its center of gravity is $6\frac{1}{2}$ in. from the small end, and its radius of gyration about the center of gravity (for oscillations in the plane of motion) is $3\frac{3}{4}$ in. The weight of the piston and wrist pin is $4\frac{1}{2}$ lb, the stroke is $5\frac{1}{2}$ in., and the cylinder bore is 4 in.

Determine the magnitude and direction of the resultant force acting on the crankpin when the crank is at 30° after the inner dead center, and when the speed is 1600 rpm, if the effective gas pressure on the piston is 250 lb per sq in.
(U.L.)

7–7. The piston and wrist pin (gudgeon pin) of a 9-in. diam × 17-in. stroke gas engine weigh 109 lb. The connecting rod, which is 46 in. long between centers, weighs 122 lb. Its center of gravity is 27.3 in. from the center of the wrist-pin bearing; its radius of gyration about an axis through the center of gravity and parallel to the wrist pin is 17.5 in. Find the transverse thrust of the piston on the cylinder walls due to the inertia of piston, wrist pin, and connecting rod, when the crank is 140° past the inner dead center. The crankshaft rotates at 270 rpm. Do not include gravitational forces.   (U.L.)

7–8. The length of the connecting rod of a gas engine is 3 ft 4 in. measured between centers, and its weight is 78 lb. The center of gravity is $9\frac{1}{2}$ in. from the crankpin center and the crank radius is 8 in. The frequency of oscillation of the rod when freely suspended from the center of the small end is 31 complete vibrations per minute.

Find (a) the magnitude of the two equivalent masses if one is considered to be at the small end, and (b) the magnitude, direction, and position of the resultant inertia force if the crank angle is 45° on the expansion stroke. The speed of the engine is 275 rpm.   (U.L.)

7–9. a) For a connecting rod, the wrist-pin center is represented by A, the crankpin center by B, and the center of gravity by G. $AG = a$, $GB = b$, $a + b = l$, and G lies in the line AB. If the rod has a mass M and a moment of inertia Mk^2 about an axis through its center of gravity and parallel to its bearing axes, show that the rod is dynamically equivalent to concentrated masses at A, B, and G given by

$$M_a = \frac{Mk^2}{a^2 + ab}, \quad M_b = \frac{Mk^2}{b^2 + ab}, \quad M_g = M\frac{ab - k^2}{ab}$$

b) The connecting rod is used in an engine with a crank of length r rotating with uniform angular velocity ω, the line of stroke of A passing through the crank center C. Establish the following method of finding the reaction at A due to the inertia of the mass M_g at G, friction being neglected:

Z is a point in AC such that the acceleration of $A = \omega^2 \cdot ZC$. Join BZ. Draw GQ parallel to AC to meet BZ in Q. Draw QM parallel to AB and CM perpendicular to AC to meet in M. Then the reaction at A is $M_g\omega^2 b \cdot CM/l$.

Hence show that for a crank angle $BCA = \theta$, if ZC is taken to be of length $r(\cos\theta + \dfrac{r}{l}\cos 2\theta)$, the reaction at A due to M_g is given to the same degree of approximation by

$$M_g\omega^2\frac{br}{l^2}(a\sin\theta + \frac{r}{2}\sin 2\theta) \quad \text{(C.U.)}$$

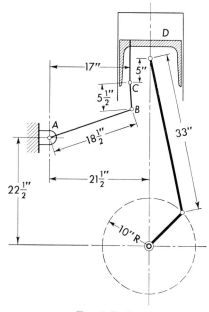

Fig. 7–P–10.

7–10. The figure shows the layout of a "walking pipe" mechanism for feeding water through the pipes AB and BC to the water-cooled piston D of an internal combustion engine. A, B, and C are hinged pipe joints, A being fixed, and C attached to the piston. The section AB is composed of a brass tube,

$\frac{3}{4}$ in. bore and $\frac{1}{8}$ in. thick; weight of brass and water 0.292 and 0.036 lb per cu in. respectively.

Determine the maximum bending moment due to inertia forces acting on the tube AB when the crank rotates at 225 rpm and is in the position 25° after the inner dead center.   (U.L.)

7-11. The four-bar linkage of the figure is part of a stitching machine mechanism actuating an awl. The disk, on which is mounted crankpin A, rotates at 3600 rpm counterclockwise about axis O. Find the torque about the axis of this disk, and all bearing loads in magnitude and direction, when (a) the configuration is momentarily as shown, in which the reaction force at B is 250 lb in the direction shown, both φ and angle $C\,D\,O$ being 60°; (b) when the angle θ is 0°, in which $F_B = 500$ lb and $\varphi = 80°$.

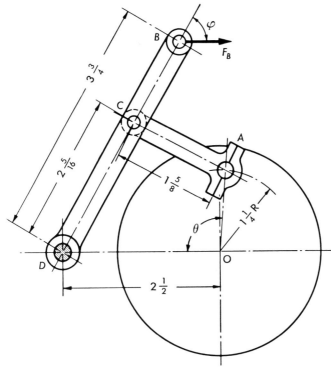

FIG. 7-P-11.

The center of gravity of link AC is 0.34 in. from A on the centerline; its radius of gyration about this point is 0.55 in., and it weighs 0.34 lb. The link BCD is a uniform steel bar $\frac{5}{8}$ in. wide in the plane of motion, and $\frac{5}{16}$ in. thick, with rounded ends, all holes being filled by the pin joints.

7-12. Find the normal force on the cam due to inertia of the mechanism, for the position shown in the figure, as the cam turns clockwise at 200 rpm about its axis O. Contact between cam and cam roll is on the toe which has a $\frac{1}{2}$ in. radius. The cam roll and bell crank together weigh 0.75 lb, with center of gravity

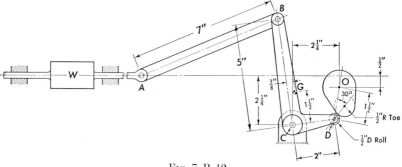

FIG. 7–P–12.

at G, about which the radius of gyration is 2.15 in. The weight of the body W that is moved is 10 lb, and the mass of the connecting rod AB is negligible. Friction and gravitational forces may also be neglected.

7–13. The figure shows a crank AB, with $1\frac{1}{4}$-in. throw, which moves a uniform steel rod BD, $4\frac{1}{2}$ in. long and of $\frac{1}{4}$ in. diam, through a sleeve C which oscillates about a fixed pivot. $AC = 2\frac{1}{2}$ in.

Neglecting the moment of inertia of C, and assuming the contact between the rod and sleeve is always at the centerline of C, find the normal force between the rod and sleeve due to the inertia of the rod, and draw a curve showing the variation of this force

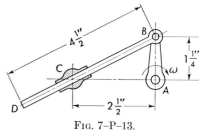

FIG. 7–P–13.

along the surface of the rod for 180° of turn of the crank. Friction may be neglected, and the rod is assumed rigid. The crank turns at 600 rpm.

7–14. The quick-return mechanism of a slotting machine is shown in the figure. The toothed sector gear meshes with a rack on the vertical ram carrying

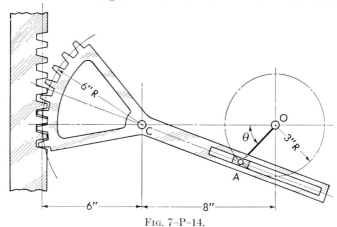

FIG. 7–P–14.

the tool box; the rack pressure angle is 20° and for the purposes of this problem it may be assumed that the contact of the teeth is on the pitch circle. The driving crank OA rotates uniformly at 90 rpm.

The ram weighs 65 lb; the sector and slotted arm is balanced so that its mass center is in the pivot axis C, and its WR^2 about this axis is 324 lb in.². The crank OA is also fully balanced, with the sliding block at A included.

Find the inertia forces at all contact points (except that between the crankpin and block at A) when the angle θ is 30°, friction and gravitational forces to be neglected.

7–15. For the quick-return slotting machine mechanism described and illustrated in Problem 7–14, plot a diagram of the variation of normal force between the sliding block and the slotted lever, for every 30° of angle θ between 0° and 180°. It may be taken that the reaction force between rack and gear segment is always tangent to the pitch circle, the effect of pressure angle being neglected. Friction and gravitational forces can likewise be ignored.

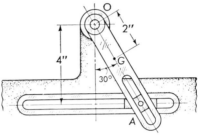

7–16. Rapson's Slide, as illustrated, is used as a reversing switch. The sliding blocks at A, each of which weighs 2 oz, are to be given an acceleration of 1000 ft/sec² from rest. Find the torque to be applied to the axle at O.

Fig. 7–P–16.

The slotted bar weighs $8\frac{1}{2}$ oz with center at G, and its radius of gyration about the axle O is 2.9 in.

7–17. The crankshaft of a cross-head type vertical engine rotates at 300 rpm. For each cylinder the stroke is 10 in.; each reciprocating mass weighs 150 lb. The connecting rod weighs 250 lb and is 18 in. long; its center of gravity is 12 in. from the cross-head wrist-pin axis, and its radius of gyration about this same axis is 7.5 in.

When the crank is 30° from the top dead-center position, and is moving downward, find the total kinetic energy of the connecting rod and reciprocating parts.

7–18. The figure shows a mechanism, called the Nurnberg Shears, for maintaining equal rotation of two parallel shafts in the same direction. The fixed

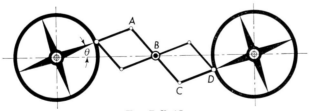

Fig. 7–P–18.

pivot B of the pantograph is midway between the axes of the wheels. The two links ABC are twice the length of the four links like CD.

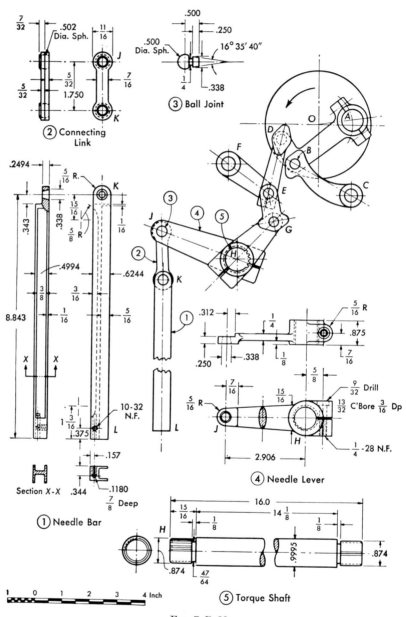

FIG. 7–P–20.

Regarding each link CD as a uniform bar of mass m and length l, and each link AC of mass $2m$, find the kinetic energy of the mechanism in terms of angle θ, when both wheels having radius r and moment of inertia I rotate at speed ω counterclockwise.

7–19. The epicyclic pump shown in Fig. 7–P–1 is to pump water on the downstroke against a constant force of 10 oz; on the upstroke there is negligible resistance. The piston and rod weigh 1 oz, the pinion weighs 2 oz, and its moment of inertia is like that of a disk of $1\frac{1}{4}$ in. diam. The crankshaft OP is balanced to include the weight of the pinion.

Use the method of energy to obtain the maximum torque required of the crankshaft, the horsepower needed, and the percentage fluctuation in energy per cycle, when the crank rotates at 600 rpm.

7–20. The operating mechanism for the needle of a certain shoe-stitching machine is shown in the center of Fig. 7–P–20. The figure also shows five details. The crank OA of the mechanism, turning about O at 3600 rpm, operates the multiple oscillating linkage shown, in which the centerlines O, C, F, and H are fixed. The driven crank GH is attached by spline to one end of a long shaft (detail 5), at the other end of which is the needle lever HJ, the connecting link, and needle bar. All members are of machine steel.

Estimate the maximum torque due to inertia to be expected in the torque shaft, assuming the rigidity of all members. Calculate the resultant angle of twist of the shaft and express an opinion of the effect on the exact needle placement. (Note that the mechanism can easily be transferred from the printed page to a drawing sheet by pricking the centers through.)

Chapter 8

FLYWHEELS AND ENGINE BALANCING

8–1. Troubles of the Reciprocating Engine. A reciprocating engine is generally used as a prime mover and is required to produce a uniform torque. This it obviously cannot accomplish if the torque is produced by a small number of pistons acted upon intermittently by internal combustion or steam pressure. To smooth out the speed and torque produced, a flywheel is required.

But then also (as taken up in the previous chapter) due to the inertia of all the moving parts, resultant shaking forces agitate the machine, and these must be minimized, at least.

These two problems are separate and are to be discussed here in sequel, the flywheel first.

Design of Flywheel

8–2. The Torque Diagram. Figure 8–1 shows a graph of the net torque T of a single-cylinder engine plotted against the crank angle θ. A procedure for obtaining this curve was explained in Chapter 7, and if this is referred to it will be seen that the inertia of the moving parts was considered, as well as the variation in pressure upon the piston.

The figure is typical of a slow-speed, two-stroke diesel engine, and similar to one for a single-acting steam engine. In the ideal engine exact repetition occurs with each 360° cycle. Torque diagrams of a double-acting steam-engine and of a four-stroke internal combustion engine have appeared as Figs. 7–21 and 7–22.

Now work is the product of torque and the angle through which the point of application of the torque has turned (if the angle is measured in radians), and therefore the area under such a torque diagram represents the work produced by the engine per cycle. In Fig. 8–1 a line is drawn showing the mean torque ($= T_m$). The most usual condition of drive is that in which the engine is required to produce a constant horsepower output at constant speed, which requires that $T_m = T_{\text{out}}$.

Then from the instant A until B (Fig. 8–1) the engine torque is in excess of the resisting torque T_m, and the engine must be accelerating. From B until A_2 it is decelerating. The shaded area between the curves T and T_m represents an excess amount of work done, resulting in the greater kinetic energy of the engine at instant B than at A. The area between the curves from B until A_2 is equal to the shaded area.

Let this area, converted into work units, be called ΔE, for it is excess energy. Then

$$\Delta E = \tfrac{1}{2}I\omega_2{}^2 - \tfrac{1}{2}I\omega_1{}^2 \qquad (8\text{–}1)$$

where ω_2 is the maximum rotational speed occurring at the instant B and ω_1 is the minimum at A (or A_2). It is plain that the larger the moment of inertia I, the smaller the variation of ω.

This then determines the size of flywheel needed. It is usual to decide on the percentage variation of speed to be tolerated, and then to solve for I. This I in eq. 8–1 is, of course, really the total equivalent rotational moment of inertia of the engine and flywheel; yet it is used generally to signify the I of the flywheel alone, which makes the flywheel slightly larger than necessary and the actual fluctuation slightly less than that value chosen.

Equation 8–1 may be improved slightly for this particular computation:

$$\begin{aligned} \Delta E &= \tfrac{1}{2}I(\omega_2{}^2 - \omega_1{}^2) \\ &= I(\omega_2 - \omega_1)[(\omega_1 + \omega_2)/2] \\ &= I(\omega_2 - \omega_1)\omega_0 \end{aligned}$$

But if

$$\omega_2 - \omega_1 = f\omega_0$$

where ω_0 is the mean speed, and f the total permissible fluctuation—the "coefficient of fluctuation"—then for the flywheel

$$I = \frac{\Delta E}{f\omega_0{}^2} \qquad (8\text{–}2)$$

The values* chosen for the coefficient f have been fairly standardized in design. For most machinery a total variation of 2 or 3 per cent is usual. For other applications:

Driven Machine	Coefficient of Fluctuation
Punch presses, rolling mills	0.20–0.05
Machine tools and machinery in general	0.04–0.02
Automobiles,† and gear transmission	0.02
Electric generators (see Art. 8–6)	0.006 or less

We include punch presses and rolling mills here as the same analysis

---

* References to the publications of Rankine, Hartnell, Theiss and many others are to be found in early editions of Kent's *Mechanical Engineers' Pocket-Book*. J. L. Astrom (*Trans. A.S.M.E.*, 1901) notes that over the years the coefficient demanded has been steadily decreasing.

† For an automobile a larger flywheel than this coefficient indicates is usually necessary since at low speeds, without undue racing, it must be able to carry the sudden load from engagement of the clutch on starting from rest and prevent stalling of the engine.

holds, although the situation is exactly reversed in the torque diagram. The drive may be produced by an electric motor, so that the steady torque line is the input; and it is the torque resistance which varies radically. Nevertheless, the areas between the two still represent the excess or deficiency of work input.

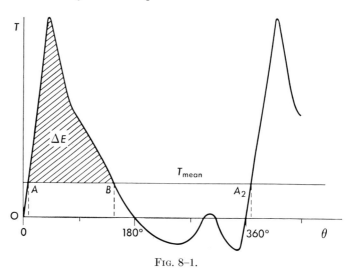

FIG. 8–1.

Example. A single-acting steam engine torque diagram, as in Fig. 8–1, is plotted to scales of 1 in. = 40 lb in. ordinate and 1 in. = 30° abscissa. The area ΔE measures 14.2 sq in. by planimeter. Find a flywheel to hold the speed within ±2 per cent of the governed speed of 300 rpm.

$$1 \text{ sq in. of diagram} = 40 \times \left(30 \times \frac{2\pi}{360}\right) = 20.94 \text{ in.-lb (work)}$$

$$\Delta E = 14.2 \times 20.94 \text{ in.-lb} = 297.4 \text{ in.-lb}$$

$$\omega_0 = \frac{2\pi}{60}(300) = 31.4 \text{ rad/sec}$$

$$f = 0.04 \text{ (being the difference between 102 and 98 per cent)}$$

Then by eq. 8–2

$$I = \frac{297.4}{0.04(31.4)^2} = 7.55 \text{ lb in. sec}^2$$

or converting to engineer's units and into feet:

$$WR^2 \text{ of flywheel} = (7.55 \times 32.2 \div 12) = 20.2 \text{ lb ft}^2$$

For the actual design of a flywheel with this WR^2 the reader is referred to design handbooks. For large spoked wheels such as are used with slow-speed engines, not more than 10 per cent of the moment of inertia is contributed by hub and spokes, the rest being in the rim. For least weight the rim radius should be greatest; the limiting factor is usually the hoop stress from centrifugal forces. A common rule is to have a velocity of 6000 ft per min for the mean radius of the rim (cast iron solid rim), although in some special designs twice this velocity is allowable. In the wheel of the example above it is not necessary to have so large a radius because of the small total inertia.

8–3. Multi-Cylinder Torque Diagrams. The torque diagram from a multi-cylinder engine can be found by adding the torques from each cylinder, but these, of course, must be spaced by the correct phase. Thus with steam engines and two-stroke internal combustion engines the phase angle for the diagram is the same as the angle between the crank throws of each cylinder in firing order. With four-stroke cycle internal combustion engines, the phase is the angle turned by the crank between successive firings of cylinders.

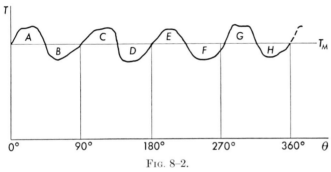

FIG. 8–2.

A two-cycle four-cylinder diesel engine will therefore have a torque diagram of four loops in each 360°, appearing like Fig. 8–2. Of course in a symmetrical engine, each loop above and each below the mean torque line should be sensibly the same, so that the flywheel size can be decided on the basis of the energy variation in 90°. But cases arise in which the diagram does not properly repeat until the 360° have elapsed. The question then arises as to what is the area ΔE.

Suppose, for instance, that the planimeter gives the following readings for the areas A, B, C, $\cdots$ of Fig. 8–2:

A	B	C	D	E	F	G	H
+0.35	−0.32	+0.36	−0.38	+0.32	−0.38	+0.37	−0.32

The flywheel's purpose is to limit the maximum variation of speed within the cycle; thus we need to find the maximum variation in the energy level. Between A and B there is a high-speed point, between B and C a low-speed one, between C and D a second high-speed point. The question before us: is the CD high more or less than the AB high? From the following summation

Loop	A	B	C	D	E	F	G	H
	+0.35	−0.32	+0.36	−0.38	+0.32	−0.38	+0.37	−0.32

Energy
Level

| 0.00 | +0.35 | +0.03 | +0.39 | +0.01 | +0.33 | −0.05 | +0.32 | +0.00 |

we see the highest high-speed point occurs between C and D, and the lowest low-speed between F and G. The maximum variation in energy level is therefore $0.39 + 0.05 = 0.44$ sq in. of the graph, larger than appears in any loop. This (when converted to energy units) is the figure to use for ΔE in eq. 8–2.

It is quite plain that the torque will be smoothest and the flywheel smallest in an engine with a given number of cylinders, if the intervals between firing or the working stroke are equal. Yet this is not always possible.

A two-cylinder steam engine, as used for example in a railroad locomotive, would best have a crankshaft with cranks opposite; yet this would mean that whenever the locomotive happened to stop at or near the dead-center position, it could not start again without a push. This would be awkward. The cranks are therefore always at 90°, and the torque diagram very uneven.

Consider vee-engines—with two banks of cylinders set at an angle. The V-8 has a four-cylinder type of crankshaft, so that the angle of the vee should be 90°. The V-12 engine 4-stroke cycle can fire regularly every sixth of a revolution if the banks are at 60° or 120°. Yet sometimes other design considerations are so strong that these angles are not adhered to, with the resultant need of a larger flywheel.

8–4. A Shorter Path to the Torque Diagram of an Engine. Once the torque diagram is produced, the calculations for a flywheel are simple. But, as described in Chapter 7, the careful procedure required to obtain it, by repeating the inertia force and working fluid force analysis for 5°, 10°, or 15° intervals through the whole cycle, is very time-consuming. It is, however, the only exact way, as exact as the draughting procedure allows, unless a purely analytic way is used.

However, if the flywheel is not designed, probably the engine is not constructed either. The masses and moments of inertia are therefore approximate, and the pressure diagram theoretical. In such circumstances why try to be so exact? There is one simplification, causing a very small error,* that can be made with regard to the connecting rod, which can cut down tremendously the labor of producing the torque diagram.

The graphical force diagram described in Arts. 7–11 through 7–14 depends upon either the actual or the dynamically equivalent connecting rod being used to obtain the inertia forces of that rod. For a series of

* Refer to Art. 8–26.

calculations, such as are necessary to obtain the torque diagram, the dynamically equivalent rod is better. Now suppose in Fig. 7–18 (7–20) that the mass M_E (being part of the connecting rod) were located at the crankpin instead of at E. The system of forces, both real and inertia, would appear as in Fig. 8–3 instead. In shifting this mass from E to B, we change also its size, in order to keep the position of the center of mass at G as before; it will be observed that this has violated the theory by obeying eqs. 7–2 and 7–3 but not 7–4, and this means we have introduced a couple to the connecting rod. But see the advantage.

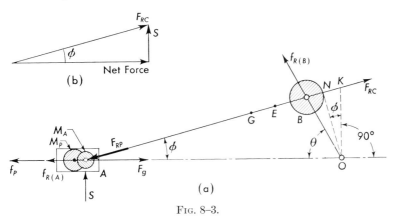

FIG. 8–3.

With the connecting rod represented by masses M_A and M_B (Fig. 8–3) the latter can produce merely a centrifugal force on the crank. All torque is therefore due to the gas pressure and inertia forces f_p and $f_{R(A)}$, which all act together on the wrist pin. The "net force" acting on the wrist pin is the gas force (pressure by piston area) less $(f_p + f_{R(A)})$. Since all forces now regarded as acting on the connecting rod are applied at the ends only, the rod is purely in compression (or tension) throughout the cycle, and Fig. 8–3b shows all forces that cause torque.

Now if the angle ϕ is known, the net turning moment on the crank is

$$Q = F_{RC} \times \overline{ON}$$
$$= (\text{Net Force}) \sec \phi \times \overline{ON}$$

which is

$$Q = (\text{Net Force}) \times \overline{OK} \qquad (8\text{–}3)$$

Therefore all that is required under this approximation is to find a quick method of ascertaining the net force, and either calculating the distance OK or measuring it on a careful drawing.

a) The net force is the gas force less the inertia force of the total "reciprocating" mass. Figure 8–4 shows a typical estimated P–V diagram assumed for a diesel engine; the theoretical diagram is used with the sharp corners rounded. The pressure scale is converted to force by

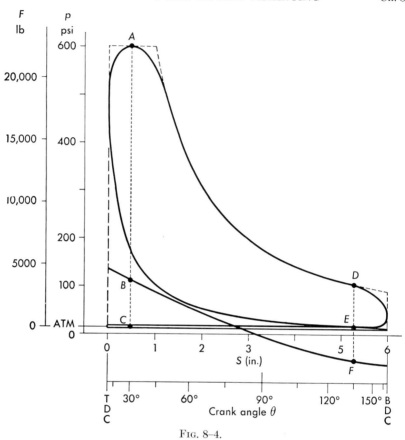

Fig. 8-4.

multiplication by the piston area. Zero force corresponds to atmospheric. Then the abscissa scale is converted to read crank angle; this involves use of the formula for piston displacement in terms of crank angle, but this relation may be found tabulated in certain texts and handbooks.* The formula is derived on page 72, eq. 2–30.

For the purposes of this illustration, the calculations are based on a 7 × 6 diesel engine, with connecting-rod–crank length ratio 5:1; the weight of the piston assembly is 12.5 lb, and the proportion (found from the location of the center of gravity) of the weight of the connecting rod to be called the reciprocating part is 4.5 lb.

* *Kent's Mechanical Engineers' Handbook*, Design and Production Volume (12th ed.; New York: John Wiley & Sons, Inc., 1950), pp. 7–04 and 7–36 to 7–38; G. D. Angle, *Engine Dynamics and Crankshaft Design* (Detroit: Airplane Engine Encyclopedia Co., 1925), pp. 12, 16, 18; F. M. Cousins, *Analytical Design of High Speed Internal Combustion Engines* (New York: Pitman Publishing Corp., 1941); H. A. Huebotter, *Mechanics of the Gasoline Engine* (New York: McGraw-Hill Book Co., Inc., 1923), p. 15; G. Lanza, *Dynamics of Machinery* (New York: John Wiley & Sons, Inc., 1911).

Now the reciprocating inertia force must be calculated for the cycle: the reciprocating mass (12.5 plus 4.5 ÷ 386 lb in. sec²) is multiplied by the acceleration of the piston. The latter is

$$a_A = r\omega^2 (\cos \theta + r/l \cos 2\theta)$$

approximately, and this may also be found from tables in the same handbook or texts. The speed ω to be taken will generally be the lowest speed at full throttle, in this case 600 rpm; but to show larger more significant values in the figure, a rather higher speed has been taken. This force is then plotted on the same diagram (Fig. 8–4), and appears as the line BF.

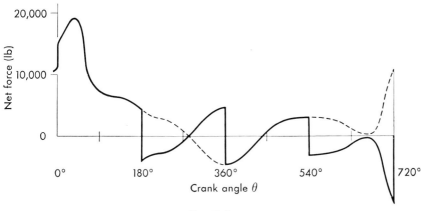

F. 8–5.

Next, a "net force diagram" is sometimes drawn, as in Fig. 8–5. The principal difference between this and Fig. 8–4 is that the angle θ is used as abscissa, so that the curve does not double back on itself as it does when displacement is the abscissa. Note certain magnitudes of the net force:

at $\theta = 30°$ after firing, gas force $= AC$, inertia resists with BC, so net force $= AB$;

at $\theta = 135°$, gas force $= DE$, inertia helping with EF, so net force $= DF$;

at $\theta = 225°$, gas force $= 0$, inertia resists with FE so net force $= -EF$.

The positive sense of the net force is defined as that which is in the same direction as the piston velocity.

b) The distance OK (Fig. 8–3) is needed last for plotting the turning moment of eq. 8–3. This may be measured or calculated: from the geometry (Fig. 8–3)

$$OK = R \sec \phi \sin (\theta + \phi) \qquad (8\text{–}4)$$

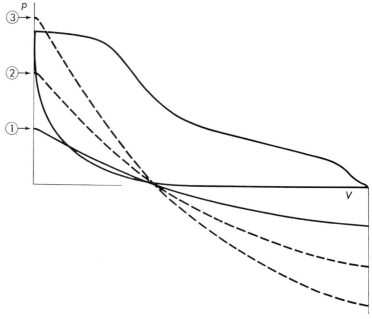

FIG. 8–6.

or

$$OK = (V_A/V_B) \cdot OB$$
$$= R(\sin \theta + \frac{R}{2L} \sin 2\theta) \qquad \text{approximately.}$$

These values also may be found tabulated in handbooks and the same texts.

An interesting sidelight on engine operation may be deduced from the combined fluid pressure and inertia curve of Fig. 8–6. It is particularly important in steam engines which use a constant maximum pressure with different throttle openings. For it is plain that the inertia curve, having a magnitude proportional to the square of the crank rotational speed, will change as speed increases from 1 to 2 to 3. At the highest speed therefore there are induced very severe alternations of stress in the engine due to the reversals of net force. Any speed at which the inertia force exceeds the maximum fluid force during the expansion stroke, such as the speed that causes curve 3, is sometimes called a critical speed of the engine.

8–5. The Shortest Cut to Determine Flywheel Size. There is an essential similarity between engines of a given type, and consequently it has been found possible to generalize on the results from calculations of many engines, and to establish typical values for the excess energy to be absorbed by the flywheel.

The excess energy is found to be roughly a certain proportion of the total energy produced by an engine per revolution; the proportion varies with the number of cylinders, the regularity of firing strokes, and the fuel used. The following table gives some values* of this proportion,

TABLE OF COEFFICIENTS K OF ENERGY FLUCTUATION

1. Steam Engines:†

Per Cent of Cut-Off	Single Cylinder	Twin-Cylinder Cranks at 90°	Three-Cylinder Cranks at 120°
0.20	0.33	0.082	0.037
0.40	0.31	0.078	0.034
0.60	0.29	0.072	0.032
0.80	0.28	0.070	0.031
1.00	0.27	0.068	0.030

2. Gasoline Internal Combustion Engines:

Firing Frequency Angles of Crank Turn	K	Engine Types			
		Cylinders	Cycle	Single or Double Acting	Crankshaft
720° regular...........	2.40	single	4 str.	single	–
360° regular...........	1.00	single	2 str.	single	–
		2-twin	4 str.	single	0°
		2-opposed	4 str.	single	180°
180°–540° alternate.....	1.60	single	4 str.	double	–
		2-twin	4 str.	single	180°
180° regular...........	0.20	single	2 str.	double	–
		2-twin or tandem	2 or 4	double	180°
		4 in line	4 str.	single	180°
240° regular...........	0.70	3 in line	4 str.	single	120°
90° regular...........	0.09	4 in line	2 str.	single	90°
		4-twin tandem	4 str.	double	90°
		8	4 str.	single	90°
120° regular...........	0.12	6 in line	4 str.	single	120°
60° regular...........	0.02	V-12	4 str.	single	120°
45° regular...........	0.01	V-16	4 str.	single	90°

3. Diesel Engines (Degler):
   Add 25 per cent to the above values for K for gasoline.

* T. Bevan, *Theory of Machines* (2d ed.; London: Longmans, Green & Co., 1948), p. 397; H. E. Degler, *Internal Combustion Engines* (New York: John Wiley & Sons, Inc., 1938), p. 300; A. Vallance and V. L. Doughtie, *Design of Machine Members* (3d ed.; New York: McGraw-Hill Book Co., Inc., 1951), p. 431.

† By permission from *Design of Machine Members*, by A. Vallance and V. L. Doughtie. Copyright, 1951, McGraw-Hill Book Company, Inc., New York.

which is called the coefficient of energy fluctuation K. From this we have

$$\Delta E = K \times \text{(Total Energy per Revolution)}$$
$$= K \times \frac{IHP \times 33,000}{N(\text{rpm})} \tag{8-5}$$

and this value for ΔE may then be used directly in eq. 8–2 to find approximately the inertia required for the flywheel.

8–6. Flywheels for Electric Generators and Close-Coupled Systems.
When an engine is arranged to drive an electric alternating generator, it is not the variation of speed within each cycle that is of prime concern, but rather the phase shift that will be produced in the generated voltage as compared with a regular sinusoidal wave; and this is of particular importance when two such generators are to be run in parallel. Thus the angular deviations of the flywheel resulting from the cyclic variations of speed must be determined, and this calculation will supplant the use of the coefficient of speed fluctuation in reckoning the necessary flywheel size.

The angular variation which is permissible will be specified by the electrical manufacturer; it is generally between $2\frac{1}{2}°$ and $3\frac{1}{2}°$ of electrical phase angle. Thus, since a complete electrical cycle transpires as the generator rotor turns past a pair of successive poles, a shift of three phase degrees on a 28-pole generator, for example, will mean that the flywheel must be large enough to be capable of maintaining a steady speed within $\pm\frac{3}{14}$ of a degree.

A graph of the angular deviation from the steady-speed position, called a flywheel displacement curve, may be derived from the turning-moment diagram by two processes of integration. Since the difference in ordinate between the actual and the mean (i.e., resisting) turning moment records the instantaneous unbalanced torque, which acts upon the moment of inertia of the flywheel and generator, the ordinate of the turning moment diagram may be changed to read angular acceleration, because $T = I\alpha$.

Three convenient methods of accomplishing this double integration without recourse to graphical integration methods are to be found in a paper by Doherty and Franklin.*

However there is an assumption in all these methods which must not be hidden: it has been assumed that the engine, with the several cranks of its crankshaft, and the flywheel may be regarded together as a single large rotating mass. Now when the engine is connected by a long or flexible shaft, or by a flexible coupling, to the machinery being driven this is a reasonable assumption.

* R. E. Doherty and R. F. Franklin, "Design of Flywheels for Reciprocating Machinery Connected to Synchronous Generators or Motors," *Trans. A.S.M.E.,* Vol. 42 (1920), p. 523.

But when the engine is close-coupled to the driven machine, as is generally the case in engine-generator sets, then the whole method presented here is inadequate. The location of the flywheel becomes as important as its size; for the shaft must be regarded as a system subject to torsional oscillations of the type discussed in Art. 3–20. The addition of a third mass, the flywheel, to the two masses, engine and generator, can control the location of the node. But further discussion of this will be deferred, to be included instead in the general discussion on the effects of flexibility in machine members, and will be found in Art. 9–11.

8–7. Sidewall Forces, Engine Rocking, and Offset Engine. Take a single-cylinder engine, and consider the crankshaft, connecting rod, and piston assembly as a "free body." The external forces acting upon this body are the force of the gas pressure, the sidewall force, the reaction at the main crankshaft bearings, and the torque resistance to the turning moment. Consider the moments of these forces about the crankshaft bearings, and it is plain that the moment of the sidewall force must be equal and opposite to the turning moment produced.

It is therefore possible to draw a graph showing the variations in this sidewall force on the piston as it travels, derived directly either from the turning moment diagram or from the force analysis.

One result of this thought is to point out the very much greater sidewall forces that occur on the explosion or driving stroke, with the result that one side of the cylinder will wear much more than the other. A method is available for modification of this situation: the centerline of the piston and wrist-pin motion can be set to pass to the driving side of the crank center (Fig. 8–7). Such an engine is called an offset (or désaxé) engine. Because of the lesser obliquity of the connecting rod on the driving stroke, the sidewall force is less, but this, of course, reflects as greater obliquity and greater sidewall force on the return stroke. This can equalize the wear admirably, and such designs have been used in recent automobile engine production (the Ford V-8 motor, to cite one case only).

Fig. 8–7.

The use of the method precludes reversibility of the engine, of course; it also adds some complications to manufacturing, which is the principal reason that it has not been adopted more often.

Another thought that arises from this discussion of the uneven torque delivery and the sidewall force is that the torque reaction is felt between the engine assembly and its mounting or foundations. With the uneven torque this causes rocking of the engine on its (usually flexible) mountings. The torque exciting this vibration is principally of the frequency of firing of the cylinders, as may be seen from the torque diagram, but it consists also of many higher harmonics. This is of great importance when the choice of mounting springs is to be made; resonance of rocking frequency must be avoided.

Reciprocating-Mass Balance of Engines

8–8. Object of Balancing. As well as rocking on its supports from the uneven torque delivery, a reciprocating engine is liable to bounce from the effect of the reciprocating masses within it. The simile has already been mentioned of the Mexican jumping bean. But, unlike the torque effect, this reciprocating effect can be wholly suppressed by proper design with sufficient number of pistons and arrangement of crankshaft.

The cause of this undesirable motion lies entirely in the masses and motion of the piston assemblies and connecting rods. It is not due to the variations in gas pressure, explosions, etc., for on every firing stroke the force upward on the cylinder head is equal to the force downward on the piston, so that the net force on the engine assembly is zero.

This problem of reciprocating balance is also distinct and separate from the problem of balancing the rotating masses. Of course, these (that is, the crankshaft and heavy ends of the connecting rods) must be properly balanced, as described in Chapter 4, and it is to be presumed that this has been done.

For the purpose of simplicity, only the slider-crank mechanism of the engine will be considered. Such reciprocating masses as the valves are ignored; their effect is generally regarded as insignificant, except in the case of the sleeve-valve engine.

8–9. Primary and Secondary Forces. The Single Engine. The balance of a single engine was investigated in Chapter 7, Arts. 11 and 12; it was not found possible to eliminate all shaking forces, although they could be reduced by the addition of a suitable counterweight to the crank.

While this result still holds, we will approach the problem from a different angle. First the approximate equivalent mass system discussed and used in Art. 8–4 is adopted for the connecting rod, in which it is regarded as two concentrated masses, one at the crankpin, the other at the wrist pin. The engine is considered then to consist of three moving masses, as in Fig. 8–8:

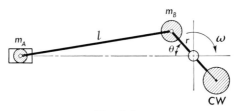

Fig. 8–8.

m_A, the reciprocating mass—consisting of the mass of the piston, rings, wrist pin, etc., with the piston rod and cross head (if any) plus the reciprocating part (usually about one-third) of the connecting rod.

m_B, the rotating mass—being the equivalent mass of the crank at the crankpin, plus the rotating part (about two-thirds) of the mass of the connecting rod.

C.W., the counterweight mass on the crank shaft, sufficient primarily to balance m_B.

The reciprocating force is the product of the mass m_A and its acceleration. The latter has already been found to be given closely by

$$a_A = r\omega^2 \ (\cos \theta + (r/l) \cos 2\theta) \tag{8–6}$$

where r = crank radius, l = connecting-rod length, ω = angular velocity of the crank in rad/sec, θ = the angle the crank has turned through from the extended dead center position (Fig. 8–8).

The two terms in this expression may be treated separately. Thus

$$\text{Reciprocating Force} = F_1 + F_2$$

$$F_1 = m_A r\omega^2 \cos \theta \tag{8–7}$$

$$F_2 = m_A r\omega^2 \ (r/l) \cos 2\theta \tag{8–8}$$

F_1 is called the "primary" force, and F_2 the "secondary" force, due to the reciprocating mass.

F_2 is secondary inasmuch as it is smaller, because of the fraction (r/l). It is also the second harmonic of the reciprocating force, tending to shake the engine with a frequency twice that of the crankshaft rotation. It is plain therefore that no additional counterweight attached to the crankshaft can modify this secondary force.

An additional counterweight on the crankshaft can improve the condition caused by the primary force, however. It cannot cure the trouble, of course, for no additional rotating force can cancel an alternating *linear* force. Suppose then that an additional counterweight (beyond any it may need for its rotational balance) is added to the crankshaft, at crank radius r but on the opposite side, and of weight equal to the weight of the reciprocating mass. Then, in Fig. 8–9, the extra radial force $m_A r\omega^2$ is separated into its components, and the horizontal component will always exactly balance the primary reciprocating force F_1 (although a small turning couple is introduced). But there still remains the other component of this centrifugal force, creating a vertical force on the engine of

$$F_V = m_A r\omega^2 \sin \theta$$

This is just as bad a condition as before; but it leads to a possible compromise. Let the additional counterweight be of mass $\frac{1}{2}m_A$, there will be a net horizontal force (to the left) of

$$F_H = \tfrac{1}{2}m_A\omega^2 \cos \theta$$

and a vertically downward force

$$F_V = \tfrac{1}{2}mr\omega^2 \sin \theta$$

These can be added to make a constant force represented by a vector revolving counter to the crank, and of magnitude $\frac{1}{2}mr\omega^2$. So this counterweight will reduce the shaking force by half, while changing it from a linear to a rotating force.

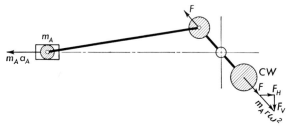

FIG. 8–9.

Nothing better can be done, unless the expense of a special device such as the Lanchester anti-vibrator (see below) is justified. We might investigate whether the counterweight $\frac{1}{2}m$ is the best possible. Suppose it is only km for $k < 1$. The two primary force components will then be

$$F_H = mr\omega^2 (1 - k) \cos \theta$$
$$F_V = mr\omega^2 (k) \sin \theta$$

The revolving vector will have magnitude

$$F = mr\omega^2\sqrt{(1 - k)^2 + (k)^2}$$

For a minimum, differentiate with respect to k and equate to zero.

$$\frac{d}{dk}[(1 - k)^2 + (k)^2] = 0$$
$$2(1 - k) - 2k = 0$$

Thus $m/2$ is the best possible.

Nothing is usually done about the secondary force.

8–10. Lanchester "Anti-vibrator." The device shown in Fig. 8–10 has many uses, for it produces a linear simple harmonic force. It was first developed by Lanchester* in England for use with an automobile engine.

Two equal gears are in mesh. Both carry counterweights of mass M at radius R. One gear is driven at speed ω and it drives the other. The

---

* F. W. Lanchester, "Engine Balancing," *Proc. Inst. Auto. Eng.* (London), 1914.

weights are set so that they are both at the bottom together. After turning through any angle θ, the horizontal components of the two centrifugal forces are seen to be collinear, equal, and opposite. Their effect is therefore nil.

But the two vertical components add. They are also always equally distant from the center. Thus the whole effect of rotation is to produce a force

$$F = 2MR\omega^2 \cos \theta$$

which will act through the pitch point of the gears, perpendicular to the line of centers.

Such a device can be applied to neutralize a primary reciprocating force in an engine. Furthermore, if it is rotated at twice the crankshaft speed, it may neutralize a secondary reciprocating force; for then the weights will turn through an angle 2θ and produce a linear force

$$F = 2MR(2\omega)^2 \cos 2\theta \tag{8-9}$$

8–11. Approximations. Two approximations are then to be accepted in this study.

The first concerns the two-mass approximation for the equivalent connecting rod, in which the larger mass is at the crankpin. The error in this is investigated later (Art. 8–26).

The other is due to the use of the shortened expression (eq. 8–6) for the acceleration of the reciprocating mass. The complete expression (Fourier series) not only shows all higher harmonics, but also shows a change even in the second term; the inertia reciprocating force* is properly

$$
\begin{aligned}
F = mr\omega^2 \Bigg[&\cos\theta + \left(k + \frac{1}{4}k^3 + \frac{15}{128}k^5 + \frac{35}{512}k^7 + \cdots\right)\cos 2\theta \\
&- \left(\frac{1}{4}k^3 + \frac{3}{16}k^5 + \frac{35}{256}k^7 + \cdots\right)\cos 4\theta \\
&+ \left(\frac{9}{128}k^5 + \frac{45}{512}k^7 + \cdots\right)\cos 6\theta \\
&- \left(\frac{5}{256}k^7 + \cdots\right)\cos 8\theta + \cdots \Bigg]
\end{aligned} \tag{8-10}
$$

where $k = r/l$. For certain common values of $\frac{1}{k}$ these coefficients are given in the table over leaf. Where the connecting rod is short, there is quite a significant variation from the approximate coefficient of eq. 8–6 in the second harmonic term.

---

* For derivation of this, see the texts on engine dynamics by F. M. Cousins, and by R. E. Root, or on the internal combustion engine by A. W. Judge, mentioned in Bibliography.

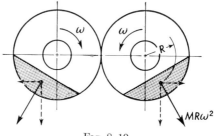

FIG. 8–10.

COEFFICIENTS OF HARMONICS OF INERTIA FORCES (eq. 8–10)

Coefficient	$\frac{1}{k} = 3$	$\frac{1}{k} = 4$	$\frac{1}{k} = 5$	$\frac{1}{k} = 6$
Primary...............	1.0	1.0	1.0	1.0
Secondary.............	0.34311	0.25402	0.20204	0.16784
Fourth Harmonic........	0.01009	0.00410	0.00206	0.00118
Sixth Harmonic.........	0.000330	0.000074	0.000024	0.000009
Eighth Harmonic........	0.0000089	0.0000012	0.00000025	0.00000007

8–12. Two-Cylinder In-Line Engine—180° Cranks. Although in this engine one piston goes up when the other goes down, balance still cannot be achieved. But the condition is better than in a single cylinder.

Let the engine be vertical and arranged as in Fig. 8–11. Suppose the reciprocating masses of each cylinder, the crank radii, and connecting rod lengths are the same. Then since the crank angle of the second is 180° in advance of the first, the vertical forces will be:

In cylinder No. 1

$$F_1 = mr\omega^2[\cos\theta + (r/l)\cos 2\theta]$$

In cylinder No. 2

$$F_2 = mr\omega^2[\cos(\theta + 180°) + (r/l)\cos 2(\theta + 180°)]$$

or

$$F_2 = mr\omega^2[-\cos\theta + (r/l)\cos 2\theta]$$

Both of these are upward when positive; the cosines take care of any change in sense. The total upward force is thus the arithmetic sum of F_1* and F_2. It appears that there is balance of primary forces, but there remains a secondary unbalanced force

$$\Sigma F = 2mr\omega^2(r/l)\cos 2\theta$$

This could be balanced by a Lanchester device.

But this is not all. The side view of the engine shows that there is a serious couple caused by the primary forces. If the distance along the

* Here, it should be noted, F_1 and F_2 refer to the total reciprocating inertia force in cylinder No. 1 and cylinder No. 2 respectively, and not to the primary and secondary components of those forces as used in eqs. 8–7 and 8–8.

crankshaft between the centerlines of the cylinders is a, this moment is

$$M = mr\omega^2 a \cos \theta$$

The secondary forces cause no couple, for they are parallel and in the same sense.

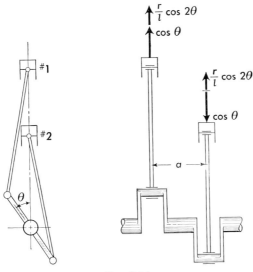

FIG. 8–11.

Our conclusion on this engine is therefore that it is unbalanced with respect to its primary couples and secondary forces.

The primary unbalanced couple can be partially eliminated by adding half counterweights at each end for the same reason as with the single cylinder. The result will be a revolving couple instead of a plane couple.

8–13. General Analysis of In-Line Engines. In a multi-cylinder engine in which all cylinders are in line and parallel and to one side of the crankshaft, we may make an algebraic sum of the inertia forces due to reciprocating masses, and also sum the moments of these forces by knowing the distance along the crankshaft from any arbitrary point to the line of action of the inertia forces.

Now if the sum of all these forces and the sum of all these moments are zero, the engine will be in complete balance with respect to reciprocating inertia.

Figure 8–12 shows such an engine. The masses m, crank radii r, and connecting-rod lengths l are presumed the same for each. Then if the crank angle of crank #1 happens to be θ_1, the crank angle of crank #2 will be θ_2, etc. The inertia forces from each piston will be

$$F_1 = mr\omega^2[\cos\theta_1 + (r/l)\cos 2\theta_1]$$
$$F_2 = mr\omega^2[\cos\theta_2 + (r/l)\cos 2\theta_2] \qquad (8\text{--}11)$$
$$F_3 = mr\omega^2[\cos\theta_3 + (r/l)\cos 2\theta_3]$$
$$\cdots\cdots\cdots\cdots\cdots\cdots\cdots\cdots\cdots$$

These are all positive upward; the cosines will take care of the fact that some might be downward. So they may be added directly: ΣF is the net total upward force. But with all the different variables θ_1, θ_2, θ_3, $\cdots$, the addition is difficult.

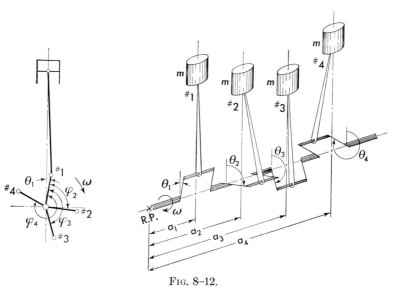

Fig. 8–12.

Note that if θ_1 is chosen, the shape of the crankshaft automatically fixes θ_2, etc. Let φ represent the fixed angle between any crank in advance of and relative to the first crank, or

$$\left.\begin{array}{l} \varphi_2 = \theta_2 - \theta_1 \\ \varphi_3 = \theta_3 - \theta_1 \\ \varphi_4 = \theta_4 - \theta_1 \\ \varphi_5 = \theta_5 - \theta_1 \\ \cdots\cdots\cdots \end{array}\right\} \qquad (8\text{--}12)$$

We may also add for the sake of symmetry

$$\varphi_1 = \theta_1 - \theta_1 = 0$$

Then the vertical force from the whole engine will be

$$\Sigma F = mr\omega^2\{\cos(\theta_1 + \varphi_1) + \cos(\theta_1 + \varphi_2) + \cos(\theta_1 + \varphi_3) + $$
$$\cos(\theta_1 + \varphi_4) + \cdots + \frac{r}{l}[\cos 2(\theta_1 + \varphi_1) + \cos 2(\theta_1 + \varphi_2) +$$
$$\cos 2(\theta_1 + \varphi_3) + \cdots]\}$$
$$\qquad (8\text{--}13)$$

Expanding the cosine terms:

$$\Sigma F = mr\omega^2\{(\cos\theta_1\cos\varphi_1 - \sin\theta_1\sin\varphi_1) + (\cos\theta_1\cos\varphi_2 - \sin\theta_1\sin\varphi_2)$$
$$+ \cdots$$
$$+ \frac{r}{l}\,[(\cos 2\theta_1\cos 2\varphi_1 - \sin 2\theta_1\sin 2\varphi_1) + (\cos 2\theta_1\cos 2\varphi_2 -$$
$$\sin 2\theta_1\sin 2\varphi_2) + \cdots]\}$$

We note a series of terms containing $\cos\theta_1$, $\sin\theta_1$, $\cos 2\theta_1$, $\sin 2\theta_1$; so factorize:

$$\Sigma F = mr\omega^2\left\{\cos\theta_1\sum_1^n\cos\varphi_n - \sin\theta_1\sum_1^n\sin\varphi_n\right.$$
$$\left. + \frac{r}{l}\cos 2\theta_1\sum_1^n\cos 2\varphi_n - \frac{r}{l}\sin 2\theta_1\sum_1^n\sin 2\varphi_n\right\} \qquad (8\text{–}14)$$

All φ's are constant, θ_1 is variable. Hence if the force ΣF is to be zero all the time the engine turns over, the coefficients of the terms in the bracket must be zero, or

$$\Sigma \cos\varphi = 0 \qquad\qquad (8\text{–}15a)$$
$$\Sigma \sin\varphi = 0 \qquad\qquad (8\text{–}15b)$$
$$\Sigma \cos 2\varphi = 0 \qquad\qquad (8\text{–}16a)$$
$$\Sigma \sin 2\varphi = 0 \qquad\qquad (8\text{–}16b)$$

The two eqs. 8–15 will show balance of primary forces and the two eqs. 8–16 will show secondary forces balanced in the engine.

Now consider rocking moments. If a reference plane is established anywhere, say in front of the engine, so that the distance along the crankshaft axis to the centerline of the first cylinder is a_1, to the second cylinder a_2, etc., as shown in Fig. 8–12, then instead of eq. 8–13 we will have the moment equation

$$\Sigma M = mr\omega^2\{a_1\cos(\theta_1 + \varphi_1) + a_2\cos(\theta_1 + \varphi_2) + a_3\cos(\theta_1 + \varphi_3) + \cdots$$
$$+ \frac{r}{l}[a_1\cos 2(\theta_1 + \varphi_1) + a_2\cos 2(\theta_1 + \varphi_2) + a_3\cos 2(\theta_1 + \varphi_3)$$
$$+ \cdots]\}$$

which factorizes as with the forces into

$$\Sigma M = mr\omega^2\left\{\cos\theta_1\sum_1^n a_n\cos\varphi_n - \sin\theta_1\sum_1^n a_n\sin\varphi_n\right.$$
$$\left. + \frac{r}{l}\cos 2\theta_1\sum_1^n a_n\cos 2\varphi_n - \frac{r}{l}\sin 2\theta_1\sum_1^n a_n\sin 2\varphi_n\right\} \qquad (8\text{–}17)$$

This gives four more conditions for balance

$$\Sigma a \cos \varphi = 0 \qquad \text{(8–18a)}$$

$$\Sigma a \sin \varphi = 0 \qquad \text{(8–18b)}$$

$$\Sigma a \cos 2\varphi = 0 \qquad \text{(8–19a)}$$

$$\Sigma a \sin 2\varphi = 0 \qquad \text{(8–19b)}$$

Equations 8–18 refer to primary moments, eqs. 8–19 to secondary moments.

8–14. The Six-Cylinder Engine. The usual crank arrangement of a six-cylinder in-line engine is illustrated in Fig. 8–13. If then the variable θ refers to the instantaneous angle of the crank of #1 cylinder past top dead center, the relative angles of the other cranks will be

$$\varphi_1 = \quad 0° = \varphi_6$$
$$\varphi_2 = 120° = \varphi_5$$
$$\varphi_3 = 240° = \varphi_4$$

Merely substituting in the eqs. 8–15 and 8–16 just derived

$$\Sigma \cos \varphi = 1 - \tfrac{1}{2} - \tfrac{1}{2} - \tfrac{1}{2} - \tfrac{1}{2} + 1 \qquad\qquad = 0$$
$$\Sigma \sin \varphi = 0 + 0.866 - 0.866 - 0.866 + 0.866 + 0 = 0$$
$$\Sigma \cos 2\varphi = 1 - \tfrac{1}{2} - \tfrac{1}{2} - \tfrac{1}{2} - \tfrac{1}{2} + 1 \qquad\qquad = 0$$
$$\Sigma \sin 2\varphi = 0 - 0.866 + 0.866 + 0.866 - 0.866 + 0 = 0$$

Hence the coefficients of all the terms in the general force equation (eq. 8–14) are zero. The engine is fully balanced as far as reciprocating inertia forces.

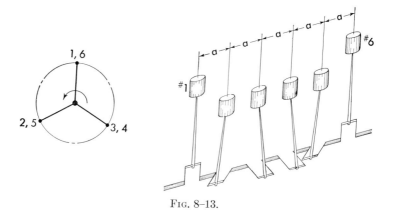

FIG. 8–13.

For analysis of moments let us suppose that the axial distances between all cylinders are the same and equal to a. Let us take moments about a point on the centerline of the crankshaft a distance a to the front of crank #1. Then

$$a_1 = a$$
$$a_2 = 2a$$
$$a_3 = 3a$$
$$\cdots\cdots$$

and by substitution in eqs. 8–18 and 8–19

$$\Sigma a \cos \varphi = \qquad a(1 - 2 \times \tfrac{1}{2} - 3 \times \tfrac{1}{2} - 4 \times \tfrac{1}{2} - 5 \times \tfrac{1}{2} + 6 \times 1) = 0$$
$$\Sigma a \sin \varphi = 0.866a(0 + 2 - 3 - 4 + 5 + 0) \qquad\qquad = 0$$
$$\Sigma a \cos 2\varphi = \qquad a(1 - \tfrac{2}{2} - \tfrac{3}{2} - \tfrac{4}{2} - \tfrac{5}{2} + 6) \qquad\qquad = 0$$
$$\Sigma a \sin 2\varphi = 0.866a(0 - 2 + 3 + 4 - 5 + 0) \qquad\qquad = 0$$

Thus all the coefficients of the moment terms in eq. 8–17 are also zero. The engine is completely balanced.

8–15. The Four-Cylinder 180°-Crank Engine. The engine is shown diagrammatically in Fig. 8–14. Suppose all reciprocating masses, crank radii, and connecting rod lengths are the same, and the spacing between cylinders is a.

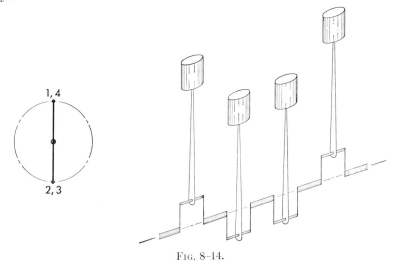

1, 4

2, 3

FIG. 8–14.

Then from eqs. 8–15 and 8–16:

$$\left.\begin{array}{l} \Sigma \cos \varphi = 1 - 1 - 1 + 1 = 0 \\ \Sigma \sin \varphi = 0 + 0 + 0 + 0 = 0 \\ \Sigma \cos 2\varphi = 1 + 1 + 1 + 1 = 4 \\ \Sigma \sin 2\varphi = 0 + 0 + 0 + 0 = 0 \end{array}\right\} \qquad (8\text{–}20)$$

since $\varphi_1 = \varphi_4 = 0°$, $\varphi_2 = \varphi_3 = 180°$.

For the moments, take for a reference plane the plane of crank #1; then $a_1 = 0$, $a_2 = a$, $a_3 = 2a$, $a_4 = 3a$. From eqs. 8–18 and 8–19:

$$\left.\begin{array}{l} \Sigma a \cos \varphi = 0 - a - 2a + 3a = 0 \\ \Sigma a \sin \varphi = 0 \\ \Sigma a \cos 2\varphi = 0 + a + 2a + 3a = 6a \\ \Sigma a \sin 2\varphi = 0 \end{array}\right\} \quad (8\text{-}21)$$

The coefficient of the third eq. 8–20 is not zero hence there is an unbalanced secondary force which will be given (by substitution into eq. 8–14) by:

$$\Sigma F = 4mr\omega^2\left(\frac{r}{l}\right)\cos 2\theta_1 \quad (8\text{-}22)$$

The third coefficient of eq. 8–21 is also not zero, so from eq. 8–17 a moment will appear. But it should be apparent that this is merely the moment of the force given by eq. 8–22. It is not an unbalanced couple. We took moments about the #1 cylinder for a reference plane; the secondary force has a coefficient $\Sigma \cos 2\varphi = 4$; hence the distance from the reference plane to the line of action of this force is

$$\frac{6a}{4} = 1.5a$$

which means that the force acts through the centerline of the engine.

That the third line of eq. 8–21 does not represent a couple may be made even clearer by repeating the computation with a reference plane located through the centerline of the engine. Then

$$a_1 = -1.5a, \quad a_2 = -0.5a, \quad a_3 = +0.5a, \quad a_4 = +1.5a$$

These give for total moment coefficients

$$\Sigma a \cos \varphi = -1.5a + 0.5a - 0.5a + 1.5a = 0$$
$$\Sigma a \sin \varphi = 0$$
$$\Sigma a \cos 2\varphi = -1.5a - 0.5a + 0.5a + 1.5a = 0$$
$$\Sigma a \sin \varphi = 0$$

There are no unbalanced moments or couples.

8–16. An Eight-Cylinder In-Line Engine. The commonest crankshaft arrangement for an eight-cylinder in-line engine (a "straight eight") is shown in Fig. 8–15. The crankshaft consists of two four-cylinder crankshafts, set at 90° to each other, one sandwiched by the other.

This may be analyzed as before by means of eqs. 8–15 through 8–19. But there is no need since we analyzed the four-cylinder in the preceding article.

Cylinders 1, 2, 7, 8 form such a four-cylinder engine. Then from eq. 8–22, they will produce an unbalanced secondary force

$$F_{1278} = 4mr\omega^2(r/l)\cos 2\theta_1 \quad (8\text{-}23)$$

This force will act in the central plane midway between cylinders 2 and 7, i.e., between cylinders 4 and 5.

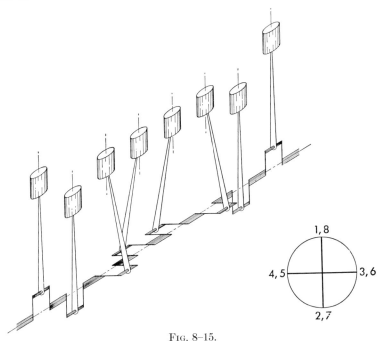

FIG. 8–15.

Cylinders 3, 4, 5, 6 form a similar engine, whose first crank is that of cylinder #3; hence the unbalanced secondary force will act in the same midplane, and be of magnitude:

$$F_{3456} = 4mr\omega^2(r/l) \cos 2\theta_3 \qquad (8\text{–}24)$$

Crank #3 is 90° ahead of crank #1 or

$$\theta_3 = \theta_1 + 90°$$

But since the force is dependent on double the angle, the force F_{3456} will be 180° in advance of F_{1278}.

$$F_{3456} = 4mr\omega^2(r/l) \cos 2(\theta_1 + 90°)$$
$$= -4mr\omega^2(r/l) \cos 2\theta_1 \qquad (8\text{–}25)$$

The forces always act in the line of the cylinders, so they may be added algebraically:

$$\Sigma F = F_{1278} + F_{3456} = 0$$

The engine is balanced in all forces and couples.

8–17. Sine and Cosine Unbalance. When neither of the two terms of the expansion whose coefficients are $\Sigma \cos \varphi$ and $\Sigma \sin \varphi$ is zero, it does not mean that there are two forces, one in line of piston motion and the other at right angles. All forces or moments are necessarily still in the line of motion of the piston—all these forces we consider are just $F = ma$ forces due to the piston's reciprocating motion and *must act in that line.*

Example. A two-cylinder twin steam engine is arranged with cranks at 90°. The two cylinders are parallel and horizontal. The first cylinder is high pressure, with a reciprocating mass of m_{hp}, and the second is the larger diameter low-pressure cylinder with reciprocating mass m_{lp}. Crank radii and connecting-rod lengths are the same for both.

Let $\varphi_1 = 0°$, $\varphi_2 = 90°$. We will not bother to go further than the primary force computation because that will demonstrate our point:

$$\Sigma m \cos \varphi = m_{\text{hp}} \cos 0° + m_{\text{lp}} \cos 90° = m_{\text{hp}}$$
$$\Sigma m \sin \varphi = m_{\text{hp}} \sin 0° + m_{\text{lp}} \sin 90° = m_{\text{lp}}$$

Total unbalanced primary force will be

$$F = r\omega^2(m_{\text{hp}} \cos \theta - m_{\text{lp}} \sin \theta)$$

Suppose $m_{\text{hp}}r\omega^2 = 562$ lb and $m_{\text{lp}} = 3m_{\text{hp}}$,

$$F = 562(\cos \theta - 3 \sin \theta) \qquad (8\text{--}26)$$

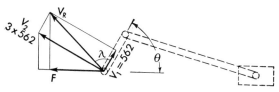

Fig. 8–16.

Note then these points:

1. The magnitude of the force is given by eq. 8–26, and, for any angular position θ of the hp crank, is found by looking up $\cos \theta$ and $\sin \theta$, and substituting.

2. If eq. 8–26 comes out positive when θ is substituted, the direction of the force is from crank toward piston.

3. The magnitude of the force is *not* the vector sum of a $(1 \cos \theta)$ force horizontally and a $(3 \sin \theta)$ force vertically.

But:

4. The force *may* be regarded as the algebraic sum of the horizontal components projected from two rotating vectors V_1 and V_2, as in Fig. 8–16. V_1 along the crank and rotating with it will have a horizontal component $562 \cos \theta$ if $V_1 = 562$ lb. If $V_2 = 3 \times 562$ and leads 90° on the crank, it will produce a horizontal component $562 (3 \sin \theta)$; in the figure it has opposite sense. The algebraic sum gives the quantity F of eq. 8–26.

This quantity is obviously also the horizontal component of the resultant vector V_R ($= V_1 +\!\!\!+ V_2$). This vector leads the crank by an angle $\lambda = \tan^{-1} 3$, and it is therefore apparent that the maximum unbalanced force will occur when this vector V_R comes into line with the line of stroke, that is when $\theta = -\lambda$, and that the magnitude of this maximum is $\sqrt{10} \times 562$ lb.

5. The facts shown vectorially and described above can also be demonstrated by doing some trigonometric manipulations with eq. 8–26, as follows:

Remember that $A \cos (\theta + \lambda) = A \cos \theta \cos \lambda - A \sin \theta \sin \lambda$. Then we may write an identity

$$F = 562 \ (\cos \theta - 3 \sin \theta) = A \cos (\theta + \lambda) \qquad (8\text{–}27)$$

and to justify this, the following must hold:

$$562 = A \cos \lambda$$
$$-3 \times 562 = -A \sin \lambda$$

By squaring and adding:

$$A^2 = 10 \times (562)^2$$

By dividing:

$$\tan \lambda = 3$$

Hence eq. 8–26 may be written

$$F = 562\sqrt{10} \cos (\theta + \lambda) \quad \text{for} \quad \lambda = \tan^{-1}3$$

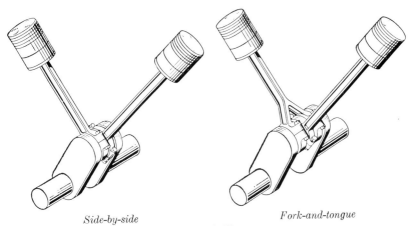

Side-by-side   Fork-and-tongue

Fig. 8–17.

8–18. The V-8 Engine (90° Crankshaft). A V-8 engine consists of two banks of four cylinders. The connecting rods of each pair of cylinders act upon the same crank, so that a four-throw crankshaft is sufficient.

The crank ends of the connecting rods may be side by side on the crankpin, or the connecting rod ends from one bank may be forked to allow the end of the other connecting rod between, as shown in Fig. 8–17. The side-by-side arrangement introduces a small couple to the engine, unless for two of the pairs of cylinders the connecting rods from one bank are forward, and for the other two, the rods from the other bank are forward.

The crankshaft, being of four throws, may either be like the standard

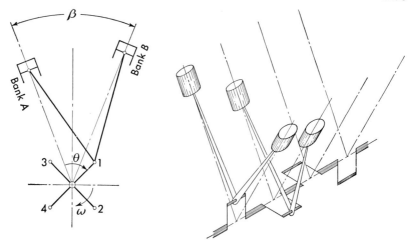

Fig. 8–18.

four-cylinder 180° type (Fig. 8–14) or be of the 90° type (Fig. 8–18). The 180° type still suffers from secondary forces unbalanced like the four-cylinder but may utilize a Lanchester anti-vibrator driven at twice crankshaft speed to achieve balance. The 90° crankshaft type is better; the analysis follows.

The general equations of Art. 8–13 apply only to in-line engines. The V-8, however, has a four-cylinder in-line engine in each bank. The general method may therefore be applied to each bank separately and the vector results added.

In bank A (Fig. 8–18), assume that all cylinder dimensions are the same, that the spacing of cylinders is a, and that moments be taken about the first crank plane. The relative crank angles are $\varphi_1 = 0°$, $\varphi_2 = 90°$, $\varphi_3 = 270°$, $\varphi_4 = 180°$. The eight balance coefficients will be:

$$\Sigma \cos \varphi = 1 + 0 + 0 - 1 = 0$$
$$\Sigma \sin \varphi = 0 + 1 - 1 + 0 = 0$$
$$\Sigma \cos 2\varphi = 1 - 1 - 1 + 1 = 0$$
$$\Sigma \sin 2\varphi = 0 + 0 + 0 + 0 = 0$$
$$\Sigma a \cos \varphi = 0 + 0 + 0 - 3a = -3a$$
$$\Sigma a \sin \varphi = 0 + a - 2a + 0 = -a$$
$$\Sigma a \cos 2\varphi = 0 - a - 2a + 3a = 0$$
$$\Sigma a \sin 2\varphi = 0 + 0 + 0 + 0 = 0$$

There is therefore in this one bank a primary unbalanced couple given (by means of eq. 8–17) by

$$M_A = mr\omega^2(-3a \cos \theta + a \sin \theta) \qquad (8\text{–}28)$$

(It is plain that it is a couple, because there is no unbalanced primary force.)

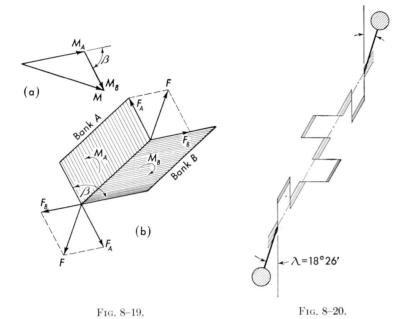

FIG. 8–19.   FIG. 8–20.

Now in bank B, there is the same four-cylinder engine. The analysis of the eight equations will give exactly the same result as eq. 8–28. However, the phase of the couple is different. If the angle between the banks (centerlines of cylinders) is β, the forces from the second bank pistons reach their maximums a crank turn of β after the maximums of the first bank. Thus at the same instant that eq. 8–28 gives M_A, we will have a primary couple in bank B given by

$$M_B = mr\omega^2[- 3a \cos (\theta - \beta) + a \sin (\theta - \beta)]$$

Let the bank angle β be $90°$.

$$M_B = mr\omega^2[- 3a \sin \theta - a \cos \theta] \qquad (8\text{--}29)$$

These two couples act respectively in their own bank planes, that is, around an axis normal to the bank plane. The vector sum of these two moment vectors, shown in Fig. 8–19(a), is given by

$$M = \sqrt{M_A^2 + M_B^2}$$

since M_A and M_B are separated by angle $\beta = 90°$. If the reader finds the vector sum of couples difficult, visualize instead the couple of forces F_A at either end of bank A, and forces F_B in bank B, which constitute the couples, and add these forces for the resultant couple of forces F, in Fig. 8–19b.

But before we add, let us transform eqs. 8–28 and 8–29 by the process suggested in the preceding article (refer to eq. 8–27). From eq. 8–28, let

$$M_A = -mr\omega^2 a(3\cos\theta - \sin\theta) = -A\cos(\theta + \lambda)$$
$$= -A\cos\lambda\cos\theta + A\sin\lambda\sin\theta$$

then

$$\begin{rcases} A\cos\lambda = +3mr\omega^2 a \\ A\sin\lambda = +mr\omega^2 a \end{rcases} \tag{8-30}$$

$$A = +\sqrt{10}\ mr\omega^2 a$$
$$\tan\lambda = \tfrac{1}{3} \quad (\lambda \text{ in first quadrant})$$

Hence

$$M_A = -\sqrt{10}\ mr\omega^2 a \cos(\theta + \lambda)$$

But using eq. 8–30, we may transform eq. 8–29 also into

$$M_B = -mr\omega^2 a\ (\cos\theta + 3\sin\theta)$$
$$= -[(A\sin\lambda)\cos\theta + (A\cos\lambda)\sin\theta]$$
$$= -A\sin(\theta + \lambda) = -\sqrt{10}\ mr\omega^2 a \sin(\theta + \lambda)$$

Thus M_A and M_B are seen to be the sine and cosine component of the same thing. This means the resultant M is a constant which is given by

$$M = -\sqrt{10}\ mr\omega^2 a \tag{8-31}$$

which makes an angle $(\theta + \lambda)$ with bank A at all times; that is, the couple rotates with the crank and holds an angle λ in advance of crank #4. But such a rotating couple may be completely balanced by adding an extra pair of counterweights to the crankshaft. Figure 8–20 shows their position. If they are placed in planes $4a$ apart, at crank radius, each counterweight will be of mass equal to $(\sqrt{10}/4) = 0.791$ of the mass of one piston assembly.

8–19. Other V Engines. Among aircraft engines especially, larger V engines than the V-8 are fairly common.

It has been shown that when 6 or 8 cylinders are in line, the engine can easily be balanced. An engine with two or more banks of cylinders, each of which has either 6 or 8 cylinders, must then also be in balance no matter what is the angle between the banks. Thus V-12, V-16, W-18, double-V-24, H-24 engine arrangements are found.

The bank angles are still of great importance because they affect the regularity of the firing impulses and the torque.

A favorite arrangement is the V-12 with 60° bank angle: this is made by Allison, Daimler-Benz, de Havilland, Hispano-Suiza, Packard, Renault, and Rolls-Royce, among others.

Isotta-Fraschini has a W-18 with three banks of 6 cylinders with 45° between banks.

The H arrangement has two crankshafts, geared together, the cylinders being parallel and opposed.

8–20. Vector Method. An alternative approach to the analytical is to consider the forces involved in an engine as the projection of rotating vectors. Thus the inertia force from one reciprocating assembly can be shown by the projections of the two vectors of Fig. 8–21.

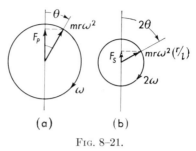

The approximate expression that we have used for the reciprocating forces consists of the primary force $F_p = mr\omega^2 \cos \theta$, which is shown in Fig. 8–21a as the vertical projection or component of the vector $mr\omega^2$ which is rotating at speed ω and has reached the position θ corresponding to the crank angle. The secondary force $F_s = mr\omega^2(r/l) \cos 2\theta$ is represented by the projection of the

(a)   (b)

Fig. 8–21.

shorter vector in Fig. 8–21b, which must have turned through an angle 2θ, and therefore must be rotating at speed 2ω.

The sum of the two projections is the unbalanced force in a single-cylinder engine.

Example 1. Let us apply this method to the 4-cylinder engine with 180° cranks.

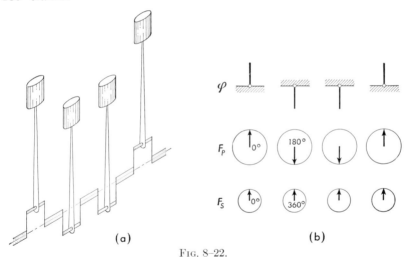

(a)   (b)

Fig. 8–22.

Figure 8–22a shows the perspective, and in Fig. 8–22b in the first row, the cranks are cut up and shown in order in their relative positions. Since the relative position is all that matters, #1 crank may as well be on top dead center.

The second row shows the four primary-force vectors, set at the position of their respective cranks. Since there are two up and two down, symmetrically placed, there will obviously be neither resultant force nor moment.

The third row shows the four secondary-force vectors. If the first is on top center, the second will have turned through twice the angle of its crank, or will have turned 360°. Thus all four are in phase. There is obviously a total secondary force

$$F_s = 4mr\omega^2(r/l) \cos 2\theta$$

but because the forces are parallel, there is no couple.

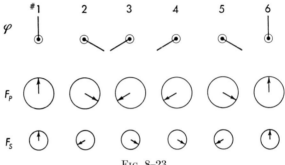

Fig. 8-23.

Example 2. The 6-cylinder considered in Art. 8–14 appears as in Fig. 8–23, which by the symmetry of its figures shows no force or couple.

Be sure to observe here that the resultant of the projections of a number of vectors is the projection of the vectors' resultant.

8–21. Two-Cylinder with Opposed Pistons. If two pistons, one on each side of the crankshaft, are connected to the same crank, there will be a doubly strong primary force, but the secondary forces will balance each other. This is because when one side is on inner dead center, the other will be on the outer center.

The solution by vectors is shown in Fig. 8–24. If piston #1 is θ_1 past

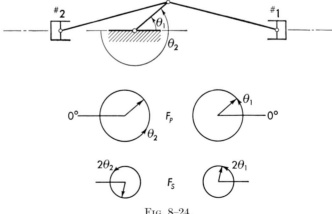

Fig. 8-24.

its inner center, piston #2 will be $\theta_2 = 180° + \theta_1$ past its inner center. The primary forces are therefore in phase, and the secondary opposite each other.

But with the primary unbalanced, this is very poor design. Consider the possibility of a 180° crankshaft, as in Fig. 8–25a. The two pistons are always in the same position relative to their own inner dead center.

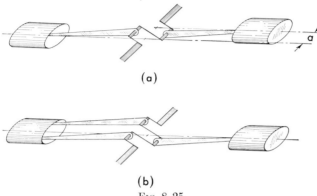

(a)

(b)

Fig. 8–25.

So the inertia forces will be identical, but directed in opposite sense. There can be no net force, but due to the staggering of crank throws there will be bad couples, both primary and secondary.

The couples may be avoided by using double connecting rods to one piston, as in the design shown in Fig. 8–25b.

8–22. Cross-Four Radial Engine and Right-Angled X Engine. Four cylinders arranged in a right-angled cross, and with the four connecting rods attached to the same crank, make an excellent engine from the point of view of dynamic balance, as will be shown.

From the point of view of torque, however, the design is limited to a two-stroke cycle engine. In a radial engine using the four-stroke cycle, the intervals of crank turn between the firing of successive cylinders can only be regular if the number of cylinders is odd. For this reason, radial engines usually have 7 or 9 cylinders.

Figure 8–26 shows the 4-cylinder engine; the top cylinder is chosen as #1, and the crank angle θ is measured for that cylinder.

If we analyze the problem by taking the forces one at a time, the following are acting:

$$\text{A force up from \#1} = mr\omega^2[\cos \theta + (r/l) \cos 2\theta]$$
$$\text{A force down from \#3} = mr\omega^2[- \cos \theta + (r/l) \cos 2\theta]$$
$$\text{A force to the right from \#2} = mr\omega^2[\sin \theta - (r/l) \cos 2\theta]$$
$$\text{A force to the left from \#4} = mr\omega^2[- \sin \theta - (r/l) \cos 2\theta]$$
$$\text{The net upward force} = F_1 - F_3 = 2mr\omega^2 \cos \theta$$
$$\text{The net force to the right} = F_2 - F_4 = 2mr\omega^2 \sin \theta$$

The total unbalanced force is therefore a constant rotating force in the direction of the crank, of magnitude $2mr\omega^2$. It can be completely balanced by the addition of a counterbalance weight to the crankshaft opposite the crankpin. The counterbalance is to have a mass twice that of a reciprocating mass, when set at crank radius.

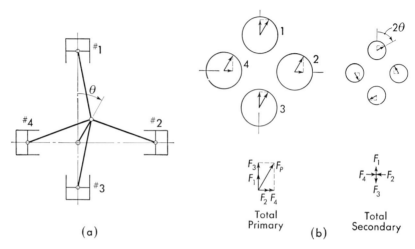

(a)

Total Primary   (b)   Total Secondary

Fig. 8–26.

The secondary forces cancel each other between opposite pairs (refer to the last article) and the couples are not of great significance, since the engine is nearly in a single transverse plane.

By the vector method shown in Fig. 8–26b the result is, of course, the same.

Since a single radial arrangement of 4 cylinders is so easily balanced, then if the four shown in Fig. 8–26a are the first cylinders of four banks, say six in each bank, so that the whole becomes a 24-X cylinder engine (or any other number in each bank), it follows that irrespective of crankshaft arrangement the engine may easily be balanced. With more than 8 cylinders, the torque impulses can be regular for a 4-cycle engine.

An example of such a 24-X cylinder engine is the Rolls-Royce "Vulture" aircraft engine, except that this engine has a 12-throw crankshaft, so that only two connecting rods are applied to each crankpin.

8–23. Radial Engines. All radial engines might be analyzed by this method, if all connecting rods were mounted on the crankpin. However it is not practical to attach seven or nine rods to the same pin, when moreover side-by-side attachment would introduce unbalanced couples.

Radial engines therefore generally use the articulated connecting rod system, with one master rod. The kinematic arrangement is shown in Fig. 8–27, and from this it is plain that the obliquity of the master rod affects the piston position and acceleration in every other cylinder.

Equation 8–8 is thus not adequate for reckoning secondary balance. But eq. 8–7 is still fine for primary balance: a moment's thought will show that there is always a large primary unbalanced force in the form of a rotating vector, which can be neutralized by an additional crank counterweight equal to half the sum of the reciprocating weights of all cylinders.

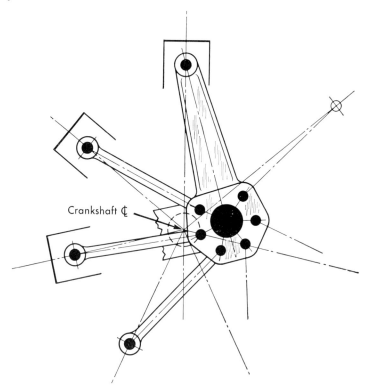

FIG. 8–27.

The secondary balance problem is rather too specialized for inclusion here. The reader is referred to the books on engine dynamics listed at the end of this chapter, or to *Mechanical Vibrations* by Den Hartog. Secondary balance requires a counterweight rotating at twice crankshaft speed.

It is to be noted moreover that the master connecting rod is always of much heavier construction than the others, so that the reciprocating weight of this one cylinder will always be rather more than the other; the result is that the engine will be subject to a reciprocating force, both primary and secondary, proportional to the excess weight of this one mass.

The articulated connecting rod construction will also have an effect

(Courtesy Nordberg Manufacturing Co.)
Fig. 8–28.

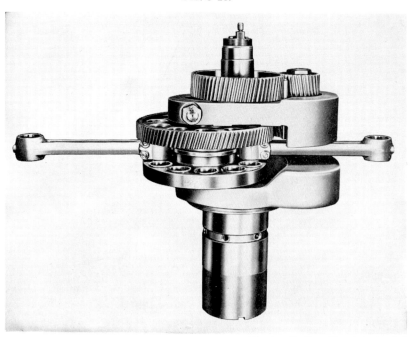

(Courtesy Nordberg Manufacturing Co.)
Fig. 8–29.

on the regularity and similarity of the torques from each cylinder. The turning moment diagram will not therefore be quite regular; but this effect on the usual 7 and 9 cylinders is slight.

A clever design that avoids the master rod construction is due to the Nordberg* Company; their patented method, shown in Fig. 8–28, is incorporated in a line of 11 and 12† cylinder 2-stroke cycle diesel and gas engines. All connecting rod big ends are attached to knuckle pins on the master bearing—a ring like the big end of the conventional master rod. The master bearing surrounds the crankpin. But then it is necessary to prevent this master bearing from rotating; it should maintain a parallel motion of gyration with the crankpin. This is accomplished either exactly by an epicyclic gear train (Fig. 8–29) of which the sun-gear is stationary, or very nearly by application of a four-bar chain after Watt's straight-line mechanism (Figs. 8–28 and 8–30). In this, two opposite connecting rods are pinned to inclined "restraining cranks" to form bell cranks such as ABC. The pivots C and D are connected by a "restraining link," and the motion of this link will be nearly linear across

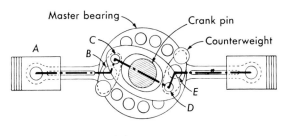

Restraining linkage

(Courtesy Nordberg Manufacturing Co.)

Fig. 8–30.

the main crankpin, being at the extreme of its eccentricity with respect to the crankpin when the crank is at right angles to the line of those two controlling cylinders. The restraining cranks BC and DE carry counterweights (Fig. 8–28) which help to counteract the unbalance of the link CD when displaced.

8–24. Use of the Balancing Machine. We turn now from the study of particular engines and their balance or unbalance as a whole, and consider in these next three articles certain side-line effects.

For the first, then, we note that in several engines special extra counterweights have been prescribed for addition to crankshafts, and if this is done, it means that the crankshaft alone is not in balance. What then shall be done about the simpler initial problem of ensuring balance of rotating parts?

* Nordberg Manufacturing Co., Milwaukee, engines described in their sales bulletins.
† Note the 12-cylinder design is possible with the 2-stroke cycle.

With an engine in which the reciprocating parts are so arranged as to counter each other, or in which the reciprocating inertia forces are left unbalanced, there remains the problem of providing proper counterweight in the crankshaft to balance the "rotating" part (generally about two-thirds) of the weight of the connecting rods. To do this, special ring clamps—each of a weight equal to the rotating part of a connecting rod—may be attached to the crankpin bearings, and the crankshaft is then balanced in a balancing machine.

For example, in a 2-cylinder engine, such weights must be included in the balancing operation.

On the other hand, with a 4-cylinder 180° crankshaft these weights are not necessary, for if the crankshaft is in balance without these four extra clamp weights, their addition in the symmetrical manner of this engine's cranks will not change the balance. They are therefore customarily omitted. Nevertheless if any cognizance is to be taken of the fact that the crankshaft will bend a little, or if each half of the crankshaft is to be balanced in order to relieve the dynamic load on the center main bearing, then the extra weights should be included, and diminution of wear of the bearings will result.

In engines that require some proportions of the reciprocating weight to be counterbalanced by the crankshaft, the clamp weights must be added according to the theory. In a single-cylinder engine then, the weight to be attached should be equal to the "rotating" connecting rod weight plus half the total reciprocating weight (Art. 8–9). In radial aircraft engines, there is needed a weight of mass equal to the "rotating" mass of all connecting rods plus half the sum of all reciprocating masses. The 90° crank V-8 engine was studied in Art. 8–18; and it is unique. Consideration will show that if a clamp weight equal to the whole weight of a connecting rod and piston assembly is added to each crankpin the crankshaft will come off the balancing machine with the correct primary couple (eq. 8–31) incorporated.

In the design of these clamp weights, it is well to line the inside surfaces with a copper coat, to prevent marring the finished crankpin bearing surface.

8–25. Turning Moment Diagrams for Balanced Engines. In any engine (such as those with 6 or 8 cylinders) in which there is both primary and secondary balance of reciprocating forces, the method (see Art. 8–4) to be followed in obtaining the turning moment diagram may be shortened by entirely ignoring all reciprocating inertia forces.

The net force may be found directly from the P–V diagram, the inertia line being absent.

8–26. Connecting Rod Effect Correction. As was pointed out in Art. 8–9 all the analysis of balancing that has been set down so far has been based upon the supposition that the connecting rod can be replaced by an approximately dynamical equivalent of two masses, one at the piston pin, the other at the crankpin.

The correct equivalent system for the connecting rod consists of a mass at the piston pin and a mass at the center of percussion, as described in Art. 7–13. It is the difference in the two results, that is, the error introduced by using the simpler method, to which we want to turn our attention.

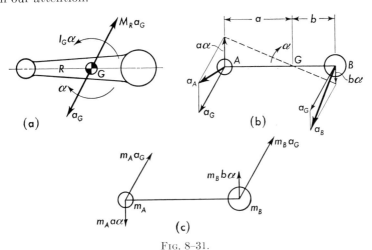

Fig. 8–31.

The plane motion of any body R can be completely specified by identifying the acceleration a_G of the center of mass, and α its angular acceleration. And the inertia effect is then completely stated as $M_R a_G$ and $I_G \alpha$ (Fig. 8–31a).

The body is now represented by two masses M_A, M_B, distant a, b from G, for which

$$m_A a = m_B b \qquad \text{(8–32, also eq. 7–2)}$$

$$m_A + m_B = M_R \qquad \text{(8–33, also eq. 7–3)}$$

but the third equation (eq. 7–4) for the moment of inertia equivalence is not satisfied. The accelerations of points A and B (a_A and a_B) are composed of the vector sums (Fig. 8–31b):

$$a_A = a_G + a\alpha$$
$$a_B = a_G + b\alpha$$

and therefore the inertia effects appear as the four forces of Fig. 8–31c. The sum of the two forces $m_A a_G$ and $m_B a_G$ is obviously $M_R a_G$ (as desired) because of eqs. 8–32 and 8–33. The vector sum of the two forces $m_A a\alpha$ and $m_B b\alpha$ is zero, for, from eq. 8–32,

$$m_A a\alpha - m_B b\alpha = (m_A a - m_B b)\alpha = 0$$

The moment about G of the two forces $m_A a_G$ and $m_B a_G$ is zero from eq. 8–32. The moment q of the other two forces is, however:

$$q = (m_A a\alpha)a + (m_B b\alpha)b$$
$$= \alpha[m_B ba + m_A ab]$$
$$= M_R ab\alpha$$

Since the dimension $b = GB$ is greater than the dimension $GE(= e)$ of the proper placement of the second equivalent mass at the center of percussion (Fig. 7–17), the approximate equivalent mass system used throughout the analysis of this chapter has introduced an error in the inertia couple of each connecting rod of

$$\text{Error in } q = M_R ab\alpha - I_G \alpha$$
$$= M_R(ab - k_G^2)\alpha$$
$$= M_R a(b - e)\alpha \qquad (8\text{–}34)$$

Such an error in reckoning a couple is not going to affect any of the foregoing calculations concerning the balance of forces in any multi-cylinder engine. These conclusions still stand. The error does affect, and must properly be included in, reckoning the rocking couples due to the uneven torque produced by an engine, if this approximately equivalent inertia system is used to produce a torque diagram, as was done in the first part of this chapter. This torque, it was noted, could never be made uniform, nor the rocking couple ever balanced, so the error is not a serious fault.

Since the error of eq. 8–34 shows an excess couple, when the approximately equivalent system is used, the side-wall forces on the cylinder walls will appear larger in the calculation than actually obtain, by the amount

$$M_R(ab - k_G^2)\alpha/(L \cos \varphi) \qquad (8\text{–}35)$$

8–27. Other Mechanisms. The reckoning of torque and of balance or unbalanced resultant forces of certain other mechanisms may be accomplished by an approach similar to that explained here for engines.

For example, in the common vane pump (Fig. 8–P–29) the motion of the vanes will be found to be the same as the motion of the pistons in the old-style rotary aircraft engines, that is, a kinematic inversion of the slider-crank radial engines.

Another device which is amenable is the Oldham coupling for connecting parallel shafts (Fig. 8–P–31).

Another engine which may be fully balanced is the wobble-plate (swash-plate) engine, with cylinders grouped around and parallel to the rotating axis. This design (Fig. 8–P–32), which gives simple harmonic motion to the pistons, is extensively used for hydraulic motors and pumps and has also produced experimental aircraft engines. These examples form the basis of three problems that follow.

The four-bar linkage mechanism is one which presents a difficult problem in balancing. The most typical form has a rotating driving crank and an oscillating follower crank, as in Fig. 8–32, and the balancing of this can only be approximate. Investigations* have however shown that very great reduction in the bearing loads can be achieved.

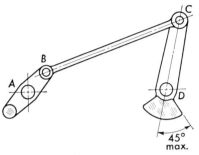

Fig. 8–32.

Consider first that the connecting rod BC is replaced by an equivalent of two masses M_B, M_C, one at each end, which divide the mass of the rod according to the position of its center of gravity. This is usually a fifty-fifty division, as the connecting rod is generally uniform. Then the driving crank AB, with this addition M_B at B, is balanced as a simple rotating body.

The driven crank CD has a rotational motion, so that a counterweight is desirable, but it also has (often very high) angular acceleration, so that the moment of inertia must be kept low. Some compromise between these conflicting objectives is necessary; the best solution depends largely on the speed of the driving crank and the mechanism dimensions; the item noted in Art. 4–10 must be reckoned, and partial balancing is also to be considered. Most frequently, however, the best results accrue when a counterweight as large as is possible is designed close around the pivot D, as in Fig. 8–32.

BIBLIOGRAPHY

ALBERT, C. D., *Machine Design Drawing Room Problems.* 4th ed. New York: John Wiley & Sons, Inc., 1948, Chap. 10, on Flywheels.

ANGLE, G. D. *Engine Dynamics and Crankshaft Design.* Detroit: Airplane Engine Encyclopedia Co., 1925.

ANGUS, R. W. *Theory of Machines.* 2d ed. New York: McGraw-Hill Book Co., Inc., 1917, Chaps. 13–16.

COUSINS, F. M. *Analytical Design of High Speed Internal Combustion Engines.* New York: Pitman Publishing Corp., 1941, Chaps. 2, 8, and 10.

DALBY, W. E. *The Balancing of Engines.* 4th ed. London: Longmans, Green & Co., 1929.

DEGLER, H. E. *Internal Combustion Engines.* New York: John Wiley & Sons, Inc., 1938, Chap. 12.

DENT, J. A., and HARPER, A. C. *Kinematics and Kinetics of Machinery.* New York: John Wiley & Sons, Inc., 1921, Chap. 6 and Appendix.

HAM, C. W., and CRANE, E. J. *Mechanics of Machinery.* 3d ed. New York: McGraw-Hill Book Co., Inc., 1948, Chap. 14.

HECK, R. C. H. *Mechanics of Machinery.* (Vol. II, "Kinematics and Dynamics.") New York: McGraw-Hill Book Co., Inc., 1925, Chap. 5.

* G. J. Talbourdet and P. R. Shepler, "Mathematical Solution of 4-Bar Linkages" (Part IV, "Balancing of Linkages"), *Machine Design*, July, 1941, pp. 73–77.

HUEBOTTER, H. A. *Mechanics of the Gasoline Engine.* New York: McGraw-Hill Book Co., Inc., 1923, Chaps. 3, 9, and 11.

JUDGE, A. W. *Automobile and Aircraft Engines.* 2d ed. London: Sir Isaac Pitman & Sons, Ltd., 1931, Chaps. 16 and 17.

LANZA, G. *Dynamics of Machinery.* New York: John Wiley & Sons, Inc., 1911, Chap. 3.

LICHTY, L. C. *Internal Combustion Engines.* 6th ed. New York: McGraw-Hill Book Co., Inc., 1951, Chaps. 17 and 18.

ROOT, R. E. *Dynamics of Engine and Shaft.* New York: John Wiley & Sons, Inc., 1932, Chaps. 4–7.

TOFT, L., and KERSEY, A. T. J. *Theory of Machines.* 6th ed. London: Sir Isaac Pitman & Sons, Ltd., 1919, Chap. 12.

PROBLEMS

8-1. A two-stroke diesel engine has a turning moment diagram which may be represented approximately as two triangles, as in Fig. 8–P–1. (a) Find the steady horsepower of the engine when the engine is running at 500 rpm. (b) Find the percentage of fluctuation in speed if the flywheel has a moment of inertia of 40 lb ft sec².

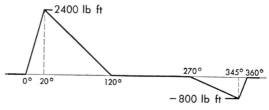

FIG. 8–P–1.

8-2. A double-acting steam engine, running at 250 rpm, gives a turning moment diagram which may be stated approximately as

$$T(\text{lb ft}) = 1600 \sin 2\theta + 1400$$

where θ is the crank angle. (a) Find the steady horsepower transmitted by the engine. (b) Find the maximum change in kinetic energy to be stored by the flywheel, and the moment of inertia of the flywheel necessary to hold the fluctuation of speed within 3 per cent total.

8-3. A double-acting steam engine has a turning moment given by

$$T(\text{lb ft}) = 1400 + 1449 \sin (2\theta - 75°)$$

where θ is the crank angle. Find the weight of the rim of the flywheel to hold the fluctuation to 3 per cent total. The speed of the engine is 200 rpm and the radius of gyration of the flywheel rim is 2 ft.

8-4. A flywheel of a rolling mill weighs 30 tons and has a radius of gyration of 2 ft 9 in. In one series of operations, the horsepower output required by the mill is constant at 260 for 3 sec, then 20 for 5 sec running light, then 165 for 6 sec, 20 again for 10 sec light, 125 for 16 sec, after which it continues to run light using 20 horsepower. If the engine supplies 80 horsepower constantly, and if the flywheel speed is 175 rpm at the commencement of the process, what will the speed at the end of the 125-horsepower output period be, and how long must the engine run light to regain its initial speed?

8–5. The work delivered by a 100-horsepower steam engine running at 300 rpm varies so that the energy level fluctuates 25 per cent above and below the mean of the energy developed per cycle. Find the weight of a flywheel needed to keep a speed fluctuation coefficient of 0.02, if the flywheel is a solid cylindrical disk of 4 ft diameter. If the disk is cast iron, what is its width?

8–6. Figure 8–P–6 represents a turning effort diagram; the numbers show the areas of the loops in square inches on the original diagram, of which this is a reduced reproduction. This original diagram was $5\frac{1}{2}$ in. long, and the vertical scale was 1 in. = 27 lb per sq in. of piston area.

a) At what point is the engine speed a maximum; and a minimum?
b) What is the maximum fluctuation of energy?
c) If the diagram is for a 12 in. by 24 in. multi-cylinder engine running at 150 rpm mean speed, find the moment of inertia of the flywheel required to limit the fluctuation of speed within a total 3 per cent of the mean.
d) Find the weight of this flywheel in terms of k, the radius of gyration, and plot the relationship for a range of W from 100 to 1000 lb.

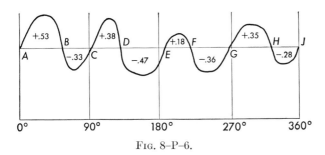

Fig. 8–P–6.

8–7. A disk, 30 in. in diameter, weighing 40 lb, acts as a flywheel in driving an air compressor through a crank and connecting rod mechanism. If the forward stroke is taken against a constant pressure of 50 psi, and the return stroke has a negligible back pressure, and if the speed is 1200 power strokes per minute maintained by a constant horsepower input, find the fluctuation in speed of the flywheel. The bore and stroke of the piston are 6 in. and 18 in., and the connecting-rod–crank ratio is 5:1. Moment of inertia of the disk $= \frac{1}{2}mr^2$. Neglect the inertia of the reciprocating parts.

8–8. A motor and flywheel of moment of inertia 15 lb in. sec² drive an oscillating table at 600 cycles per minute with simple harmonic motion through a scotch yoke mechanism. The stroke is one inch, and the table assembly weighs 120 lb. There is a constant frictional couple against the rotation. Find the percentage of fluctuation from mean speed of the motor.

8–9. A double-acting "unaflow" single cylinder Skinner steam engine is governed to run at 248 rpm. Dimensions are as follows: stroke = 13.0 in., bore = 10.125 in., piston rod diameter = 1.9375 in., length between centers of the connecting rod (crankpin to crosshead) = 34.6875 in., total rotating weight =

Crank End

Head End

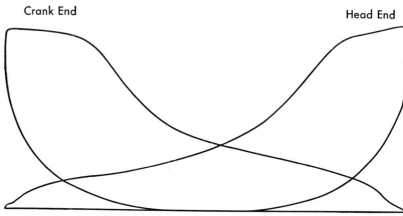

FIG. 8–P–9a.

170 lb equivalent at crankpin, total reciprocating weight = 333 lb equivalent at crosshead pin. (a) Use the tabulation method to calculate the piston displacement in terms of crank angle for each 15°. For example:

$$s = R\left(1 - \cos\theta + \frac{R}{2L}\sin^2\theta\right)$$

(b) Calculate by tabulation the inertia force of the reciprocating mass. (c) Reproduce the indicator diagram taken from this engine given by Fig. 8–P–9a; maximum pressure is 127 psi; show upon it the inertia force line. Then make a sketch of the net force diagram. (d) Calculate the "effective crank radius" for the turning moment. (e) Tabulate all forces and calculate turning moment. (f) Plot turning moment or torque effort diagram (show both vertical scales). (g) By planimeter, find the mean torque and so find steady horsepower. Also find ΔE, the maximum excess energy. (h) Measurements of the rim of the two cast steel flywheels are shown in Fig. 8–P–9b. From this, find the coefficient of fluctuation of the engine.

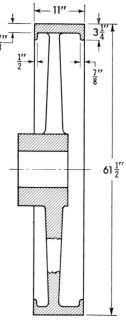

FIG. 8–P–9b.

8–10. If you have a steam engine in your laboratory, take the dimensions of this engine and sample indicator cards. Then, follow the procedure suggested in Problem 8–9, finally taking measurements of the flywheel in order to determine the coefficient of fluctuation for which the engine is designed.

8–11. From the data of Problem 8–9, make the same calculations for the coefficient of fluctuation maintained by the flywheel, but make full use of any tables available for displacement, acceleration, etc. (e.g., in *Marks' Handbook*), instead of computing them.

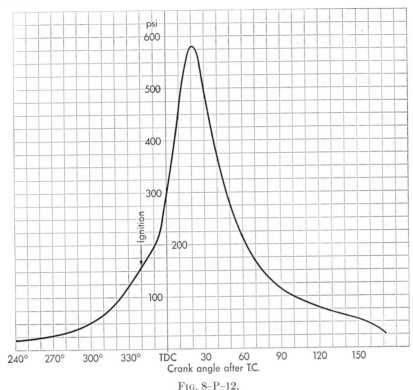

Fig. 8–P–12.

8–12. Obtain the turning moment diagram for a single-cylinder four-stroke cycle gasoline engine of a size typical in an automobile, as given by: bore = 3.5 in.; stroke = 3.75 in.; weight of piston (complete) = 600 grams; length of connecting rod = 7.5 in.; weight of connecting rod = 500 grams, to be divided in the ratio 65:35 for rotating: reciprocating parts. Figure 8–P–12 shows the pressure–crank-angle relation in the firing stroke at 1000 rpm full throttle, with spark advance 20° before top center, as given by oscilloscope records. IMEP is 140 psi. Find the value of the excess energy ΔE.

8–13. From the single-cylinder turning moment diagram derived in Problem 8–12 for 1000 rpm, draw a 6-cylinder turning moment diagram by adding six equal single diagrams spaced 120° apart. Find ΔE.

8–14. The actual pressures occurring in consecutively fired charges in a cylinder may vary. The oscilloscope record of Fig. 8–P–14 shows incipient knock on the 1st, 2nd, and 3rd firing strokes, and different characteristics of the others. Investigate the effect of these variations on the turning moment, and find the ratio of the maximum force on the main bearing when detonating to that when firing normally.

The figure shows the pressure–crank-angle diagrams for six successive firing strokes in a single cylinder; consider these, however, the six successively firing cylinders of an engine. The four sharp jumps each cycle in the curve are "pips"

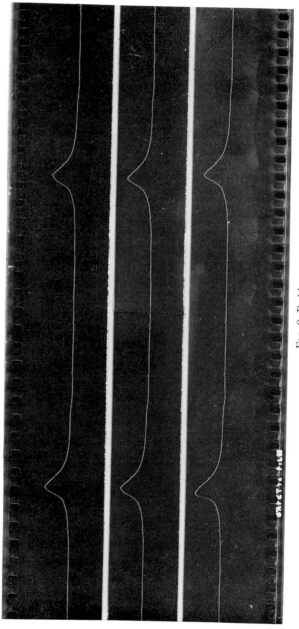

Fig. 8–P–14.

recording the instants at which the crank is 80° before and 40° after its top center
—these enable the time scale to be determined; engine speed is 600 rpm. For
the vertical scale the maximum pressure of the sixth firing stroke was reckoned
at 550 psi (gauge). The engine dimensions are the same as in Problem 8–12.

In the following, assume each reciprocating mass m, crank throw r, and the
spacing between each cylinder and its neighbor a, to be equal unless otherwise
stated.

8–15. Investigate the balance of a 3-cylinder in-line engine, with cranks at
0°, 120°, 240°. State the unbalance (if any). What remedies are available?

8–16. A 5-cylinder in-line engine has cranks (reading in order) at 0°, 144°,
288°, 216°, 72°. Investigate the balance of reciprocating masses.

8–17. A two-stroke 8-cylinder in-line engine, with a crankshaft that fulfils
the need of regular 45° firing intervals (with cylinders at opposite ends of the
bank firing alternately), uses the firing order 1–8–2–6–4–5–3–7. (a) Write an
expression for the unbalance of this engine. (b) Specify a pair of Lanchester
anti-vibrators, aligned with front and rear cylinder centerlines, to remedy the
trouble.

8–18. A two-stroke 6-cylinder in-line engine has a crankshaft with throws at
0°, 120°, 240°, 60°, 300°, and 180°. Find the unbalance of the engine, and
specify a Lanchester counterbalancing arrangement.

8–19. In the usual arrangement for a four-stroke 6-cylinder (cranks 0°, 120°,
240°, 240°, 120°, 0°), the inclusion of an oil pump at the center main bearing
necessitates that the spacing between cylinders No. 3 and No. 4 is 50 per cent
more than the spacing of all other neighboring cylinders. Determine if this
engine will be balanced.

8–20. A vertical marine two-stroke diesel with forced scavenge has six cylinders
in line, and crankshaft as in Problem 8–18, but outside of these six (being #1 and
#8 of eight cylinders in line) are two scavenger pump cylinders. If the crank
throws on these pumps are to be the same as for the working pistons, find the
ratio of the reciprocating pump mass to the reciprocating working piston mass,
and the crank angles of the two pump cylinders, needed to bring the engine into
primary balance.

8–21. A locomotive has four cylinders, two outside the wheels and two inside
the frame, and all forward of the crankshaft. If the crank of the cylinder on the
right hand outside is on top dead center, the next crank is at 180°, the next at
270°, and the left outside at 90°. The two outside cylinders are high-pressure and
have a reciprocating weight of 150 lb; the two inside are low-pressure (with
bigger bore) and reciprocating weight of 300 lb. The space between the two inside cylinders is 26 in., and between both high-pressure and neighboring low-
pressure 20 in. Find the magnitude of any primary or secondary unbalanced
forces or couples when the wheels turn at 270 rpm. All crank radii are 12 in., and
connecting rod lengths 4 ft.

8–22. A V-8 has the conventional 180° crankshaft (cranks at 0°, 180°, 180°, and 0°). Show that this engine, with angle between the banks 90°, symmetrical about the vertical, has a horizontal unbalanced reciprocating force. Find the magnitude of this force in an engine of stroke $4\frac{1}{2}$ in., turning at 3000 rpm, and in which each reciprocating mass weighs 1 lb, and for which the crank–connecting-rod ratio is $1:4\frac{1}{2}$.

8–23. A 4-cylinder horizontally opposed pancake engine has four crank throws at 0°–180°–180°–0°. Cranks 1 and 3 are attached to pistons in the right bank; cranks 2 and 4 to the left bank. Check the balance.

8–24. Is any arrangement of a 4-cylinder pancake engine fully balanced?

8–25. A radial engine has 3 cylinders of which the centerlines are in a plane and make 120° with each other. All connecting rods work on the single master crank rotating around the center of the star. Find an expression for the unbalance of the engine, if any.

8–26. Prove that if a 9-cylinder radial engine could have all connecting rods working off a single crankpin, and be wholly in a plane, the engine could be fully balanced by the addition of a single extra counterweight to the crank.

8–27. Investigate the balance of all the harmonics of reciprocating forces in a conventional 6-cylinder engine, for which the first and second have been shown (Art. 8–14) to be completely balanced. (Use eq. 8–10 for the force, and the vector method of Art. 8–20.)

8–28. Investigate the balance of all harmonics of reciprocating forces in a conventional straight 8-cylinder engine with crankshaft as in Fig. 8–15.

8–29. A sliding-vane pump has four vanes, as in Fig. 8–P–29, which are free to slide in the four equally spaced slots in the rotor. Centrifugal force keeps these vanes in contact with the inside surface of the circular housing, which has a radius R. The centers of the rotor and the housing are separated by amount e. Each vane has mass m and radial length $2a$. Find the unbalanced force on the housing as the rotor turns at speed ω.

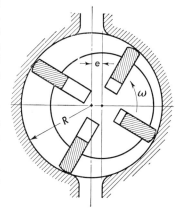

8–30. Write an expression for, and draw the graph of, the torque needed to drive the vane pumps of the preceding problem, neglecting all pneumatic or hydraulic effects. Assume a friction coefficient of 0.10 between vanes and housing, but neglect friction between vanes and rotor.

8–31. The Oldham coupling is a device for transmitting a drive from one shaft to another which is parallel, but may be displaced slightly. Figure 8–P–31 shows a commercial product; the two forks, orthogonally placed, contain the center member or "spider," which weighs $\frac{1}{4}$ lb. Find the net inertia force when the shafts are out of line by $\frac{1}{8}$ in. and turning at 1000 rpm.

FIG. 8–P–29.

FIG. 8–P–31.

8–32. (a) Show that in the barrel-type swashplate motor* (Fig. 8–P–32) the motion of each reciprocating mass is simply harmonic. (b) Then show that the engine is fully balanced as to primary forces, provided that the cylinders (any

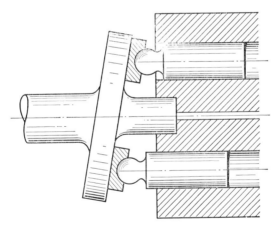

FIG. 8–P–32.

number) are equally spaced around the shaft. (c) Show that the unbalanced couple from the reciprocating inertia forces may be perfectly balanced by the couple from the rotating swashplate, if the thickness of the latter is suitably chosen. Write down this requirement.

* R. Hadekel, "Swashplate Mechanisms," *Machine Design*, February, 1953, pp. 141–45.

Chapter 9

FLEXIBLE MACHINE MEMBERS IN MOTION

9–1. Flexibility. In Chapter 7 it was found that, due to their motion, the members of a machine sustain a system of forces from inertia together with the system of forces reckoned to transmit useful energy from one part to another. Reactions at all joints and contacts may be found when the members are assumed rigid. But whenever there are forces or reactions acting upon machine members, those members will undergo strain and will carry corresponding stress. For no actual member is a rigid body.

It was discussed in Chapter 7, Art. 7–10, that in some cases the strain will cause significant changes in the geometry of the mechanism, and thus increase or decrease the forces of inertia, causing further effect on the strain; an example of this is the case of a whirling shaft (page 153).

In other cases the strain causes little or negligible geometrical change, so that the stresses are readily computed from the loading. An example is the connecting rod of an engine.

But even in the second type the analyst must be on the alert to suspect stresses due to vibration resonance. In dealing with members of machines moving at reasonably low speeds, vibration of the members may safely be ignored. But let the speeds increase, and it is as if a new system of forces took charge. For instance, if the engine mechanism is to rotate at a speed that is within ten percentage of the natural transverse vibrational frequency of the connecting rod, the deflections from this cause must be reckoned. Luckily most members are made so stiff that their lowest natural frequencies are very high.

In the illustrative examples of stress in members, on the following pages, the cases are arranged in groups according to the type of inertia force occurring. At first we approach a few where centrifugal force is the cause, for that is probably of the most common occurrence.

9–2. Effects of Centrifugal Force. In Figs. 9–1 and 9–2 the same shaft carries the same eccentric mass, and in rotation therefore the same centrifugal force is effective at the same position relative to the supports of the shaft. As it has been developed already, the reactions at the two bearings will be the same in the two cases, because the magnitude of these reactions depends only upon the location of the resultant centrifugal force. But with the connection of the mass to shaft being different, as shown in the figures, the stresses resulting in the shaft will be different. For stress depends not on resultant forces but on the shape of the members.

Suppose in the two cases that the centrifugal force F is known; then below the two figures there are shown the shear force and bending moment diagrams. In Fig. 9–1 the shear force is of constant magnitude

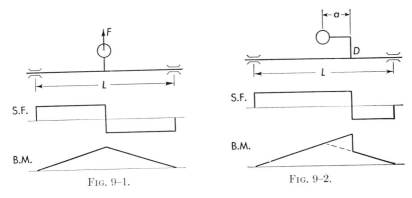

FIG. 9–1.   FIG. 9–2.

$F/2$, and the maximum bending moment is $FL/4$ where L is the length of span. The load F is presumed at midspan. In Fig. 9–2 the spur carrying the mass is attached to the shaft at a point D distant a from midspan. Due to F, the shear force is still $F/2$ in magnitude across the span but the bending moment reaches a maximum of $\frac{1}{2}F(L/2 + a) = F(L + 2a)/4$ and higher stresses result. The discontinuity in the bending moment diagram is of an amount equal to the moment Fa applied by the spur at the point D.

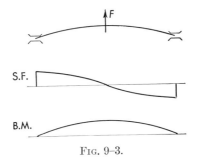

FIG. 9–3.

Completely different stresses must also be noted when we compare cases in which loads are applied in concentrated form with those in which loads are applied in distributed form. In Fig. 9–3 the curved shaft is such that the sum of all centrifugal forces acting upon the various elements across the span has the same resultant F acting at midspan as in Fig. 9–1. Then the reactions at the bearings will be the same as those of the case in Fig. 9–1, but the stresses will not. The shear from the distributed load (Fig. 9–3) varies continuously across the span with a maximum of $F/2$ at each end; the bending moment will also be a curve, to be found by integration of the shear force diagram.

9–3. Whipping Stress in a Rotating Shaft. To determine the stresses in a rotating shaft which is bending due to whirling, it is necessary to find first the deflections suffered. This entails the use of the theory developed in Chapter 4, to obtain the natural frequency of transverse vibration. Then from the ratio of the running speed to the critical speed, the deflection may be found approximately by the Rayleigh method.

Now when a shaft or beam is bent, the bending moment or curvature causes tensile stresses on the convex side of the curve, and compressive stresses on the concave side. The maximum stress is at the outer fiber, and is given by the well-known relation

$$S_{\text{max}} = \frac{My}{I} \qquad (9\text{--}1)$$

In this, M is the moment at the section, I the sectional (area) moment of inertia and y the distance to the extreme fiber from the neutral axis. Due to the shearing forces, there will also be shear stress across the section. At any distance y' from the neutral axis this shear stress is given by

$$S_s = \frac{VQ}{Ib} \qquad (9\text{--}2)$$

where V is the shear force, Q the statical moment about the neutral axis of that part of the cross-sectional area lying between the line at y' and the extreme fiber, and b is the breadth of the cross section at y'. The maximum shear stress thus often occurs at the neutral axis (though not in I-beam section) where the bending stress is zero, and near bearings. It is usually very much smaller than bending stresses, and therefore is frequently ignored.

Example. A uniform round steel shaft, 1.25-in. diameter, held in bearings 6 ft apart, rotates at 1000 rpm. When stationary the shaft has a slight initial curvature amounting to 0.005 in. at midspan. Find the maximum whipping stresses.

The critical speed is found approximately as follows, by the Rayleigh method (refer to pages 167–68):

Assume the maximum shaft deflection in transverse vibration

$$y = A \sin \frac{\pi x}{L} \qquad (a)$$

and that this varies with time (at every station x along the shaft) in simple harmonic manner as

$$\delta = y \sin \omega_n t$$

Then

$$\text{K.E.}_{\text{max}} = \frac{1}{2}\frac{w}{g}\int_0^L (y\omega_n)^2\, dx \quad \text{in.-lb}$$

$$\text{P.E.}_{\text{max}} = \frac{1}{2}EI\int_0^L \left(\frac{d^2y}{dx^2}\right)^2 dx \quad \text{in.-lb}$$

Equating:

$$\omega^2_n = \frac{EIg}{w}\left(\frac{\pi}{L}\right)^4 \frac{\int A^2 \sin^2 \pi x/L \cdot dx}{\int A^2 \sin^2 \pi x/L \cdot dx} = \left(\frac{\pi}{L}\right)^4 \frac{EIg}{w} \quad (\text{rad/sec})^2$$

For the shaft

$$w(\text{lb per inch length}) = 0.346 \text{ lb/in.}$$
$$L(\text{inches span}) = 72 \text{ in.}$$
$$E(\text{modulus}) = 30 \times 10^6 \text{ psi}$$
$$I(\text{area moment}) = \frac{\pi}{64} \cdot (1.25)^4 = 0.120 \text{ in.}^4$$

So $\omega_n = 120.5$ or $N_{\text{crit}} = 1150$ rpm.

The central deflection due to whipping at the running speed (that is additional to the original curvature) is then

$$A = \frac{0.005}{\left(\dfrac{1150}{1000}\right)^2 - 1} = \frac{0.005}{0.323} = 0.0155 \text{ in.}$$

if damping is neglected. In this case damping is not very significant; it cannot arise from intermolecular friction in the shaft, for the shaft is not flexing back and forth, but rotating with the same fiber outermost. Damping therefore can be due only to air friction which is slight, and from friction at the bearings which is located where the deflection is small.

To ignore damping, it should be noted, is to be on the safe side from the designer's point of view; for calculations on this basis can only lead to figures for stress larger than will actually occur.

Returning then to the equation of the deflected shape, (eq. a), the central deflection A has been found, and from that the bending moment at any point x can be found as

$$M = EI\frac{d^2y}{dx^2} = EIA\left(\frac{\pi}{L}\right)^2 \sin\frac{\pi x}{L}$$

From the maximum bending moment (when $\sin\frac{\pi x}{L} = 1$) the maximum tensile stress in the outer fiber at midspan is

$$S_t = \frac{Mc}{I} = E \cdot c \cdot A\left(\frac{\pi}{L}\right)^2 = 553 \text{ psi}$$

Not very large. But turn now to the shear stress. The maximum shear force occurs at the bearing where it is due to the sum of the centrifugal forces distributed over one-half the span. The radius of each element is the arithmetic sum of the original curvature and the deflection of y, for the shaft rotates below critical speed. The original shape can also be assumed sinusoidal without much possible error; thus the maximum shear force is

$$V = \frac{w}{g}\omega^2 \int_0^{L/2} (A + 0.005) \sin \frac{\pi x}{L} \, dx = \frac{w}{g}\frac{L}{\pi}\omega^2(A + 0.005)$$

$$= 6.13 \text{ lb}$$

Obviously the maximum shear stress is a much smaller quantity. Actually in a round cross section it is 133 per cent of the average stress, and occurs at the neutral axis. Hence the maximum shear stress in the shaft is

$$S_s = 1.33\frac{V}{\text{Area}} = 6.6 \text{ psi}$$

The results of this problem are particularly interesting in that they confirm (for this case) the general rule laid down by designers: a machine is satisfactory if it avoids all critical speeds by at least ten per cent.

Many problems removed from the notion of whirling shafting may yet be solved by an analysis similar to the above example. For instance, the side rod of a locomotive coupling the driving wheels has a parallel motion with plane circular path. The transverse component of the centrifugal forces will therefore act to set up whipping in the vertical plane; the stress from bending can be found when the deflection of the rod from straight is found.*

9–4. Radial Rods or Columns. When a bar projects from a rotating boss, the centrifugal force of the outermost end is carried by the penultimate section. Then at that section a further item of centrifugal force is added, and so on, so that the tensile stress increases toward the root of the bar.

The tensile stress at the root must be the product of the whole mass and the acceleration of the center of gravity of the bar, divided by the root area, for it has been proved already (page 9) that the resultant of all centrifugal forces of any body is the same as if the mass were concentrated at the center of gravity.

Now just as this applies to the whole bar, it must also apply to any

* See also M. W. Davidson, "Whip Stress in a Locomotive Main Rod at 100 Miles per Hour," *Trans. A.S.M.E.*, Vol. 62 (1940), p. 133.

part of the bar. The stress at any section will be due to the centrifugal force of that part of the bar which is outside that section.

For example, the round bar of cross-sectional area A and length $2L$, shown in Fig. 9-4, is mounted perpendicularly to the shaft O-O, with center on the centerline. The shaft and bar rotate about axis O-O. The tensile stress at any radius y may be found as follows:

(Since the bar is mounted symmetrically, the shaft and bar are balanced. Assume then that the shaft remains straight.)

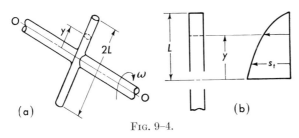

FIG. 9-4.

At any radius y the length of the bar outside this section is $(L - y)$ with the center of its mass at radius $(L + y)/2$. If the specific weight of the bar is ρ, the centrifugal force carried by the section at y is

$$\left[\frac{\rho A}{g}(L - y)\right]\left(\frac{L + y}{2}\right)\omega^2$$

and the tensile stress at section y is

$$S_t = \rho(L^2 - y^2)\omega^2/2g$$

The stress therefore increases according to a parabolic law, as shown in the graph in the figure at (b). Note however that L has been assumed a constant, whereas in fact, especially at very high speeds, it stretches.

Example. A turbine consists of a solid disk of diameter 16 in., into the rim of which are inserted the steel blades, in the manner shown in Fig. 9-5. Investigate the maximum stresses, when maximum running speed is 10,000 rpm (1047.2 rad/sec).

The stresses will always be greatest at the inside end of a given section. At section A-A, therefore, where the blade sectional area, measured by planimeter, is 0.147 sq in., the stress is found as follows:

Weight of blade outside section A-A = 0.283 × 1.062 × 0.147 =
0.0442 lb

Radius of center of gravity = 8.781 in.
Centrifugal force = 0.0442 × 8.781 × (1047.2)²/
386 = 1103 lb

Tensile stress (section A-A) = 7500 psi

The specific weight of steel is taken as 0.283 lb per cu in.

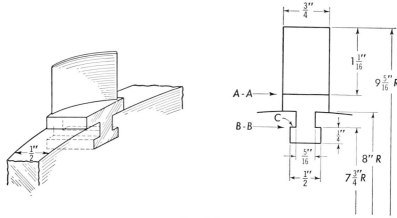

FIG. 9–5.

At section B–B there are added the centrifugal forces due to the packer (volume $\frac{1}{4}$ in. $\times$ $\frac{1}{2}$ in. $\times$ $\frac{3}{4}$ in.) and the dovetail neck ($\frac{1}{4}$ in. $\times$ $\frac{1}{2}$ in. $\times$ $\frac{5}{16}$ in.).

Additional centrifugal force

$$= [0.283 \times (1047.2)^2/386] \times [(\tfrac{1}{4} \times \tfrac{1}{2} \times \tfrac{3}{4} \times 8.125) +$$
$$(\tfrac{1}{4} \times \tfrac{1}{2} \times \tfrac{5}{16} \times 7.875)]$$
$$= 860 \text{ lb}$$

Total centrifugal force $= 1963$ lb

Tensile stress (section B–B) $= 1963/(\tfrac{5}{16} \times \tfrac{1}{2}) = 12{,}570$ psi

The shoulders C of the dovetail must carry not only the above centrifugal force but also that from the wide part of the blade dovetail.

Additional centrifugal force

$$= [0.283 \times (1047.2)^2/386] (\tfrac{1}{4} \times \tfrac{1}{2} \times \tfrac{1}{2} \times 7.625)$$
$$= 383 \text{ lb}$$

Compression on shoulders $= 2346/(\tfrac{3}{16} \times \tfrac{1}{2}) = 25{,}000$ psi

These calculations ignore stress concentrations. At the root of the blade there will usually be adequate fillets, but at the inside of the dovetail the corners have very small radius, so that the tensile stress at section B–B may easily be double that calculated near those corners.

The last calculation in the foregoing example shows a case where centrifugal force may cause compressive stresses in a radial bar.

In Fig. 9–6 some bars are shown projecting inward from a rotating ring. In this case the bars must be considered as columns in compression, and the possibility of buckling at speed arises. The tendency to buckle is greatly aggravated if there is any slight variation in speed, for this causes the columns to sway.

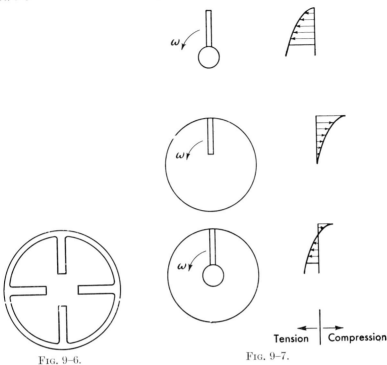

Tension | Compression

FIG. 9–6.   FIG. 9–7.

When a radial bar is anchored at both inside and outside ends, both the tensile and compressive systems are superimposed, with the result that the stress magnitude throughout can be approximately halved (Fig. 9–7). Thus the blades of the turbines, as in the example above, are usually restrained at their outer ends by a thin hoop or shroud. The amount of compressive stress at the outer ends depends upon the stiffness of the shroud ring.

9–5. Hoop Stress. A thin hoop or ring (Fig. 9–8) subjected to centrifugal forces presents exactly the same problem as that of a thin tube

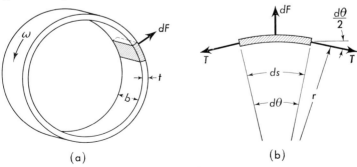

(a)   (b)

FIG. 9–8.

under internal hydraulic pressure. Similarly a heavy ring, or wheel rim, is analogous to the thick-walled cylinder problem.

In the figure a ring of mean radius r, small thickness t, and width b rotates at angular velocity ω. On an element of arc length ds, which subtends $d\theta$ at the center, the centrifugal force is

$$dF = (\rho bt\ ds)(r\omega^2/g) = \rho btr^2 d\theta(\omega^2/g) \qquad (9\text{-}3)$$

where ρ is the specific weight (e.g., lb/cu in.).

From the equilibrium of forces shown in the figure at (b), by resolving radially

$$2T \sin\left(\frac{d\theta}{2}\right) = dF$$
$$T\ d\theta = dF$$

Thus the tensile hoop stress is

$$S_t = T/bt = \rho r^2\omega^2/g \qquad (9\text{-}4)$$

This is often written

$$S_t = \rho V^2/g \qquad (9\text{-}5)$$

where V is the rim velocity. It is independent of both the thickness and width of the hoop, so long as the thickness is small, as in the hypothesis.

The comparison with the hydraulic case is made in eq. 9–3, in which the centrifugal force is seen to be equivalent to an internal pressure of

$$p = \rho tr\omega^2/g$$

Because the hoop stress is dependent on rim velocity, it is common in the design of machine parts, such as flywheels, to see the rim velocity specified.

An important consequence of hoop stress is an increase in diameter of the hoop. Thin rings and collars which are given a shrink fit to a shaft may loosen themselves at speed.

The circumferential strain as a result of the stress in eq. 9–4 is

$$e_t = E\rho r^2\omega^2/g$$

But the ratio of change in circumference to original circumference is also the ratio of change in diameter to original diameter: where δ represents a small finite change

$$\frac{\delta(\pi D)}{\pi D} = \frac{\delta D}{D} = e_t$$
$$\delta D = E\rho D^3\omega^2/4g \qquad (9\text{-}6)$$

This is the change in diameter effected by the stress.

9–6. Stresses in a Rotating Disk. The solution of this problem is considerably more difficult than the last. It is included here because it is a problem of great significance and also because it will introduce the student to a typical method employed in the mathematical theory of elasticity.

In common with all problems that are statically indeterminate it is necessary to write equations of statical equilibrium, and also equations of geometry based on strain, and then to correlate stress and strain.

The following assumptions* are made: that the disk is of elastic, iso-tropic, and homogenous material, and that the stress parallel to the axis of rotation is uniform across the thickness of the disk at any given radius. Thus the stresses and strains can be taken as a two-dimensional system; there can be no warping of the disk and no shear stresses at all.

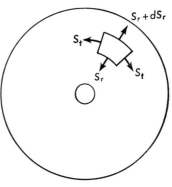

FIG. 9–9.

The disk is considered as a series of narrow, concentric rings, each of radial thickness dr. Each ring (as in the last problem) tends to expand, but the next outer ring will prevent some of this expansion, while the next inner ring will increase it. There is therefore radial stress s_r, as well as hoop stress s_t.

When an element of a body, as shown in Fig. 9–9, is subjected to stress s_r in one direction it will have extension in that direction and contraction in the two perpendicular directions, so that the strains in the radial and tangential directions will be

$$e_r = \frac{1}{E}(s_r - \nu s_t) \left.\begin{array}{c} \\ \\ \end{array}\right\}$$
$$e_t = \frac{1}{E}(s_t - \nu s_r) \left.\begin{array}{c} \\ \\ \end{array}\right\} \qquad (9\text{–}7)$$

where ν is Poisson's ratio.

The cylindrical element of the disk shown in the figure has volume $(b \times r\,d\theta \times dr)$. The centrifugal force is then

$$dF = \frac{\rho b r^2 \omega^2}{g}\, dr \cdot d\theta$$

where b is the (uniform) disk thickness, and ρ its weight per unit volume. The equilibrium of radial outward forces will therefore be found by equating the force to the products of each stress and the area upon which it acts.

$$(s_r + ds_r)[(r + dr)d\theta \cdot b] - s_r[r\,d\theta \cdot b] - 2s_t[b \cdot dr]\sin d\theta/2 + (\rho b r^2 \omega^2/g)dr \cdot d\theta = 0$$

* For the effects of various assumptions see J. Prescott, *Applied Elasticity*, New York: Dover Publications, 1946, p. 326–46.

With $\sin d\theta/2 = d\theta/2$, and all terms involving the third order of small quantities discarded, then dividing by $(b\, dr \cdot d\theta)$ we have

$$r\frac{ds_r}{dr} + s_r - s_t + \rho r^2 \omega^2/g = 0 \tag{9-8}$$

If the last term above is omitted, this is the same equation derived in many machine design books for thick-walled cylinders (Lamé's equations).

Now the geometrical relations give the other necessary data. Suppose the ring of radius r expands a small but finite amount u. The circumference $2\pi r$ then reaches $2\pi(r + u)$, and the strain in the tangential sense is the ratio

$$e_t = \frac{2\pi(r + u) - 2\pi r}{2\pi r} = u/r \tag{9-9}$$

In the radial sense the expansion at r is u and at $r + dr$ it is $u + du$ $\left(\text{strictly } u + \dfrac{du}{dr}\, dr\right)$, and therefore the strain is the proportional extension on length dr or

$$e_r = \frac{(u + du) - u}{dr} = \frac{du}{dr} \tag{9-10}$$

Transform eqs. 9-7 to express stress in terms of strain

$$s_r = \frac{E}{1 - \nu^2}(e_r + \nu e_t)$$

$$s_t = \frac{E}{1 - \nu^2}(e_t + \nu e_r)$$

From eqs. 9-9 and 9-10

$$\left. \begin{array}{l} s_r = \dfrac{E}{1 - \nu^2}\left(\dfrac{du}{dr} + \nu\dfrac{u}{r}\right) \\[3mm] s_t = \dfrac{E}{1 - \nu^2}\left(\dfrac{u}{r} + \nu\dfrac{du}{dr}\right) \end{array} \right\} \tag{9-11}$$

Substitute in eq. 9-8

$$\frac{d^2u}{dr^2} + \frac{1}{r}\frac{du}{dr} - \frac{u}{r^2} + \left(\frac{1 - \nu^2}{E}\right)\rho r\omega^2/g = 0 \tag{9-12}$$

This can be solved for u, if it is noted that the first three terms can be combined, so that

$$\frac{d}{dr}\left[\frac{1}{r}\frac{d(ur)}{dr}\right] + \frac{(1 - \nu^2)}{E} \cdot \frac{\rho r\omega^2}{g} = 0$$

whence

$$u = Ar + \frac{B}{r} - \frac{(1 - \nu^2)\rho\omega^2}{8Eg}r^3 = 0 \tag{9-13}$$

This then is the radial expansion u of any elemental ring of radius r. A and B are arbitrary constants of integration, which may be determined by the boundary conditions. From the relations in eqs. 9–11

$$s_r = C_1 + C_2/r^2 - \frac{(3 + \nu)\rho r^2 \omega^2}{8g} \tag{9–14}$$

$$s_t = C_1 - C_2/r^2 - \frac{(1 + 3\nu)\rho r^2 \omega^2}{8g} \tag{9–15}$$

where C_1, C_2 are arbitrary, but related to A, B.

Two common cases occur: either the disk is solid, or it has a hole in its center.

1. SOLID DISK. The arbitrary C_2 must be zero, or both stresses would be infinite at the center. C_1 may be found since at the outside radius r_0 the radial stress must be zero or

$$C_1 = \frac{(3 + \nu)\rho \omega^2}{8g}(r_0)^2$$

Then

$$s_r = \frac{(3 + \nu)\rho \omega^2}{8g}(r_0^2 - r^2)$$

$$s_t = \frac{\rho \omega^2}{8g}[(3r_0^2 - r^2) - \nu(3r^2 - r_0^2)]$$

At $r = 0$ both stresses are equal to C_1.

2. DISK WITH CENTRAL HOLE. C_1, C_2 are determined by the two boundary conditions. There can be no radial stress s_r at the hole radius r_i or the outside radius r_0. Equation 9–14 will yield then

$$0 = C_1 + \frac{C_2}{r_0^2} - \kappa r_0^2$$

$$0 = C_1 + \frac{C_2}{r_i^2} - \kappa r_i^2$$

where κ is short for $(3 + \nu)\rho \omega^2/8g$. Now solving for C_1, C_2

$$C_2 = -\kappa r_i^2 r_0^2$$
$$C_1 = \kappa(r_i^2 + r_0^2)$$

so that the stresses become fully expressed as

$$s_r = \kappa(r_i^2 + r_0^2 - r^2 - r_0^2 r_i^2/r^2)$$
$$s_t = \kappa(r_i^2 + r_0^2 + r_0^2 r_i^2/r^2 - \{(1 + 3\nu)/(3 + \nu)\}r^2)$$

The hoop stress is always a maximum at the boundary of the inner hole. The radial stress is a maximum at the root mean radius $\sqrt{r_0 r_i}$.

In turbine rotors, in order to hold the hoop stress down to a reasonable value, the rotor is made considerably thicker toward the center. The ideal rotor section may be shown to have a thickness diminishing exponentially with the radius. To design the section of a rotor, several approximate methods of analysis have also been devised which involve merely a routine numerical procedure; an example of the "sum and difference" method of Donath is given by Timoshenko. Recent papers undertake to combine in the analysis stresses due to a temperature gradient in the wheel.

9–7. Skew Rotor. Effect of Centrifugal Couples. If a non-symmetrical body is attached to a rotating shaft there will be centrifugal moments due to the product of inertia of the body about the axis, but the flexible yielding of the body and of the shaft will affect their magnitudes. Various assumptions are permissible in order to obtain an approximate answer, and the example following illustrates two such assumptions.

Example. A steel shaft of $\frac{1}{2}$-in. diameter, simply supported between bearings 18 in. apart, carries at midspan a cross bar of rectangular ($\frac{3}{4} \times \frac{1}{2}$) section and 8-in. length. The bar is set at 45° to the axis of rotation (as in Fig. 9–10). It is desired to find the stresses when the shaft rotates at 3000 rpm.

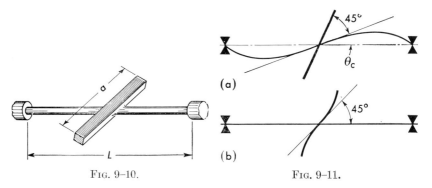

FIG. 9–10.   FIG. 9–11.

Several assumptions are alternatively possible; for instance:

1. The cross bar will not bend significantly but the shaft will flex to a double curvature (Fig. 9–11a). But it is reckoned that the centrifugal forces of the shaft itself, thus caused, will be too small to affect the shape of the shaft.
2. The centrifugal forces of the shaft are included as well as the centrifugal couple from the rigid cross bar.
3. The cross bar is reckoned to bend, and the shaft to remain stiff (Fig. 9–11b).
4. Both bend.

The relative importance of the terms will become apparent in the development of the following:

1. The shaft is bent to a double curvature by the centrifugal couple from the cross bar. The couple is not known because the inclination of the cross bar is increased from 45° by the angle θ_c (Fig. 9–11) of inclination of the shaft. Let the couple be C, and the reactions at the bearings will then be $R = C/L$ when L is the span (Fig. 9–12).

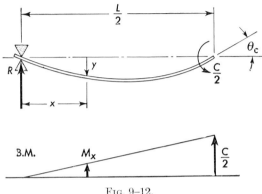

Fig. 9–12.

By the theory of flexure of beams, the shape of the shaft may be found from the bending moment M_x at any position x from the left bearing:

$$-EI\frac{d^2y}{dx^2} = M_x = \frac{C}{2}\frac{x}{L/2} = \frac{C}{L}x \tag{9–16}$$

Two integrations of this give

$$y = -\frac{C}{6EIL}x^3 + \theta_0 x + y_0$$

where θ_0, y_0 are constants of integration which are determined by the conditions that $y = 0$ at $x = 0$ and $x = L/2$; thus

$$y_0 = 0 \quad \text{and} \quad \theta_0 = \frac{CL}{24EI}$$

and

$$y = \frac{Cx}{6EIL}\left(\frac{L^2}{4} - x^2\right) \tag{9–17}$$

Differentiate and set $x = L/2$ to find the slope at the center

$$-\left[\frac{dy}{dx}\right]_{x = L/2} = \theta_c = \frac{CL}{12EI} \text{ radians} \tag{9–18}$$

Regarding the cross bar, the couple that is exerted depends upon the product of inertia and the speed.

$$C = I_{xy}\omega^2$$

If the cross bar is regarded as slender, this is

$$C = \frac{1}{2}\left(\frac{W}{g}\frac{a^2}{12}\right)\omega^2 \sin 2(45° + \theta_c)$$

where a is the length of the cross bar (Fig. 9–10). But more accurately (refer to eq. 6–18, page 242) it is

$$C = -\frac{W}{2g}\left(\frac{a^2}{12} - \frac{b^2}{12}\right)\omega^2 \sin 2(45° + \theta_c) \tag{9-19}$$

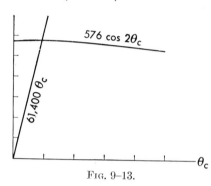

576 cos 2θ_c

61,400 θ_c

θ_c

FIG. 9–13.

for this includes the counter-moment due to the breadth of the bar.

For equilibrium, the couples C occurring in eqs. 9–18 and 9–19 must agree; we solve for the angle

$$\frac{W(a^2 - b^2)\omega^2}{24g}\cos 2\theta_c = \frac{12EI}{L}\theta_c \tag{9-20}$$

This sort of transcendental equation must be solved graphically, and numerical substitution is needed.

$$L = 18 \text{ in.}; E = 30 \times 10^6 \text{ psi}$$

$$I \text{ (cross section of shaft)} = \frac{\pi}{64}(\tfrac{1}{2})^4$$

$$W = 0.283 \times 8 \times \tfrac{3}{4} \times \tfrac{1}{2} = 0.849 \text{ lb}$$
$$a = 8, b = \tfrac{1}{2}, \quad a^2 - b^2 = 63.75 \text{ sq in.}$$
$$\omega = (\pi/30)3000 = 314.2 \text{ rad/sec}, g = 386 \text{ in./sec}^2$$

Hence

$$576 \cos 2\theta_c = 61,400\theta_c \tag{9-21}$$

From the sketch of the graph in Fig. 9–13, it is plain that θ_c is very small: it will be more accurate then to compute by putting $\cos 2\theta_c = 1 - \tfrac{1}{2}(2\theta_c)^2$ or even to unity:

$$1 - 2\theta_c^2 = 106.5\theta_c$$
$$\theta_c = 0.0094 \text{ radians} = 0.538 \text{ degrees}$$

From the left-hand side of eq. 9–21 then, since the maximum bending moment is $C/2$ occurring at the center of the shaft (Fig. 9–12), the maximum stress in the shaft is

$$s_t = \frac{Mc}{I} = \frac{576}{2} \cdot \frac{0.25}{I} = 23{,}480 \text{ psi}$$

And in the cross bar the bending moment is also $C/2$ from the centrifugal couple of each half, so that

$$s_t = 9216 \text{ psi}$$

2. When the centrifugal force on the shaft itself is to be included it is easiest to start with the fourth-order equation of the loading on the shaft (refer to page 178). If w is the weight of the shaft per inch run

$$EI \frac{d^4 y}{dx^4} = \frac{w}{g} y \omega^2$$

which has for general solution

$$y = A_1 \sin px + A_2 \cos px + A_3 \sinh px + A_4 \cosh px$$

Substitution confirms that $p^4 = \dfrac{w}{g} \dfrac{\omega^2}{EI}$. We shall deal only with the half-span because of the discontinuity at the cross bar. In the equation above, from the manner of support and loading, the four constants are found:

$y = 0$ at $x = 0$	$A_2 + A_4 = 0$
$-EI\dfrac{d^2 y}{dx^2} = 0$ at $x = 0$	$-A_2 + A_4 = 0$ so $A_2 = A_4 = 0$
$y = 0$ at $x = L/2$	$A_1 \sin pL/2 + A_3 \sinh pL/2 = 0$
$-EI\dfrac{d^2 y}{dx^2} = C/2$ at $x = L/2$	$A_1 \sin pL/2 - A_3 \sinh pL/2 = C/2EIp^2$

Whence

$$A_1 \sin pL/2 = C/4EIp^2$$

Finally

$$y = \frac{C}{4EIp^2}\left(\frac{\sin px}{\sin pL/2} - \frac{\sinh px}{\sinh pL/2}\right) \tag{9–22}$$

If a check on this solution is desired, the reader will find agreement between two expressions for the reaction force R at the left-hand bearing, one by the shear force

$$R = EI\frac{d^3 y}{dx^3}\Big]_{x=0}$$

the other by taking moments about the center

$$\frac{RL}{2} = C + \int_0^{L/2} \frac{w}{g} y \omega^2 \left(\frac{L}{2} - x\right) dx$$

The slope θ_c is found as the derivative of y (eq. 9–22).

$$\theta = -\frac{dy}{dx}\bigg]_{x=L/2} = \frac{C}{4EIp}\left[\coth\frac{pL}{2} - \cot\frac{pL}{2}\right] \qquad (9\text{-}23)$$

and this is solved together with eq. 9–19 for the couple from the cross bar. Numerical substitution produces the following:

$$w = 0.283 \times \pi(\tfrac{1}{4})^2; \quad p^4 = 1.543 \times 10^{-4}; \quad p = 0.1115 \text{ rad/in.}$$

Corresponding to the right-hand side of eq. 9–21 we now get

$$C = 60{,}700\,\theta_c$$

The stresses are virtually unchanged; the angular deflection increases a little to 0.0095 radians, which is as expected.

Thus, except for the fact that this second solution is no longer or more difficult than the first, there appears no justification for it. However, if the cross bar were set more nearly normal to the shaft, the gyroscopic couple would be more sensitive to slight changes in the angle of inclination.

The further investigation of assumptions such as those listed in (3) and (4) on page 394 is left for the student.

9–8. Effects of Tangential Acceleration—The Swinging Pendulum.
When dealing with the reactions caused by angular acceleration on a pendulum or any crank, it was sufficient to deal with the *resultant* of all inertia forces which was found to act through the center of percussion. It must be emphasized again, this resultant must not be regarded as if it were a concentrated load when stresses are to be investigated.

Consideration of the field of the inertia forces from successive elements of a swinging or rotating body such as the uniform bar of Fig. 9–14 shows that they will increase linearly with the radius r from the fixed axis. The reaction R at the bearing will be equal to the sum $M\bar{r}\alpha$ where $\bar{r}$ is the radius of the center of gravity, and equilibrium is maintained by the couple $I_0\alpha$ that must be applied externally to achieve the angular acceleration α.

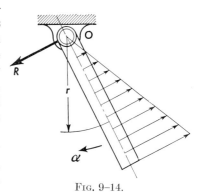

Fig. 9–14.

In the body, therefore, the shear is a maximum equal to R at the center, and diminishes parabolically to zero at the free end. The expression for the shear force at any radius x is

$$S_x = \int_l^{r=x}\left(\frac{w}{g}r\alpha\right)dr \qquad (9\text{-}24)$$

where l is the maximum length and w the weight per unit length.

The bending moment will also (in the illustration) be a maximum equal to $I_0\alpha$ at the center, increasing from zero at the free end. At radius x it is expressed by

$$\text{B.M.}_x = \int_l^x \left(\frac{w}{g}r\alpha\right)(r - x)dr \qquad (9\text{–}25)$$

On the other hand, if the angular acceleration is not caused by an external torque applied at the center, but by the weight of the body itself, as in an oscillating pendulum, the conditions are markedly different.

Example. A rigid pendulum swings through 90° amplitude either way under the influence of its own weight. Find the maximum shear and bending moment when it is horizontal.

We choose the horizontal to eliminate centrifugal forces. Figure 9–15 shows at (a) the loading. At (b) the shear forces due to inertia are given by the curve S_i, and those due to weight by S_w. The resultant is shown as a heavy dotted line. At (c) in the figure the maximum bending moment is seen to occur (of course) where the shear force is zero.

(If the reader should desire to draw the forces, etc., acting upon an element of length, no couple $\delta I\alpha$ should appear on such a figure. The couple $I\alpha$ for the whole is merely a convenient notation to express the difference between the uniformly increasing system of forces $mr\alpha$ shown in Fig. 9–15a, and a constant distributed force $m(l/2)\alpha$ which is the mean value of $mr\alpha$.)

For the shear at any x, eq. 9–24 becomes

$$S_i = \frac{w}{2g}\alpha(l^2 - x^2) = \frac{W}{g} \cdot \frac{l}{2} \cdot \alpha\left(1 - \frac{x^2}{l^2}\right)$$

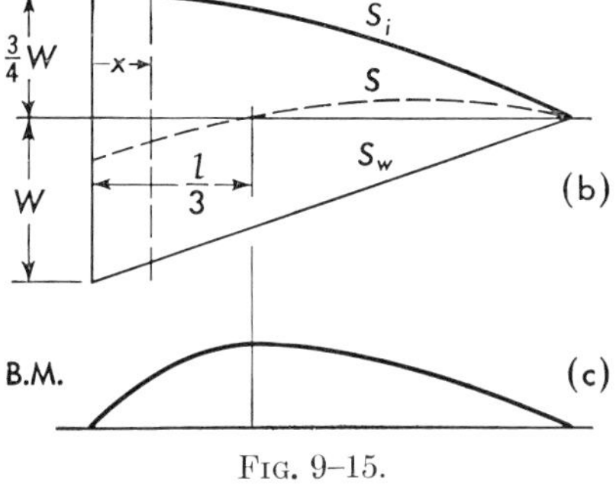

Fig. 9–15.

if $W = wl$. And the total shear

$$S = \frac{w\alpha}{2g}(l^2 - x^2) - w(l - x)$$

The angular acceleration α may be found by the moment of the resultant forces (see page 23) to be $3g/2l$, and when this is entered in the above:

$$S = \frac{3}{4}W\left(1 - \frac{x^2}{l^2}\right) - W\left(1 - \frac{x}{l}\right)$$

$$= -\frac{1}{4}W\left(1 - \frac{4x}{l} + \frac{3x^2}{l^2}\right) \qquad (9\text{--}26)$$

The shear is zero at a point one-third out, a maximum (in the positive sense) two-thirds out, that is, at the center of percussion, and a maximum in the opposite sense at the pivot. Here it has the value $W/4$, which is equal to the reaction R_V.

Consider the pendulum divided at radius x and between x and l treated as a free body. The bending moment at x must equal the moment of all forces about that section, or

$$\text{B.M.}_x = \int_x^l \left(\frac{w}{g}r\alpha - w\right)(r - x)dr$$

$$\text{B.M.} = \frac{Wx}{4}\left(1 - 2\frac{x}{l} + \frac{x^2}{l^2}\right) \qquad (9\text{--}27)$$

This might also be obtained directly from eq. 9–26 by integration. The maximum moment at $x = l/3$ is

$$\text{B.M.}_{\max} = Wl/27$$

so that the maximum stress, if the thickness of the pendulum is b, is

$$S_t = \frac{Wlb}{54I}$$

It is to be hoped that the student detected the approximation latent in this solution of the problem. It is the same matter discussed in Art. 9–1—that we have taken the pendulum to suffer stress and not strain; for the inertia loading was calculated under the assumption that the centerline remained straight. And this is a contradiction in terms.

Maybe the pendulum was rigid enough; but what about a swinging chain or rope? This is a problem studied in Classical Mechanics; it is rather involved and will not be taken up here. But it is plain that the swinging chain cannot carry bending moments at all, and consequently the stresses imposed on it by its motion are less.

The question is then posed: does increased flexibility of machine members generally reduce stress? And is it, per se, desirable in design?

The general answer is in the negative; flexibility is a property that finds its chief use in the isolation of shock, as a cushion.

9-9. Flexibility and Natural Frequency of Mechanisms. Consider the problems of an engineer engaged in the design of a mechanism that is part of an automatic machine. Perhaps it is a cam moving a swinging follower which turns a shaft to move a tool, as in many screw machines, or a four-bar linkage which operates a clamp or jaws.

In most such machines the prime requisite is that the tool should be advanced or the part moved in a predetermined manner. Exact timing is important also. This being so, there is no room for flexibility in the drive or linkage. The motion must be positive, and actuating links are made as stiff as possible.

But there is another aspect: in this type of mechanism the motion is generally some sort of reciprocation; that is, the velocity of the driven members is not constant. Therefore there is a continual change in the kinetic energy of the linkage. Some member, the tool perhaps, is stationary, then it must be advanced, then stopped and retracted. In most cases the distance over which this energy change is to be accomplished is very small, which results in very high forces, unless the mass of all driven members is kept at a minimum.

This creates somewhat of a contradiction—for if the members are to be inflexible, they are generally sturdy and have greater mass. However if they are stiffer they are also able to take the higher stresses concomitant with greater mass.

Example. The swinging arm of a cam follower is mounted upon a torque shaft which transfers the motion from the enclosed "works" of the machine to the front, where it moves a reciprocating tool by means of a slider-crank mechanism. The original design calls for a solid shaft; would a hollow torque tube be better?

The torsional stiffness of a shaft is given by GJ/L (eq. 3-30, p. 117), where J is the polar area moment of inertia of the section. Now the energy is proportional to the polar mass moment of inertia I; and $I = \rho J$ where ρ is the specific mass of the material, if I is interpreted as the moment of inertia per unit length. Thus if the shaft in the design is changed from solid to hollow for equal torsional strength, its rotational energy will remain unchanged. An increase in stiffness, of any section, will increase the effective mass proportionately. However since the energy of the system is comprised of that of the following slider-crank as well as that of the shaft, an increase in the stiffness of the shaft will produce a lesser increase in the over-all effective mass.

For increased precise control of the tool, there is nothing to choose between hollow and solid shafts, though an increase in stiffness of the torque shaft is good. But note the far greater benefit that accrues if the shaft can be shortened, for then stiffness increases while mass decreases.

Greater stiffness, less mass—this is synonymous with increased natural frequency; for $\omega^2 = k/m$. And this is the third item for design consideration. Every mechanism should be thought of in terms of a simple spring–mass system, in which one end of the spring is moved in a certain desired manner, and in which it is hoped that the mass at the other end of the spring will move in the same manner; that is, as reckoned by kinematics on the rigid-body assumption. Two examples of this have already been given in Art. 5–8. It is plain that the motion of the driven members will never be *exactly* as reckoned; and the error, the undesirable difference, will become very great if the natural frequency of the mechanism should agree too closely with the frequencies involved in the imposed motion, for then resonance may occur.

We may summarize all three aspects of this discussion then by saying that the natural frequency of a mechanism should be high if precise control of the movement of the driven members is desired. The natural frequency of the mechanism here refers to the frequency with which the body at the free end of the linkage would oscillate if given a sharp hammer blow while the driving crank or cam is stationary.

There are occasions in which softer, more flexible links are desirable however; in these the softness is to act as a cushion. Suppose a drive-shaft that is known to carry torsional vibrations of a high frequency is to drive a four-link chain. If the connecting link is made stiff there may be danger of resonance. But if the connecting link is made thin, it will act as a cushion filtering out the high frequency and responding only to the slower principal motion of the driving crank. Precise definition of the position of the driven crank is absent, of course; but it is not available anyway if the drive-shaft motion contains the torsional.

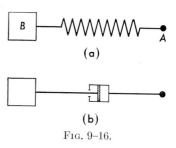

(a)

(b)

Fig. 9–16.

So it is with the control of any shock loading. A soft cushion, a flexible connection, will transfer only part of the shock to the neighboring members, storing the remainder as strain energy within itself. Thus the instantaneous stresses are greatly lowered. But after the shock is past, the strain energy will work out of containment, and this may start a free vibration. It is generally required therefore that, wherever shock is encountered, damping be incorporated together with cushioning, so that the energy may be dissipated.

A damper may be regarded fundamentally in two ways: first, it is a device for dissipation of stray vibrations; second, it acts to modify and counteract the effect of a spring under sustained forced vibrations. For if a body B, as in Fig. 9–16a, is connected to a moving point A by a spring, the body will move more for low-frequency and less for high-frequency oscillations of the point, whereas, if as in the figure at (b) the connection is a dashpot, the response of the body is more for the high frequency and less for the low.

9–10. A Flexible Cam-Follower System. As an illustration of some of the remarks in the preceding article, we take a cam and its follower which is to move a mass. The follower may be of any form, with several links perhaps between the actual cam-roll or mushroom and the major body to be moved, yet it may always be simulated or simplified to the system shown in Fig. 9–19.

For the motion that is to be designed into the cam, we consider a rise through a height h from a static base position to a dwell at the top. This is the type of motion that a cam mechanism is peculiarly well adapted to produce, beyond the capabilities of most other mechanisms.

Such a rise may be accomplished in many ways, but the four most common methods, as the student of kinematics will know, are by constant velocity, by simple harmonic motion, by constant acceleration and deceleration,* and by so-called "cycloidal" motion, or by combinations of these. These four are represented by the following equations:

(i) $s = vt$ $\qquad\qquad$ for $0 < t < T$ $\qquad\qquad$ (9–28)

$\qquad$ with $v = h/T$

(ii) $s = \frac{1}{2}h(1 - \cos pt)$ $\qquad$ for $0 < t < T$ $\qquad\qquad$ (9–29)

$\qquad$ with $p = \pi/T$

(iii) $s = \frac{1}{2}at^2$ $\qquad\qquad$ for $0 < t < T/2$, and$\left.\right\}$ (9–30)

$\qquad s = h - \frac{1}{2}a(T - t)^2$ $\qquad$ for $T/2 < t < T$

$\qquad$ with $a = 4h/T^2$

(iv) $s = v\left(t - \dfrac{1}{p}\sin pt\right)$ $\qquad$ for $0 < t < T$ $\qquad\qquad$ (9–31)

$\qquad$ with $v = h/T$ and $p = 2\pi/T$

Radial cams are of two types, the open radial or disk cam, and the positive radial, either with a groove in the face or with two followers. Each has its problems in operation. On the open radial cam the follower must not be permitted to separate from the cam, and this is likely to occur theoretically (by rigid follower assumptions) at or before the cam position giving maximum deceleration, although actually somewhat later (because of flexibility). A spring is needed to prevent this separa-

* Often called "parabolic" or "gravity" motion.

tion, yet it must not be too strong, for friction and contact stresses must be a minimum.* On the positive cams no spring is needed, and the problem arises when the contact of the follower shifts from one side of the track to the other. This movement is usually less than two or three

FIG. 9–17.

FIG. 9–18.

thousandths of an inch, and as such might be thought unimportant. Yet it is not so—the impact can be very high as Fig. 9–18 demonstrates. Figure 9–17 is a photograph of a face cam, and Fig. 9–18 is a closer view of its track that is worn out by these impacts—the cam-roll follower was thrown with such force across the track the first time that it bounced back and forth half a dozen times.

A study of this impact problem is given in the following example, in which a rise of a given height to a dwell is to be obtained theoretically with simple harmonic motion. It is plain that cross-over of the follower

* See J. A. Hrones, "An Analysis of the Dynamic Forces in a Cam-Driven System," *Trans. A.S.M.E.*, Vol. 70 (1948), p. 473.

in the track will occur with zero acceleration; that is, when the inertia forces change sign.

Example. The follower system of a closed-track face cam is shown in simplified form in Fig. 9–19. In this the cam-roll is assumed to have negligible mass: it is connected by a push rod (or other linkage), of stiffness k, to the principal mass M. (If the mass of the push rod itself is to be incorporated, then presumably M should represent the principal mass plus some proportion of this other mass; that is, M is the equivalent mass of the system.)

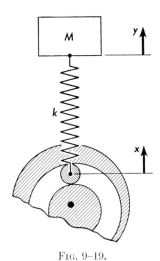

FIG. 9–19.

The displacement diagram of the cam shows that it gives to the cam-roll a motion x given by

$$x = \tfrac{1}{2}h(1 - \cos pt) \quad \text{for } 0 < t < T$$

where $p = \pi/T$ and T is the time for the whole rise h (see eq. 9–29). After $t = T$, there is a dwell so that the equation is $x = h$.

The mass M will move with a motion y caused by the force transmitted through the spring. Thus the displacement of M from its initial static position is given by y in the equation

$$k(x - y) = M\ddot{y} \tag{9–32}$$

if damping is neglected. Now substituting x and setting $k/M = \omega^2$ for the natural frequency

$$\ddot{y} + \omega^2 y = \tfrac{1}{2}\omega^2 h(1 - \cos pt)$$

This has a general solution (complementary plus particular)

$$y = A \sin \omega t + B \cos \omega t + \frac{h}{2}\left(1 - \frac{\omega^2}{\omega^2 - p^2} \cos pt\right)$$

when A and B are arbitrary. For our case, initially $y = \dot{y} = \ddot{y} = 0$, so that $A = 0$ and

$$B = +\frac{h}{2}\left(\frac{p^2}{\omega^2 - p^2}\right)$$

or

$$y = \frac{h}{2}\left(1 - \frac{\omega^2}{\omega^2 - p^2} \cos pt + \frac{p^2}{\omega^2 - p^2} \cos \omega t\right) \qquad (9\text{-}33)$$

This is, of course, only within the limits $0 < t < T$ during which x changes. At $t = T$ we may find from this how much the displacement y differs from h and find the velocity $\dot{y}$, and so find the starting conditions for a simple harmonic oscillation of y about the position $y = h$, which will in actual conditions gradually die down.

Differentiating y, we have

$$\dot{y} = \frac{h\omega p}{2(\omega^2 - p^2)}(\omega \sin pt - p \sin \omega t) \qquad (9\text{-}34)$$

$$\ddot{y} = \frac{h\omega^2 p^2}{2(\omega^2 - p^2)}(\cos pt - \cos \omega t) \qquad (9\text{-}35)$$

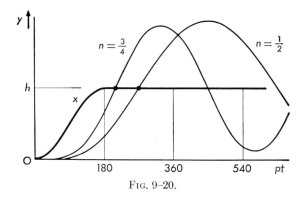

Fig. 9–20.

(i) Let k be soft so that $\omega < p$. Then over the period of the rise, that is for $0 < t < T$, the acceleration $\ddot{y}$ will never be zero. The cross-over must occur after the rise is theoretically supposed to be completed. The graphs (Figs. 9–20, 21, and 22) show two cases when $\omega = \frac{1}{2}p$ and when $\omega = \frac{3}{4}p$—and they compare the displacement (Fig. 9–20), the velocity (Fig. 9–21), and the acceleration (Fig. 9–22) of the body M having the motion y to the theoretical motion x that is designed into the cam.

Let $\omega = np$; then at $t = T$ when the cam starts its dwell, the displacement y is

$$y_T = \frac{h}{2}\left(1 - \frac{n^2}{n^2 - 1}\cos \pi + \frac{1}{n^2 - 1}\cos n\pi\right) \tag{9–36}$$

since $pT = \pi$; the follower is thus short of its goal by

$$h - y_T = \frac{1 + \cos n\pi}{2(1 - n^2)}h \tag{9–37}$$

and the velocity at this same instant is (from eq. 9–34)

$$\dot{y}_T = \frac{hnp}{2(1 - n^2)}\sin n\pi \tag{9–38}$$

The amplitude of the simple harmonic motion of frequency ω that follows will be (by eq. 3–28)

$$A = \sqrt{(1 + \cos n\pi)^2 + \sin^2 n\pi}\left(\frac{h}{2(1 - n^2)}\right)$$

$$= \frac{h}{2} \cdot \frac{\sqrt{2(1 + \cos n\pi)}}{(1 - n^2)} \tag{9–39}$$

Zero acceleration will of course occur with maximum velocity of this simple harmonic motion. And thus the cross-over of the cam-follower will occur when the velocity of mass M is $V_c = Anp$. The less this is, the less will be the shock of this exchange.

$$\text{Shock} \sim \frac{V_c}{\frac{1}{2}hp} = \frac{n}{1 - n^2}\sqrt{2}\sqrt{1 + \cos n\pi} \tag{9–40}$$

(ii) Let k be stiffer so that $\omega > p$. Now the response of the mass M shows a motion of a type similar to that described in Art. 5–8. Figures

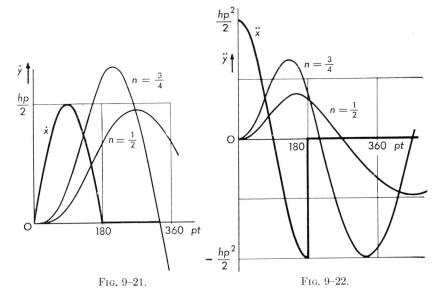

FIG. 9–21.   FIG. 9–22.

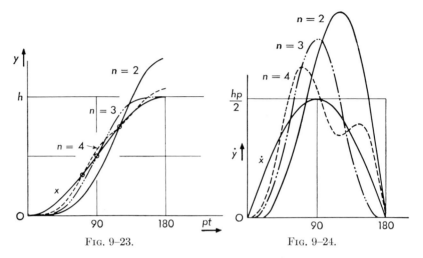

Fig. 9–23.   Fig. 9–24.

9–23, 9–24, and 9–25 show respectively the displacement, velocity, and acceleration of the mass compared with that of the cam, for the cases $\omega/p = 2, 3, 4$. These are calculated directly from eqs. 9–33, 9–34, and 9–35.

As before, the mass is not able to follow the cam with a suddenly applied acceleration; it catches up and overshoots. It is to be noted that the maximum velocity, which occurs at the first zero of acceleration, and which is the velocity shock of cross-over, gets less as the follower is made stiffer. But at the same time the pressures between cam and follower become more, for these are proportional to the acceleration; and also the motion y corresponds more closely to the desired motion x designed into the cam.

We conclude, in general, that for such a cam and follower, the fol-

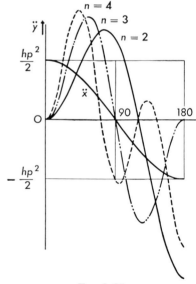

Fig. 9–25.

lower system should be as stiff as possible. However, there is an upper limit—for in practice cams are manufactured from a master cam (cam leader) which has been made by a scalloping process. The scallops are of course filed away, yet there will surely be left a high-frequency wave; the follower then must be soft to this high frequency while being stiff to the principal cam motion frequency p.

9–11. Flywheel on Flexible Shafting. The natural torsional vibrations of rotating bodies upon a shaft have a direct effect upon the effectiveness of a flywheel in serving its designed purpose. As mentioned in Art. 8–6, this is generally overlooked; a paper by Andriola,* however, brings light upon the subject.

When a flywheel is to be designed, it should always be borne in mind that the situation is described† by Fig. 9–26, which is the same as Fig. 3–20 and described in Art. 3–15. In this case a certain mass—the engine—suffers from a forced torsional vibration superimposed on its steady mean rotation and caused by the regular impulses of the firing.

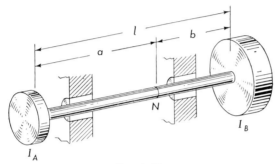

FIG. 9–26.

This mass is connected by a flexible shaft to the driven machine, of effective mass moment of inertia I_B; and it is to be decided how large shall be the mass I_A so that its angular velocity changes shall be held below a chosen value. And this is fine, so long as the whole engine can be regarded as a single rigid rotor such as I_A; which is to say, that the lengths of the flexible crankshaft within the engine are small compared to the equivalent length of transmission shaft between engine and driven machine. There is also, of course, the qualification that the natural frequency of the system, as in Fig. 9–26, shall not approach resonance with the frequency of the engine firing strokes or its harmonics.

The close-coupled system typical of an engine–electric-generator set does not fulfill this requirement, for all the lengths of shaft are comparable, unless the generator and flywheel are very close and connected by a very large diameter shaft. Furthermore, as described in Art. 8–6, in the generator the purpose of the flywheel is not to limit the velocity changes of the engine but the amplitude of oscillation of the generator. Thus the problem is principally the analysis of torsional vibration.

The solution to such a problem cannot be undertaken here; standard

---

* A. D. Andriola, "The Problem of Flywheel Effect and Speed Regulation for Diesel-Engine-Driven Machinery," *Trans. A.S.M.E.*, Vol. 60 (1938), pp. 119–25.

† This is to be recognized as an oversimplification, of necessity in that we have limited all discussion to a single degree of freedom in vibration; nevertheless it contains the correct orientation.

procedures are described in most texts on vibration. Our purpose here is rather to show how the consideration of the flexibility of the shaft has radically changed the whole approach to the problem of the selection of a flywheel.

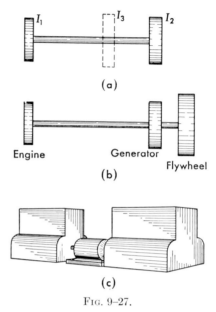

(a)

Engine   Generator
                                    Flywheel
(b)

(c)

Fig. 9–27.

There is also the matter of the location of the flywheel in the close-coupled systems. Suppose in Fig. 9–27a the engine is represented by I_1 and the generator by I_2. It is then most common to see the flywheel added as shown by I_3. Yet this is very near the node of the oscillations of I_1 against I_2. As is observed by Andriola, if the position for I_3 should happen to be exactly at this node, the most tremendous flywheel would have no controlling effect on these oscillations.

Suppose, however, that the flywheel be mounted on the side of the generator away from the engine, as in Fig. 9–27b; then the generator may be placed at the node, and it will receive little or no torsional vibrations from the engine.

Another excellent arrangement uses two equal engines with the generator between (Fig. 9–27c).

BIBLIOGRAPHY

Parallel references:

LAURSON, P. G., and COX, W. J. *Mechanics of Materials.* 2d ed. New York: John Wiley & Sons, Inc., 1947, "Shear and Bending in Shafts, Beams," pp. 132 and 339.

TIMOSHENKO, S. *Strength of Materials.* 2d ed. (Vol. I.) New York: D. Van Nostrand Co., Inc., 1940, "Shear and Bending in Shafts, Beams," pp. 109 and 171.

———. *Ibid.* (Vol. II.) "Stress in Flywheel Spokes," p. 98.

Specialized or advanced references:

Stodola, A. *Steam and Gas Turbines.* Transl. by L. C. Loewenstein from 6th German ed. (Vol. I.) New York: McGraw-Hill Book Co., Inc., 1927, "Stresses in Rotating Disks—Turbine Wheels," p. 373.

Timoshenko, S. *Strength of Materials.* (Vol. II.) New York: D. Van Nostrand Co., Inc., 1930, "Rotating Disks," p. 537.

PROBLEMS

9–1. The steel blades of a turbine have a section of $\frac{3}{16}$ sq in., and extend from a radius of 12 in. to radius 15 in. The turbine speed is 6000 rpm. Find the maximum load and stress in the blade, neglecting the shroud effect.

9–2. A small gas turbine rotor has 33 blades projecting from the 5-in. diameter disk, which can be taken to have a constant thickness of 1.25 in. The blades have a radial length of 0.906 in. and 0.11 sq in. section. The rotor disk is solid without any central hole, and turns at 35,000 rpm. Find the maximum stresses at this speed, assuming the material to be steel. (Actually it is a cobalt-nickel-chrome-iron alloy.) Note that the blades should be taken to produce a uniform tensile load around the periphery of the disk.

9–3. Find the tensile hoop stress in the rim of the cast steel steam-engine flywheel, the dimensions of which appear in Fig. 8–P–9b (p. 376), when it rotates at the governed speed of 248 rpm.

9–4. A certain soil-compactor uses the Lanchester device of two out-of-balance eccentrics counter-rotating about parallel shafts at 950 rpm to produce together an alternating vertical force of 9000 lb maximum. Each eccentric disk is mounted on a steel shaft in bearings 6 in. apart. Taking into account the flexibility of the shaft, and assuming the housing stationary, find the diameter of shaft needed so that the stress of bending shall not exceed 15,000 psi.

9–5. Solve the problem of Art. 9–7 in which the same bar is set at an angle of 60° to the shaft initially.

9–6. Part of a beater consists of three arms which project from the end of a cantilever shaft. The shaft is of $\frac{1}{2}$ in. diam steel and overhangs its bearings by 6 in. The beating arms are set around the shaft 120° apart, and are welded to the end of the shaft, so that they make an angle of 30° with the shaft centerline, forming a pyramid as shown in Fig. 9–P–6. Each arm is a round $\frac{1}{4}$-in. diam steel bar 6 in. long.

If while the shaft is turning at 3000 rpm one of the arms breaks off, is there danger that this will also cause the shaft to fracture before the machine can be stopped?

Fig. 9–P–6.

9–7. In a simple reciprocating engine the connecting rod has a length of 40 in. between centers. The weight of the rod, which may be considered as uniformly distributed between centers, is 40 lb. The crank radius is 8 in.

For an engine speed of 300 rpm estimate the bending moment at the midpoint of the connecting rod due to inertia forces when the crank and connecting rod are at right angles.   (U.L.)

9–8. The steel connecting rod of an engine is 11 in. long between centers, and of the section shown in the figure. It is attached to a crank of 2.5-in. throw, which rotates at 2500 rpm. Find the maximum bending stress due to the maximum transverse component of its own inertia loading. Assume deflections are negligible.

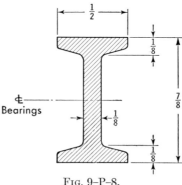

FIG. 9–P–8.

9–9. A uniform steel beam, 2 in. × ½ in. section and 6 ft long, is pivoted at its center where it is keyed to a shaft. The axis of this shaft is vertical and parallel to the 2-in. sides of the beam. A torque from the shaft produces an acceleration of $5g$ horizontally at the end of the beam. Neglect any induced curvature of the beam, and draw its bending moment diagram and find the maximum stress during this acceleration.

9–10. Two locomotive side rods have identical dimensions but one is made of 17ST aluminum alloy while the other is made of SAE 1045 steel. Considering whipping stress only, which may be operated at the higher speed? Calculate the ratio for a given factor of safety.

9–11. The ends of a uniform rod AB of length l and mass m slide in fixed straight guides at right angles. If the end A has a constant velocity v, and gravity and friction are neglected, show that the maximum bending moment in the rod is $\dfrac{mv^2}{9\sqrt{3}} \dfrac{\cos\theta}{\sin^3\theta}$ at a point distant $\dfrac{l}{\sqrt{3}}$ from A, where θ is the angle at A between the rod and the guide.   (C.U.)

9–12. A six-cylinder diesel, direct coupled to an alternator, transmits 1200 hp at 400 rpm. Assuming the flywheel and engine rotating parts may be regarded as equivalent to a disk of moment of inertia 1450 lb ft sec², which is connected by a solid steel shaft 8 ft long and of a diameter sufficient to transmit the power with maximum stress 30,000 psi, find the moment of inertia of the generator rotor required to keep the angular deviation below $\pm\frac{1}{4}$ degree (mechanical). The energy fluctuation may be taken from the table on page 343.

9–13. A positive radial cam actuates a follower that consists of a push rod with cam-roll, which moves a rocking lever and, by means of a connecting link, a sliding table weighing 185 lb. The cam is laid out to give a special motion to the table: the displacement (in inches) of the cam-roll for each 10° of cam rotation during the rise from rest are as follows:

Cam Angle (deg.)	10	20	30	40	50	60	70	80	90
Roll Displacement	0.080	0.215	0.439	0.730	1.112	1.500	1.898	2.250	2.561
	100	110	120	130	140	150	160	170	180
	2.789	2.949	3.049	3.155	3.410	3.781	4.132	4.422	4.500

In the machine with the cam turning once every 4 sec a troublesome chatter of the table develops. The engineers in "trouble-shooting" determine the strength of the connecting members as follows: under 100-lb compressive load the push rod contracts 0.0012 in., the connecting link 0.0165 in., and with 100 lb on both pins the rocking lever bends 0.237 in. Masses of these members are small in comparison with the table.

Find the cause of the chatter.

9–14. Make an analysis similar to that of Art. 9–10 for a cam designed to produce "cycloidal" motion. Take the cases of $\omega = 2p$ and $\omega = 3p$.

9–15. A slider-crank mechanism is used to give a stroke of $2r$ to the cutter of a nibbling machine, which oscillates n times per minute. The crank is mounted on a short shaft with a belt pulley, which is driven by a vee-belt from another pulley which rotates at constant speed. The mechanism may be regarded as consisting of two equivalent masses: a reciprocating mass m in the cutter, and a rotating mass of crank and pulley with moment of inertia I. The connecting rod and crankshaft are inflexible in comparison with the belt which has a stiffness k. The connecting rod can be assumed very much longer than the crank radius.

Determine a criterion for the stiffness of the belt in terms of the other data.

Chapter 10

GOVERNORS

10–1. Automatic Control. The term "governing" is broadly applied to any process by which the output of a machine, particularly a prime mover, is controlled according to a desired standard. For example, a steam engine may be governed to run at a constant speed, or a pump may be governed to produce a constant pressure. In any case, the action of the governor is to respond to the speed or pressure produced and, if there is any deviation from the amount desired, to act on the supply to correct the output. Thus a governor is a device for automatic control.

Here only the speed-responsive governor will be considered. There are two common purposes in such governing: (a) to hold the speed of a prime mover as closely as possible to a constant speed, under varying conditions of load; or (b) to act as an overspeed shutoff safety device. The latter purpose is generally very easy to accomplish. For instance, on the driven shaft of a steam turbine a small arm carries a centrifugal weight. The radius of the weight is controlled by a spring, but varies with speed. At usually 10 per cent over-speed the arm is extended sufficiently to hit against a stationary lever which operates a ratchet to shut down the steam supply.

The "constant-speed" governor may work on the same principle of centrifugal force, but involves a great many further considerations. Not only must it change its configuration with speed, but, for instance, the forces causing it to change must be strong enough to make the controlling device change correspondingly. The governor must be both powerful and sensitive.

There are several types of speed-controlling governors. Some operate by centrifugal forces and are called *flyball* governors. There are two classes of these, in which (a) centrifugal force acts against gravity, or (b) centrifugal force acts against a spring. Then there are those that operate by the tangential acceleration forces due to change in speed, and these are called *inertia* governors. There are also hydraulic governors and the hit-and-miss type. These will be dealt with in succession.

10–2. Methods of Governing. The methods by which the governing is accomplished depend upon the type of prime mover. In every prime mover there must be an exact balance at all times between the supply of available energy and the work that has to be done. Any excess of supply will produce unbalanced torques or forces, which will cause acceleration. The governor is arranged to act on either the quantity or the quality of the motive fluid. In a steam engine the ordinary methods of control are (a) to open or close a throttle valve located in the inlet steam pipe, thereby limiting inlet pressure; or (b) to vary the point of cutoff by acting on the eccentric driving the steam valve, thus changing the quantity of steam admitted. In a gasoline engine, and in steam turbines, the method of throttling is used. In diesel engines the volume of fuel injected is governed by variable-stroke injection pumps or by-passed injection pump. In gas engines the hit-and-miss scheme is sometimes used.

Gravity Controlled Flyball Governors

10–3. The Watt Governor. About 1764 James Watt invented for use with his original steam engine a governor using the principle of the simple conical pendulum. Two flyballs are suspended on thin arms from a point A (Fig. 10–1) on a rotating vertical axis. This spindle is driven through gears or belt by the output shaft of the prime mover. As the angular velocity increases, the centrifugal force of the balls causes them to fly out, thereby raising the sleeve D by means of the lower links BD. In the sleeve a groove is cut, and one end of a stationary lever rides in the groove. This lever operates the controlling device (for example, the throttle).

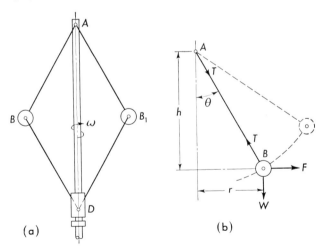

(a)   (b)

Fig. 10–1.

If the load on the prime mover is reduced, the speed will rise, the radius of the balls increase, and the sleeve rise. The highest position of the sleeve and lever must therefore correspond to a closed throttle, and

the lowest position to a wide-open throttle. The high and low positions of
the sleeve—the total sleeve travel—are generally fixed by stops.

To analyze the action of the governor, consider the forces acting on
the balls as shown in Fig. 10–1b. For the simplified analysis which
follows, the weights of the sleeve, the upper ball-arms, the lower links,
and friction are all ignored. The tensions in the lower links are therefore
negligible, and only three forces are considered. By taking moments
about the apex point A, the equation of equilibrium is found to be:

$$\frac{W}{g}r\omega^2 h = Wr \tag{10-1}$$

or

$$h = g/\omega^2 \tag{10-2}$$

where h is called the *"height"* of the governor, which is also given by

$$h = r \cot \theta$$

The tension in the arms, if that is wanted, can be found from the
summation of vertical forces:

$$T \cos \theta = W \tag{10-3}$$

Equation 10–2 is very significant in that it shows that neither the
weight of the balls, nor the length of the supporting arms, has any
influence on the height of the governor. Figure 10–2 shows graphically
the relation between height and the speed in rpm.

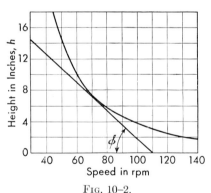

FIG. 10–2.

Secondly, it shows that the governor is quite unsuitable for high
speeds of operation. Above 100 rpm the change in position of the sleeve
for considerable percentage changes in speed is so slight that it could
not control a valve satisfactorily.

It might then be suggested that a speed-reduction gear between
engine shaft and governor spindle would allow this governor to be used
with higher-speed engines. That this is not a satisfactory remedy will
be shown in Art. 10–8.

10-4. The Loaded or Porter Governor. A great improvement on the simple Watt governor is achieved by the addition of a large central weight to hold the sleeve down. This design is generally ascribed to Charles T. Porter; and it is obvious that greater centrifugal forces— that is, greater speeds—are needed to bring the flyballs to the same radius. We shall analyze such a governor by two different methods, first by the tensions in the links, then by an equivalent system and virtual work.

In Fig. 10-3a let the supporting arms AB be equal in length to the links BD. The balls B, weighing W each, are at radius r and height h, and the center weight or load is L. The weights and masses of the arms and links are supposed negligible. Since triangle ABD is isosceles, both angles DAB and BDA may be called θ. The effect of the tension T' in the lower arms is most easily reckoned by considering the effect of its two components, T'_V and T'_H. From the vertical forces acting at D

$$T'_V = L/n \tag{10-4}$$

if there are n balls. And then from the direction of T'

$$T'_H = T'_V \tan\theta = T'_V \cdot \frac{r}{h} \tag{10-5}$$

Now take moments about A of the forces acting on the arm AB and flyball. The component T'_V acts with the weight; the other, T'_H, acts against the centrifugal force, so that:

$$(W + T'_V)r = (F - T'_H)h$$

$$= Fh - T'_V\frac{r}{h} \cdot h$$

or

$$(W + 2T'_V)r = Fh$$

$$(W + \frac{2}{n}L)r = \frac{W}{g}r\omega^2 h$$

$$h = \frac{g}{\omega^2}\left(1 + \frac{2L}{nW}\right) \tag{10-6}$$

It is also plain that this equation can be used for the simple Watt governor, if it is desired to include in its analysis the slight weight L of the sleeve. This would then be a little more accurate than to use the highly simplified eq. 10-2.

A different means of obtaining the above eq. 10-6 for the loaded Porter governor is to use the principle of work to obtain an "equivalent system." It is as follows:

Comparison between the analyses of the simple conical pendulum and the loaded governor shows at once that the latter is more involved because of the tension in the lower links, acting to hold down the balls.

Let us suppose then that it is possible to replace the loaded governor in Fig. 10–3a by a conical pendulum (Fig. 10–3b) which has the same geometry as the top half of Fig. 10–3a. We will call this an "equivalent system" if it acts like the original. Now the radial forces on the original

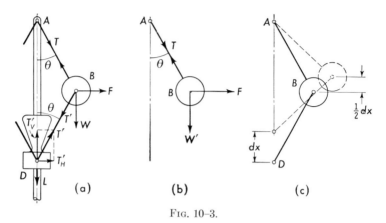

FIG. 10–3.

are only the centrifugal forces F of the balls, so we put the same on the imaginary equivalent system. (The radial component of the tension T'_H is not included because it is an *internal* force between members of the original.) The downward force W' on the balls in the equivalent will be due in part only to their own weight for it must also take care of the downward pull of the central load in the original. The problem is then to find W' in terms of W and L.

If the loaded governor and its equivalent are both moved through a small change in configuration, the equivalence will be shown if the change in potential energies of the two is the same. Let the sleeve be raised an infinitesimal amount dx. From the geometry of the figure shown in Fig. 10–3c, it appears that the balls will rise $\frac{1}{2}dx$. Then the increase in the potential of the real governor (Fig. 10–3a) with n balls will be

$$L\,dx + nW(\tfrac{1}{2}dx)$$

And in the imaginary governor (Fig. 10–3b) it will be

$$nW'(\tfrac{1}{2}dx)$$

Equating the two:

$$L\,dx + nW \cdot \tfrac{1}{2}dx = nW'\tfrac{1}{2}dx$$

$$W' = W + \frac{2}{n}L \qquad (10\text{–}7)$$

Now we have accomplished a transformation of the loaded Porter governor into a much simpler equivalent governor. As in the analysis of the Watt type, the equation of moments about the hinge pin A (Fig. 10–3b) will show the relations for the governor of Fig. 10–3a.

$$W'r = Fh$$

$$\left(W + \frac{2}{n}L\right)r = \left(\frac{W}{g}r\omega^2\right)h$$

which is eq. 10–6 again.

The change in potential energy is called "virtual work." It is virtual because the displacement is only dx which is infinitesimally small. In this example it was not necessary to make dx infinitesimal because eq. 10–7 holds for all configurations of the governor; yet in other types, for instance, if AB and BD were not equal, W' may be found to vary with different values of the angle θ, or height h.

10–5. Porter Governor with Extended Arms. The Porter governor for low-speed operation is frequently designed with the upper arms extended beyond the point of attachment of the lower links. Furthermore, the points of attachment, A or D, of these arms are often not on the axis of rotation. These two possibilities are illustrated in Fig. 10–4a, and of course the equations already derived do not apply unless modified.

The height of such a governor is still by definition the height of the cone described by the supporting arms and flyballs, as shown in the figure.

Example. Use the principle of virtual work to find the height of a Porter governor at any speed ω rad/sec, if there are two balls of 4 lb each, and a central load of 25 lb. The governor appears as in Fig. 10–4a with $AC = CD = 6$ in., $AB = 10$ in., $AA_1 = DD_1 = 2$ in. The masses of the arms and links are negligible.

Let Fig. 10–4b be the equivalent system, with L' acting down at the joint C. From the linkage ACD, if D moves up dx, C moves up $\frac{1}{2}dx$. The downward load *per ball* at D is 12.5 lb. Hence for equivalence

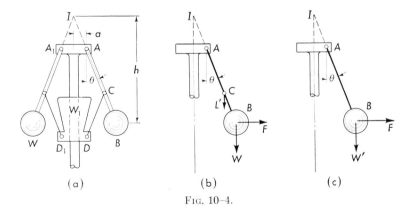

(a)   (b)   (c)

FIG. 10–4.

$$12.5 \, dx = L'\tfrac{1}{2}dx$$

$$L' = 25 \text{ lb}$$

(Note that it is as if the whole of the load L were acting at C on each flyball arm.) Now moments must be taken about point A (Fig. 10–4b):

$$L' \cdot AC \sin \theta + W \cdot AB \sin \theta = F \cdot AB \cos \theta \qquad (10\text{–}8)$$

$$\left(L'\frac{AC}{AB} + W\right) \tan \theta = F = \frac{W}{g}r\omega^2$$

but

$$\tan \theta = r/h$$

$$\left(\frac{6}{10} \cdot 25 + 4\right) = 4h\frac{\omega^2}{g}$$

$$h = \frac{g}{\omega^2} \cdot \frac{19}{4}$$

It is important to see that it is not a good idea to take moments about point I instead of using eq. 10–8. Since in Fig. 10–4b link ACB is carrying three forces, the line of action of the resultant at A is not along the centerline of ACB; and in the equation $\Sigma M_I = 0$ the moment of this reaction at A would have to be included.

However, if the equivalent system of Fig. 10–4c is chosen, in which case by virtual work

$$W' = \left(W + \frac{AC}{AB}L'\right) = \left(W + \frac{AC}{AB}L\right) \qquad (10\text{–}9)$$

then the arm AB is but a two-force member, the reaction at A must be along AB, and it is immaterial whether moments are taken about A or I.

10–6. Speed Regulation. Droop. It is necessary at this point to define a few governor operation terms.

It is evident from eqs. 10–2 and 10–6 that the governors considered so far have one particular height for any one speed. But since the height controls the sleeve position and thus the throttle (or whatever controlling device is used), then there is no possibility of having such a governor serve its primary function of holding the engine to a constant speed.

If the load on the engine is increased, the only way of making the throttle open more is to allow a slight lowering of the speed.

Thus the best compromise is to limit the speed variation between full load and idling (open and closed throttle). The percentage of variation in speed is called the *speed regulation* of the governor and is expressed as the percentage

$$\frac{N_{\max} - N_{\min}}{N_{\mathrm{av}}} \times 100$$

where $N_{av} = \dfrac{N_{max} + N_{min}}{2}$ rpm. In most gravity-controlled designs its

value is between 5 and 10 per cent, although with some spring-controlled governors this can be halved.

Speed droop has the same meaning, although generally it refers to the percentage by which the full-load speed droops below the idling speed. The droop is often shown in a graph of speed against load, as in Fig. 10–5.

Speed regulation has also sometimes been called "static fluctuation."

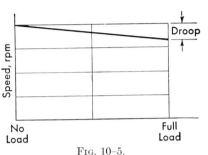

Fig. 10–5.

10–7. Controlling Force. Stability. The controlling force of a governor is equal and opposite to the radial outward force required to hold the governor in any position when stationary. The controlling force is therefore the resultant of the tensions in the arms and the weight of the ball. Since equilibrium is found (when rotating) in the balance of centrifugal force against these same inward forces, the controlling force is equal and opposite to the centrifugal force when in steady speed rotation. It is usually quoted for *each* ball. Many things about a governor can be seen by making a graph of the variation of the controlling force with the radius of the flyballs, and this is called a *characteristic* diagram (e.g., Fig. 10–14). It will be taken up later.

However, it should be plain that the stability of a governor depends upon the characteristics of the controlling force. Stable equilibrium, it will be remembered, means that if any body is displaced from its state of equilibrium by some transient outside force, it will try to get back, probably by a damped oscillatory motion.

Consider any flyball governor, not necessarily of the types considered. Let it be in equilibrium at a given radius and speed; then the centrifugal force F is equal and opposite to controlling force C. Now something knocks the balls out to an increased radius (no change in speed). To be stable, the balls must try to get back to the original radius corresponding to that (unchanged) speed. But centrifugal force has increased proportionately to the radius change. Therefore the controlling force must increase at a greater rate than increases in radius, so that the net force is a restoring force.

10–8. Regulating Force. Strength. Work Capacity. The regulating force of a governor is defined as the force that a governor can exert at the sleeve when a given change of speed occurs. In other words, it is the force that will operate the control mechanism: the bigger it is the quicker will a governor overcome frictional resistances and get to its new position. The change of speed used for comparisons is one per cent.

It is to be observed that the force is due to the increase in centrifugal force, and it must be reckoned *before there is any change in configuration*.

Example. Find the regulating force exerted by the Porter loaded governor of Fig. 10–3.

For any constant speed condition, eq. 10–6 holds:

$$\left(W + \frac{2}{n}L\right) = \frac{W}{g}h\omega_1^2$$

The only way to write a similar equation of *equilibrium* of this governor, when the speed is increased from ω_1 to ω_2 without any corresponding change in either h or r—that is, the only way to keep the governor in the same configuration when the speed increases—would be to hang an additional load ΔL on the sleeve. So

$$W + \frac{2}{n}(L + \Delta L) = \frac{W}{g}h\omega_2^2 \qquad \omega_2 > \omega_1$$

Then this additional force ΔL at the sleeve is the regulating force the governor is exerting to get itself to its new equilibrium position. Subtracting the two equations above

$$\frac{2}{n}\Delta L = \frac{W}{g}h(\omega_2^2 - \omega_1^2)$$

$$= \left(W + \frac{2}{n}L\right)\left[\left(\frac{\omega_2}{\omega_1}\right)^2 - 1\right] \qquad (10\text{--}10)$$

If $\omega_2 = (1 + p)\omega_1$ where p is the fractional increase in speed, and if $p = 0.01$, i.e., 1 per cent, then

$$\text{Regulating force} = \Delta L = \left(L + \frac{n}{2}W\right)[(1 + p)^2 - 1]$$

$$= 0.0201\left(L + \frac{n}{2}W\right) \qquad (10\text{--}11)$$

The regulating force is also commonly called the governor *effort* and it is always reckoned without friction.

The *strength* of the governor is the maximum force that the governor can exert at the sleeve when running at any speed. This is also called the *powerfulness** of the governor. It is the force that the governor would exert downward on the sleeve if the rotation suddenly stopped. It is the regulating force for a 100 per cent speed change and can obviously then be measured (exactly as controlling force is measured) when the governor is static, in which case it will be the force upward at the sleeve required to hold any given configuration of the governor.

* Sometimes wrongly abbreviated to "power."

The *work capacity* of the governor in any configuration is the integral product of the strength and the distance the sleeve has moved up from its lowest position, or work capacity $= \int F\,dx$ where F is the strength and x the position of the sleeve.

The work capacity is important in governors where it is possible to change the design for a greater strength with shorter sleeve travel, as, for example, by changing the lever ratio of the bell cranks of the Hartnell spring governor. The work capacity is not changed by such tricks.

The A.S.M.E. Test Code for Speed-Responsive Governors provides for a test for "work capacity for one per cent change in speed." This entails finding the regulating force and the sleeve travel due to one per cent change in speed, in both full-throttle and idling positions, and taking the average of the products.

Example. Find the regulating force for one per cent change in speed of the loaded governor with extended arms described in the example in Art. 10–5.

Equation 10–8 gives

$$\frac{AC}{AB}L' + W = \frac{W}{g}h\omega_1^2$$

where $L' = L = 25$ lb.

For $\omega_2 = 1.01\omega_1$, an additional load ΔL is needed at the sleeve to hold the original configuration.

$$\frac{AC}{AB}(L + \Delta L) + W = \frac{W}{g}h\omega_2^2$$

$$\frac{AC}{AB} \cdot \Delta L = \frac{W}{g}h\omega_1^2(1.01^2 - 1^2)$$

or using eq. 10–8 again

$$\tfrac{6}{10}\Delta L = (4 + \tfrac{6}{10} \cdot 25)(1.0201 - 1)$$

$$\text{Regulating force} = \Delta L = 0.6365 \text{ lb}$$

This is the same through the whole range of sleeve travel.

10–9. Effect of Friction. Sensitiveness. Unfortunately there are two distinct common meanings for the term "sensitiveness" (sometimes called "sensitivity").

If it were not for friction, the sensitiveness of a governor would be related inversely to the speed regulation. A governor with close speed regulation would be very sensitive to changes in speed. Such a concept is used in many texts and references. "Sensitiveness" is there defined as the movement of the sleeve (in inches) for a one per cent change in speed. However, if speed regulation is a term to be used, there is no great advantage in using this also.

The alternate and more practical use of the term "sensitiveness" is concerned with the quick response of a particular governor in overcoming its friction. The A.S.M.E. Test Code specifies a method of measuring it, and defines it as the per cent change in speed necessary to cause change in the position of the *complete* mechanism (governor and controlling device) when the speed is changed slowly. Thus such matters as the tightness of the pin joints, the lack or supply of oil, all affect the sensitiveness. In the search for more sensitiveness, governors are often equipped with ball-bearing pivots, knife-edge bearings, etc.

Friction in a governor has a further effect in that the governor will have a different configuration according to whether it approaches equilibrium from the higher- or lower-speed side. The difference in these two speeds is then a measure of the sensitiveness.

For example, in the Porter governor, let it be assumed that the arms are equal, that there are two balls, and also that the frictional resistance to any change in configuration may be referred to the sleeve. We therefore insert in eq. 10–6 a friction force L_f, acting up or down according to the pending movement, which is the total effective frictional effect on the governor, and obtain

$$h = \frac{g}{\omega^2}\left(\frac{W + L \pm L_f}{W}\right)$$ (10–12)

There are thus two limiting values of h at which the governor will be in equilibrium at any one speed. The larger occurs when the friction acts downward $(+L_f)$, and when the speed is increasing, the lesser (with $-L_f$) with decreasing speeds. The greater the friction, the less the sensitiveness.

Example. Find the sensitiveness of a Watt governor rotating at 10 rad/sec. It has two balls of 25 lb each, and the upper and lower links are equal (Fig. 10–1a). Presume an effective frictional force of 2.5 lb at the sleeve.

Suppose it is at first rotating in its central equilibrium position. Then from eq. 10–2

$$h_1 = \tfrac{386}{100} = 3.86 \text{ in.}$$

Using equation 10–12, holding h_1 unchanged, add friction while increasing the speed to ω_2 until

$$h = 3.86 = \frac{g}{\omega_2^2}\left(\frac{25 + 2.5}{25}\right)$$

$$\omega_2^2 = 100(1.1) \qquad \omega_2 = 104.6$$
$$\text{Sensitiveness} = 4.6 \text{ per cent}$$

Sensitiveness is thus given for this example by $\left[\left(\dfrac{W + L_f}{W}\right)^{1/2} - 1\right]100$,

for $L = 0$. In practical analyses L_f is hard to find, and is variable.

Frictional damping is sometimes introduced into a governor that is subject to "hunting," that is, to fluctuations of speed and configuration. A governor that has a small coefficient of speed regulation is often subject to such hunting, and a viscous dashpot is attached to cure it. The *rapidity* with which a governor will settle down to a new position of equilibrium after a change in the load is important, and the A.S.M.E. Code has a test to measure in seconds the time for this settling down. The motion will be a damped vibration actuated by the regulating force.

10–10. Centrifugal Effect of the Arms. If the masses of the upper and lower arms in the governors studied are to be taken into consideration, the equation of moments about the pivot point of the supporting arms will still give the relations between the height or configuration of the governor and its speed; but there are four additional terms.

Consider, for instance, the Porter governor of Fig. 10–4, for which eq. 10–8 was derived. Let the weight of the upper arms AB be w_1 and that of the lower links CD be w_2.

a) CENTRIFUGAL MOMENT, M_1, OF THE UPPER ARMS. Let the pivot A be at a radius a from the centerline of rotation. In Fig. 10–6a let $(x + a)$ be the radius of any element of mass dm vertically below A a distance y. Then the centrifugal force acting on the element is

$$dF = (x + a)\omega^2 \cdot dm$$

The moment of the sum of all these elemental forces about point A is

$$M_1 = \omega^2 \int (x + a) y \, dm$$
$$= \omega^2 \int xy \, dm + \omega^2 a \int y \, dm$$
$$= \omega^2 \left(I_{xy} + \frac{w_1}{g} a \cdot \overline{AG} \cos \theta \right) \qquad (10\text{–}13)$$

if $\overline{AG}$ is the distance from A to the center of mass of the rod.

If the rod can be regarded as a uniform rod of small cross section then from Chapter 6 (eq. 6–9) we may write

$$I_{xy} = \frac{1}{3} \frac{w_1}{g} l^2 \sin \theta \cos \theta$$

where l is the length of the rod, i.e. $l = AB - r$, if r is the radius of the sphere of a flyball.

b) GRAVITY MOMENT, M_2, OF THE UPPER ARMS. The effect of the gravity forces of the distributed particles comprising the body is the same as if the mass of the rod were concentrated at its center of gravity G. Hence

$$M_2 = w_1 \overline{AG} \cdot \sin \theta \qquad (10\text{–}14)$$

In many practical problems it may be as easy to find the center of gravity M (Fig. 10–6a) of the arm and ball combined, and this can be used similarly.

Example. A uniform rod of length l acts as a simple conical pendulum. Neglecting the weights of any lower links find the relation between speed and angle θ, Fig. 10–6b.

From eqs. 10–13 and 10–14, the centrifugal moment M_1 (since $a = 0$), and the gravity moment M_2 are

$$M_1 = I_{xy}\omega^2 = \frac{\omega^2}{3}\frac{w_1}{g}l^2 \sin\theta \cos\theta$$

$$M_2 = w_1(l/2)\sin\theta$$

Hence

$$l\cos\theta = \frac{3g}{2\omega^2} \tag{10–15}$$

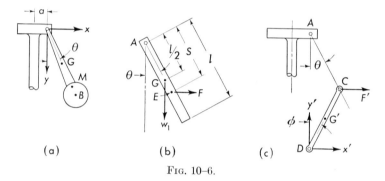

(a)   (b)   (c)

FIG. 10–6.

A further interest will show that in this case if the total centrifugal force of the rod F were presumed acting at the center of percussion E (with respect to the support point A), this will give the same centrifugal moment M_1. For suppose $AE = s$

$$F = \frac{w_1}{g}(AG\sin\theta)\omega^2$$

$$\frac{w_1}{g}(AG\sin\theta)\omega^2 \cdot s\cos\theta = M_1 = (I_A\sin\theta\cos\theta)\omega^2$$

$$s = k_A^2/AG$$

where k_A is the radius of gyration of the rod about A.

c) CENTRIFUGAL MOMENT M_3 ABOUT A DUE TO LOWER LINKS. The moment about D of the centrifugal forces due to the mass w_2/g of the lower arms is found exactly as for the Case (a). Thus if the radius of D is a, the moment is given by

$$M_D = \omega^2(I_{x'y'} + \frac{w_2}{g}a\overline{DG'}\cos\phi) \tag{10–16}$$

where the axes x', y', and angle ϕ are shown in Fig. 10–6c. Since all the centrifugal forces and the reaction at D are directed radially outward, the reaction F' at the pin C is also directed radially outward, and thus the moment about the pin A is

$$M_3 = F' \cdot AC \cos \theta \qquad (10\text{–}17)$$

where

$$F' \cdot CD \cos \phi = M_D$$

For the common case $AC = CD$ and $\theta = \phi$,

$$M_3 = M_D \quad \text{(in magnitude)}$$

d) GRAVITY MOMENT M_4 ABOUT A DUE TO LOWER LINKS. If there is no load L of the sleeve, the force at D must be horizontal. The downward force w_2 at G' is therefore transmitted as an equal downward pull at C. Hence

$$M_4 = w_2 \cdot AC \sin \theta \qquad (10\text{–}18)$$

Thus for the governor of Fig. 10–4 the equation of moments about the hinge point A is

$$[W \cdot AB + w_1 AG + (L + w_2)AC] \sin \theta$$
$$= \omega^2 \left[\frac{W}{g}(a + AB \sin \theta)(AB \cos \theta) + \frac{w_1}{g} aAG \cos \theta + I_{xy} + \right.$$
$$\left. \frac{w_2}{g} aDG' \cos \theta + I_{x'y'} \right] \qquad (10\text{–}19)$$

10–11. Isochronism—Parabolic and Crossed-Arm Governors.

The primary purpose of any governor is to hold the speed of the prime mover constant. The governors considered so far have compromised on this, allowing of necessity a small coefficient of speed regulation. It is possible to arrange a governor so that it is in equilibrium in all possible configurations at the same speed. Such a governor is called *isochronous*.

But, except in some more complex forms of modern governor, an isochronous governor is not stable,* and so is useless. Imagine such a governor running at a certain speed with a certain setting. A slight increase in speed occurs with a slackening of the load; immediately the balls fly to their maximum position, closing the throttle entirely. The engine slows quickly, and at the instant the speed is a fraction below the governor speed, the throttle is opened to its fullest. So a cycle of speeds above and below a mean continues—an extreme case of hunting. The internal friction of the governor tends to modify this somewhat.

Isochronous governors are, however, of considerable theoretical interest. A possible design is shown in Fig. 10–7, in which the balls move in a parabolic track. For one of the geometrical properties of a parabola is

---

* This is theoretically a case of neutral, not unstable, equilibrium, if friction is ignored.

that the subnormal is of constant length, which is proved as follows: at any point (x_1, y_1) on the curve $y = mx^2$,

the slope $\dfrac{dy}{dx} = 2mx_1$, so that the slope

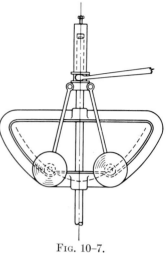

of the normal is $-1/(2mx_1)$. But the slope of the normal is the ratio $-h/x_1$ where h is the subnormal on the y-axis, which is also the height of the governor. Thus for any such parabola

$$h = \frac{1}{2m} \qquad (10\text{--}20)$$

The moment equation of the conical pendulum (eq. 10–2) shows that there is only one height corresponding to a given speed, and vice versa. Since the parabolic governor has a constant height, it has also only one speed for all positions of the balls. It is isochronous.

Fig. 10–7.

The crossed-arm governor (Fig. 10–8) is a design which is an outcome of this theory, for it can be made to approach isochronism quite closely, by so designing the lengths of its links that the path of the balls approaches the parabola. For this, the length of the arm b is made equal to the radius of curvature of the parabola at the lowest point, where the angle θ is the smallest for which the governor is designed, and the pivot point A is at the center of this curvature.

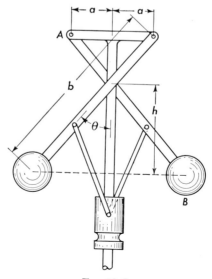

Fig. 10–8.

For the parabola, the radius of curvature at the point (x_1, y_1) is

$$R = \frac{\left[1 + \left(\frac{dy}{dx}\right)^2\right]^{3/2}}{d^2y/dx^2} = \frac{[1 + (2mx_1)^2]^{3/2}}{2m} = h[1 + (x_1/h)^2]^{3/2} \qquad (10\text{--}21)$$

But $x_1/h = \tan\theta$, so

$$R = h(1 + \tan^2\theta)^{3/2} = h\sec^3\theta \qquad (10\text{--}22)$$

The crossed-arm governor, therefore, is designed with $b = R$, and since also from the geometry (Fig. 10–8)

$$h = b\cos\theta - a\cot\theta \qquad (10\text{--}23)$$

so

$$a = b\sin\theta - h\tan\theta = h\tan^3\theta \qquad (10\text{--}24)$$

Example. Design a crossed-arm governor to run at 72 rpm, and determine its speed regulation if the arms may move from 30° to 40° positions.

The lengths must be determined at the lowest position for stability. Thus

(eq. 10–2) $\qquad\qquad h_1 = 35{,}235/N^2 = 6.79$ in.
(eq. 10–22) $\qquad\qquad b = 6.79\sec^3 30° = 10.45$ in.
(eq. 10–24) $\qquad\qquad a = 6.79\tan^3 30° = 1.305$ in.

Now by eq. 10–23, which is true for all values of θ:

$h_2 = 10.45\cos 40° - 1.305\cot 40° = 6.450$
$N_2 = \sqrt{35{,}235/6.450} = 73.9$ rpm

The speed regulation is therefore 2.6 per cent, while the flyballs move upward by an amount

Rise $= b\cos 30° - b\cos 40° = 1.045$ in.

which can be doubled by suitable connecting links to the sliding sleeve—a very large motion.

10–12. Proell Governor. A gravity-loaded governor that utilizes an inverted conical pendulum is the Proell governor, shown in Fig. 10–9. It also can be designed for very close speed regulation under slow-speed conditions.

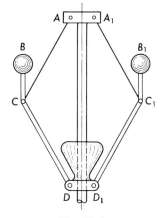

Fig. 10–9.

Spring-Controlled Flyball Governors

10–13. The Hartnell Governor. Spring-controlled governors have many advantages over the gravity-controlled types that have been described. The latter were chronologically the earlier development, but are basically better suited to the slower-speed engines.

The spring-controlled governor may be operated at very high speeds, and with proper proportioning can be both powerful and capable of very close regulation. It can be much smaller in over-all size and, since it does

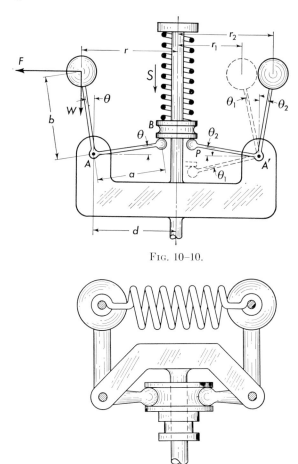

Fig. 10–10.

Fig. 10–11.

not depend upon gravity, it may revolve about a horizontal or inclined axis. The spring or springs that are used to counteract the centrifugal force may be placed upon the axis of rotation, as shown by the design of Fig. 10–10 and Fig. 10–P–18; or they may be transverse, as in Fig. 10–11 or Fig. 10–15. The controlling movement used to operate the throttle of the engine is still taken from a sleeve or "speeder-rod" which moves axially upon the revolving axle.

The axial-spring design of Fig. 10–10 is due to W. Hartnell, and is probably the most commonly used. We will take this as the example for description and analysis. The balls are mounted on a rigid right-angle bell crank, pivoted at A in a spider rotating with the axis. As the speed increases, the balls fly outward, forcing the upward movement of the sleeve B, and compressing the spring. The equation of motion may be obtained by taking moments about the pivot point A:

$$Fb \cos \theta + Wb \sin \theta = (S/n)a \cos \theta \qquad (10\text{–}25)$$

where $F = (W/g)r\omega^2$ is the centrifugal force, and S is the downward force on the sleeve, which is divided by n, the number of balls (usually two) to find the spring force on each arm.

Now if we divide by $\cos \theta$, we have

$$Fb + Wb \tan \theta = (1/n) \cdot Sa \qquad (10\text{–}26)$$

Here it has been assumed that the axis of rotation is vertical. If, however, it is horizontal, the effect of the gravity force W is zero on the sleeve as a whole, and a simpler equation results:

$$Fb = (1/n)Sa$$

or

$$\left(\frac{W}{g}\right)r\omega^2 = \left(\frac{1}{n}\right)\left(\frac{a}{b}\right)S \qquad (10\text{–}27)$$

This equation can frequently be used also for the vertical case, because of the following consideration: the governor can be adjusted so that the angle θ_1 at the low speed (see Fig. 10–10) is inside the vertical, i.e., negative, by the same amount that the angle θ_2 is outside, or $\theta_2 = \theta_1$. Then for a given change in radius, θ will be a minimum. Now $\tan \theta$ will be small, and in eq. 10–26 we have the product of $\tan \theta$ with W, which at high speeds is also very small compared with F. So the second term is negligible compared with the first.

If eq. 10–27 is used, it can be seen immediately that this governor can easily be made isochronous by appropriate choice of a spring. For consider two speeds ω_1, ω_2

$$\frac{W}{g}r_1\omega_1^2 = \frac{1}{n}\frac{a}{b}S_1$$

$$\frac{W}{g}r_2\omega_2^2 = \frac{1}{n}\frac{a}{b}S_2$$

Then

$$\frac{r_2}{r_1} \cdot \frac{\omega_2^2}{\omega_1^2} = \frac{S_2}{S_1} \qquad (10\text{–}28)$$

For isochronism $\omega_1 = \omega_2$, so

$$\frac{r_2}{r_1} = \frac{S_2}{S_1} \qquad (10\text{–}29)$$

A considerable amount of information can be deduced from this equation. We note that for an isochronous form of this governor, neglecting gravity, the spring force must increase in proportion to the increasing radius of the balls. Now take it that r_2 is greater than r_1, and suppose another spring stiffer than the isochronous one is installed, but it is such that the pressure exerted in position r_1 is the same. Then at radius r_2, the spring force will be greater than the isochronous S_2; hence from eq. 10–28 ω_2 must be greater than ω_1. This provides a stable governor. And conversely, a spring with lesser stiffness than the isochronous one will produce an unstable governor.

Equation 10–29 also determines the initial pressure of the isochronous spring. For suppose the bottom stop of the sleeve is removed so that the balls can reach the centerline position $r_1 = 0$; then by eq. 10–29 $S_1 = 0$. By the geometry of the figure, with the innermost position r_1 (not zero), the spring will be compressed a distance $(a/b)r_1$ from its position producing zero force, i.e., from its free length. Thus if the spring stiffness is k (lb/in.), the initial force at the position r_1 is

$$S_1 = k(a/b)r_1 \tag{10–30}$$

but at this position it must float the governor (allow the sleeve just to raise off the bottom stop) at the desired isochronous speed ω, or by eq. 10–27

$$S_1 = n \cdot \frac{b}{a}\frac{W}{g}r_1\omega^2$$

or

$$k = \frac{b^2}{a^2} \cdot n\frac{W}{g} \cdot \omega^2 \tag{10–31}$$

Thus choosing the speed at which the governor is to run isochronously will fix the value of the spring constant through eq. 10–31, and with k known, the choosing of the minimum radius of operation will fix the value of the initial spring pressure through eq. 10–30.

Two things have been neglected above, of course, and these are (i) the effective increase in initial spring pressure due to the weight of the sleeve (this applies only in the case of the vertical governor), and (ii) the frictional force. This latter is troublesome; it makes an otherwise isochronous governor unstable on increasing speeds, and is a principal factor in making them useless in practice.

10–14. Characteristic Curve. If a graph of controlling force be plotted against the radius of the balls, the properties of any governor appear very plainly, as was first shown by Hartnell.* Such a graph is called a "characteristic curve" for the governor, as mentioned already in Art. 10–7. We continue the study of the Hartnell governor and note first

* *Proc. Inst. Mech. Engrs.* (London), 1882.

that the controlling force of this governor is the inward force at the balls due to the spring, or the right-hand side of eq. 10–27.

$$\text{Controlling force } C = (1/n)(a/b)S \qquad (10\text{–}32)$$

Since the spring force is related to the radius by conditions of geometry, for this governor the graph of C against r will be a straight line, Fig. 10–12. (For Watt and Porter governors, it is a curve, but the following theory still holds.)

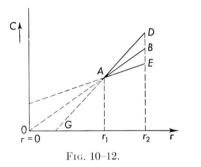

Fig. 10–12.

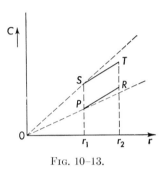

Fig. 10–13.

In Fig. 10–12 the origin must be reckoned at $C = 0$. The line AB then shows a condition where the controlling force is directly proportional to the radius, or the condition of isochronism, as explained. The line AD shows a higher value of controlling force at D than that for isochronism, hence a higher speed ω_2. So if the curve for a particular governor is steeper than that of the line through the origin, we will have $\omega_2 > \omega_1$, or a stable condition. Similarly for the curve AE, we have $C_E < C_B$ or $\omega_2 < \omega_1$, which shows an unstable condition.

If the characteristic curve is a curve such as occurs with the Porter governor, then for stability the *slope* of the curve at every point must be greater than the slope of the line joining such point to the origin.

The effect of tightening down the spring in a Hartnell governor is shown to be dangerous by Fig. 10–13. Assume PR is the characteristic curve of a governor. Since PR is steeper than OP, the governor is stable. Now a small amount of tightening of the spring will increase the controlling force at a given radius, and hence the governor will operate at a slightly higher speed. But suppose a further tightening is effected, so that the controlling force at r_1, due to the initial tension in the spring, is shown by point S. The spring stiffness is not changed, so the slope is the same, and ST will be the characteristic curve. But now the governor will no longer be stable, for the slope ST is less than the slope OS. The condition of stability is seen to be that the characteristic curve, when produced backward to cut the line $C = 0$, shall give a point which has a positive value of r, such as point G (Fig. 10–12). A negative value of r shows instability and a value $r = 0$ shows isochronism.

The characteristic curve can also be used very simply to show the speed regulation. If the curve is as shown in Fig. 10–14, remember that equilibrium occurs with the balance of controlling and centrifugal forces. Hence at point M (the high-speed point) the ordinate is $mr_2\omega_2^2$ and the abscissa is r_2. The angle subtended at the origin is

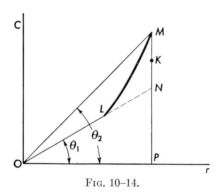

FIG. 10–14.

$$\tan \theta_2 = \frac{mr_2\omega_2^2}{r_2} = m\omega_2^2 = \frac{MP}{OP}$$

Similarly at the lowest speed point L

$$\tan \theta_1 = m\omega_1^2 = \frac{NP}{OP}$$

The coefficient of speed regulation $= \dfrac{\omega_2 - \omega_1}{\omega_{\text{mean}}} = 2\dfrac{\omega_2^2 - \omega_1^2}{(\omega_2 + \omega_1)^2}$

$$= \frac{1}{2}\frac{\omega_2^2 - \omega_1^2}{(\omega_{\text{mean}})^2} = \frac{1}{2}\frac{(\tan \theta_2 - \tan \theta_1)}{\tan(\theta_{\text{mean}})} = \frac{1}{2} \cdot \frac{MN}{KP} \qquad (10\text{–}33)$$

where K is actually halfway between the arithmetic and the geometric mean points of MP and NP.

Sometimes the abscissa of the characteristic curve represents the displacement of the sleeve instead of the radius. In this case regulating force can be read from the curve, instead of speed regulation.

Example. Design a Hartnell governor to run at 900 rpm with 5 per cent speed regulation. The design limits the flyball radius from a minimum of 1 in. to a maximum of 3 in. Find the weights, the minimum spring pressure, and the necessary spring stiffness, for a $\frac{1}{2}$-lb regulating force on 1 per cent change of speed.

Assume that there are to be two flyballs, and that the governor is to rotate about a horizontal axis.

From the mean speed and speed regulation

$$\omega_{mean} = \frac{2\pi}{60} \cdot 900 = 30\pi$$

$$\omega_2 = 30.75\pi$$
$$\omega_1 = 29.25\pi$$

At any speed ω, from eq. 10–27, the spring force is

$$S = 2(b/a)mr\omega^2$$

The regulating force L is therefore given by the general relation

$$L = 2(b/a)mr[(\omega + \delta\omega)^2 - \omega^2]$$

This will then vary, being more at the higher speeds. If the minimum must be $\frac{1}{2}$ lb and $\delta\omega$ is 1 per cent of ω

$$S_1 = L/0.0201 = 24.875 \text{ lb}$$

$$\frac{b}{a}W = 0.57 \text{ lb}$$

Hence the bell-crank ratio b/a should be about 2:1 to reduce the size of the weights to the more reasonable figure of 0.285 lb.

Now for the high-speed condition (eq. 10–28)

$$S_2 = 78.5 \text{ lb}$$

and the spring stiffness

$$k = \frac{78.5 - 24.9}{\frac{1}{2}(3 - 1)} = 53.6 \text{ lb per in.}$$

If this is too stiff a spring, then allow weights of 0.57 lb on $b/a = 1:1$ and $k = 26.8$ lb per in.

Note that if this same control is to be exercised by a governor in which the weights are allowed to move from 1-in. to 2-in. radius only, the weight, size, and lever ratio possibilities are the same, but the spring has to be a little stiffer; the corresponding figures for k are 54.8 lb per in. and 27.4 lb per in.

10–15. Other Spring-Controlled Governors. It has been pointed out that sensitiveness is a very important property of an actual governor. The Hartnell governor is inherently bad in this respect because the centrifugal forces are balanced by the central spring through the bell crank and thus there must be large forces at the pivot and at the sleeve contact points, involving a relatively large amount of friction.

The governor in Fig. 10–15 is the Jahns governor, and it overcomes this trouble very nicely by having the springs in the radial line of the centrifugal forces. The governor in Fig. 10–11 also does this, but the springs in Fig. 10–11 are not adjustable. In both designs it is plain that the bell crank has to transmit only the regulating force to the sleeve, and friction will be much less.

The governor in Fig. 10–16 is one of the standard designs of the

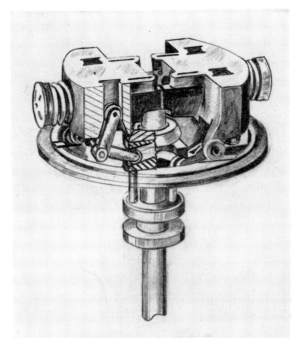

(Redrawn by permission of the Massey Machine Co.)
FIG. 10–15.

Pierce Governor Company. It is seen in the figure that the designers favored the adjustability of the spring control (speed setting) *while running* over the advantage, stated above, of the Jahns design. Friction is minimized by ball-bearing journals and a thrust bearing (1) between the rotating sleeve (2) and the rocker yoke (3). The governor control spring (4) is ingeniously arranged to have two adjustments: first the screw (5) may be adjusted, changing the spring force at the low-speed position, and thereby the mean running speed; second, the auxiliary screw (6) may be adjusted, thereby changing the moment arm of the spring force about the axis of yoke (3) and control lever (7). This has the same effect as changing the spring stiffness, thus giving closer speed regulation; the effect is the same as if in the Hartnell governor the bell-crank arm were adjustable. Thus both speed and speed droop are adjustable.

10–16. Vibrations of a Governor. If, because of a sudden change in load, a flyball governor finds itself out of equilibrium, it will move toward the new position; but unless there is considerable damping, it will overshoot the mark and oscillate radially in and out as it rotates.

The time for settlement of such oscillations, depending on the damping, has already been defined as the measure of the *rapidity* of the governor. But the frequency of the oscillations is also important because of the danger of resonance with the variations in torque output from

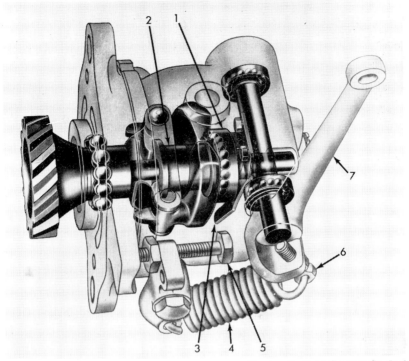

(Courtesy the Pierce Governor Co., Inc.)

Fig. 10-16.

the engine. The flywheel is designed (Chapters 7, 8) to hold down the magnitude of these speed fluctuations in the engine, but near resonance even a small magnitude can cause great sympathetic oscillations. This is a form of *hunting*, though the usual type of hunting is much slower and is dependent on the time of response of the engine to a governor change.

Consider a governor with weights moving radially in a plane against springs, such as in the Jahns governor. Assume that at speed ω, the equilibrium radius is r. But suppose that by a sudden decrease from a higher speed, the weights are at a greater radius $(r + x)$. The excess controlling (spring) force will be kx on each weight, and the excess centrifugal force will be $mx\omega^2$. Hence if the masses and other effects of the bell cranks, etc., are ignored, the radial acceleration $\ddot{x}$ is given by the equation of motion

$$m\ddot{x} = mx\omega^2 - kx \qquad (10\text{-}34)$$

Therefore simple harmonic oscillations will be set up, with natural frequency

$$f = \frac{1}{2\pi}\sqrt{\frac{k}{m} - \omega^2} \text{ cycles per sec} \qquad (10\text{-}35)$$

Due to the changing radius, there will also be a Coriolis acceleration component, $2\dot{x}\omega$, in direction perpendicular to $\dot{x}$, that is, in the direction of the tangential velocity as x increases. The acceleration components are shown in Fig. 10–17, which is a top view. Resolving forces in the tangential line gives

$$R = 2m\dot{x}\omega$$

where R is the side reaction from the guides of the weights. The two forces R form a couple on the governor tending to cause a change in the

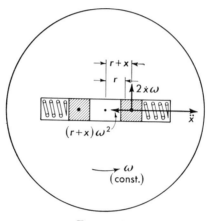

FIG. 10–17.

speed ω, probably having little effect; but also from R there will be frictional forces μR which should be included in eq. 10–34, and which will dampen out the oscillation.

Example. The weights of the governor of Fig. 10–17 have a natural frequency of 25 cycles per sec when the governor is static. Investigate possible resonance with the double-acting steam engine to which it is to be attached. Assume the governor rotates at engine speed.

$$\text{Static Frequency} = 1/2\pi\sqrt{k/m} = 25 \text{ cycles per sec}$$

therefore,

$$k/m = (50\pi)^2$$

The principal harmonic of torsional impulses (causing speed fluctuations) will occur twice per revolution in this engine. There will be resonance therefore, if

$$\sqrt{k/m - \omega^2} = 2\omega$$

$$k/m = 5\omega^2$$

$$\omega^2 = (50\pi)^2/5$$

$$\omega = 10\pi\sqrt{5}$$

$$\text{Engine speed} = N = 60\omega/2\pi = 671 \text{ rpm}$$

The derivation of the equation of motion for the oscillations of a governor which has its flyball attached to a moving pivoted arm, such as both the Porter* and the Hartnell types, is more complex than the type considered, because of several other components of acceleration due to the curvature of the path of the balls about both the axis of rotation and the pivot of the arm. There is three-dimensional curvature.

10–17. Isochronous Hydraulically Operated Governor. Any flyball governor may be made to be both isochronous and stable by including a hydraulic system in the mechanism by which the governor sleeve motion controls the fuel valve setting (throttle). An example of such a device arranged to be actuated by a Hartnell governor is shown in Fig. 10–18; and this is a Woodward design.†

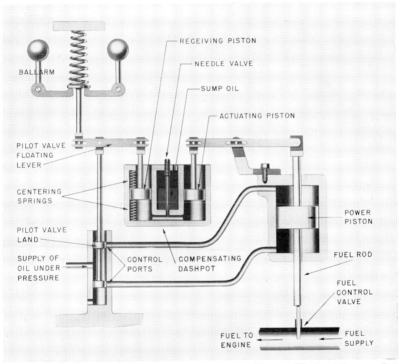

(Courtesy Woodward Governor Co.)

Fig. 10–18.

In general, it has been shown that the Hartnell governor is stable when the minimum spring force is greater than that given by eq. 10–30, and the stiffness is equal to or more than that given by eq. 10–31. This

---

*See J. D. Dent and A. C. Harper, *Kinematics and Kinetics of Machinery* (New York: John Wiley & Sons, Inc., 1921), pp. 194–98.

† Reproduced by permission from the bulletin *Elementary Principles of Diesel Engine Governing* of the Woodward Governor Co., Rockford, Illinois.

was apparent on the characteristic diagram. But a governor to be stable always has also a speed droop, if a direct connection is made between the speeder rod (sleeve) and the throttle. The arrangement of the Woodward governor, to be described, uses a governor which has a considerable droop for the sake of stability. It is not on this account that the governor is isochronous.

Secondly, the fuel control mechanism of Fig. 10–18 shows a pilot valve and power piston. This may be used alone, and is an amplifier for the regulating force produced by the governor. Suppose the speeder rod ran directly to the pilot valve. Then the slightest movement of the speeder rod would open one or other of the control ports and the high-pressure supply would feed oil to the power piston, which is of relatively large diameter. As a result a highly sensitive governor is obtained which is yet able to deliver a very strong regulating force.

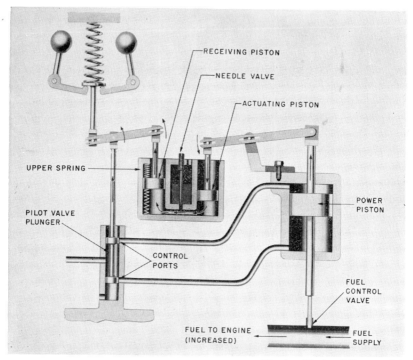

(Courtesy Woodward Governor Co.)

Fig. 10–19.

Now with these two preliminaries understood, the action of the design in the figure may be described. The governor is designed with droop; the two pistons of the compensating dashpot act as a droop remover. Suppose the governor mechanism is in the position shown by Fig. 10–18, running at half-load: the throttle or fuel-control valve is in a mean position. Then the load on the engine is increased. The immediate effects follow in rapid succession—the engine speed falls, and the governor balls close in to a lesser radius, depressing the speeder rod. The pilot-valve floating lever pivots about the right-hand end, depressing the pilot valve which admits oil to the lower side of the power piston while opening the upper side to an oil exhaust line. The power piston rises, opening the throttle, and also pushing down the actuating piston in the dashpot. The trapped oil here pushes the receiving piston up, and since the speeder rod position is fixed, this raises the pilot valve and stops any further motion of the power piston.

The position shown in Fig. 10–19 is thus arrived at. And now two relatively slower actions start. First, the engine will respond to the greater fuel supply, and in regaining its former speed will cause the governor flyballs to increase their radius of rotation, raising the speeder rod. Second, between the two pistons of the compensating dashpot is a needle valve; the receiving piston feels the influence of the upper of the centering springs and is lowered by this force as the oil bleeds out through the valve. (It is obviously not able to move the actuating piston.) If then the needle valve is correctly adjusted, these two motions synchronize, the pilot-valve floating lever merely turns and no motion is imparted to the pilot valve.

As a result, the flyballs may return to exactly their former radius, signifying that the engine has regained its former speed—i.e., isochronous control—and the throttle is in a more open position, which takes care of the increased load. This arrangement therefore provides a governor which is isochronous and stable, both sensitive and powerful.

Shaft and Inertia Governors

10–18. Shaft Governors. Many high-speed engines are fitted with a governor attached directly to the flywheel and rotating about the crankshaft. Such shaft governors have a feature not active in the flyball governors: since the motion of

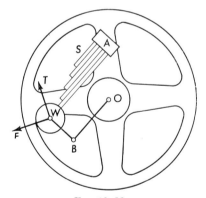

Fig. 10–20.

the governor relative to the flywheel is in the same plane as the rotation of the flywheel, it is possible to make use of the tangential inertia force as well as the centrifugal.

Consider the simple form of the Robb governor (Fig. 10–20). The ball W is restrained from flying out by the leaf spring S anchored at A. Its position controls the configuration of the linkage WB and BO, which is shown in simplified manner. Let the direction of rotation of the flywheel be counterclockwise, and let the motion of OB, clockwise relative to the flywheel, cut down on the steam inlet.

At a certain speed ω_1 we shall assume an equilibrium condition. Now if the speed should increase to ω_2, there will be an increase in the centrifugal force F, or an outward force

$$\Delta F = (W/g)r(\omega_2{}^2 - \omega_1{}^2)$$

which will bend the spring farther out, cutting down on the steam supply, and thus achieve the usual governor action. But in increasing the speed from ω_1 to ω_2, there must have been an angular acceleration α acting counterclockwise. Hence another force

$$T = (W/g)r\alpha$$

arose which supplemented the other in achieving the same result. Moreover, the tangential force T occurred sooner than the other; the angular acceleration α probably had its full value for a fraction of a second, and as a result of this the final value of the angular velocity ω_2 was reached. Hence the effect of the tangential force is to give the governor more effort, and to quicken the response.

Note that for a decrease in speed, the two effects still supplement each other; for the centrifugal force is reduced, giving a net inward effect ΔF, and the tangential force T is also reversed in direction. However, if the direction of rotation of the flywheel is reversed (making it clockwise) the two effects act against each other, resulting in a sluggish response.

Now if this governor were made with a longer spring, or if by some other means the angle between the line of action of the tangential force and the line of motion of the ball were increased, it is apparent that the tangential effect could be made the principal effect. When a shaft governor is so designed that the tangential effect is predominant, it is referred to as an *inertia governor*.

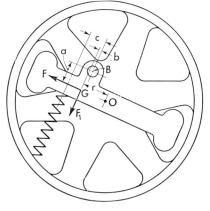

Fig. 10–21.

10–19. Rites Inertia Governor. This is one of the best known of shaft governors, and is shown by Fig. 10–21. The governor consists of a heavy bar pivoted to the flywheel at some eccentric point B. The center of gravity of the bar is at G and the center of rotation of the flywheel at O. The moment of the centrifugal force about B is opposed by that of the spring when the bar is rotating in equilibrium at some speed ω_1.

Let the speed increase from ω_1 to ω_2. Then, provided there has been no change in configuration and thus no increase in spring force, we have the regulating moment due to centrifugal action

$$M_c = (W/g)r(\omega_2^2 - \omega_1^2)a \qquad (10\text{–}36)$$

where a is the moment arm of the force about B as shown.

Quite independently of this, the change in speed was accompanied by an angular acceleration α causing another moment about B

$$M_T = (W/g)r\alpha b + I_G\alpha \qquad (10\text{–}37)$$

where I_G is the mass moment of inertia of the bar about its center of gravity.

These two effects can be made to supplement or oppose each other according to the direction of rotation of the flywheel and the relative positions of O, G, and B. Obviously if the moment M_T due to the tangential inertia forces opposes that due to the centrifugal forces, the governor will be very sluggish. If such a governor is to be mounted on a flywheel which may run in both directions, that is, if the engine is reversible, it is necessary to suppress the moment M_T as much as possible by proper choice of the positions of the points O, G, and B, using the centrifugal effect only.

The general analysis of the equilibrium of the Rites governor forms a very nice example of the application of the Coriolis forces; for it should be observed that while the governor has any motion relative to the wheel, the radius of its center of gravity is changing. The reader is referred to the very careful explanation of this by Seeley and Ensign in their text.* However, the result of such analysis is the same as given in eqs. 10–36 and 10–37 above.

10–20. Hit-and-Miss Governor. Another interesting inertia governor of quite a different type is the hit-and-miss governor, shown in Fig. 10–22. It has a linear, not rotational, motion, using the linear inertia force $f = ma$.

This type was used on slow-speed, gas-burning reciprocating engines. These engines had two inlet valves, one for air and one for fuel. The former opened every stroke, but the opening of the latter was regulated by the governor. The cam or eccentric of the valve drive operated the slide A which carried a bell crank B, one end of which was in line with the slide and sharpened to a knife-edge. At slow speeds the knife advanced with the slide and entered a dovetail C on the valve stem, thus pushing the valve open. At overspeeds the inertia of the weight D

---

* F. B. Seeley and N. E. Ensign, *Analytical Mechanics for Engineers* (3d ed. 1941, and previous editions only; New York: John Wiley & Sons, Inc.), p. 401.

attached to the bell crank caused it to lag behind the slide, thus lowering the knife which missed the dovetail. So the gas valve never opened
on that stroke.

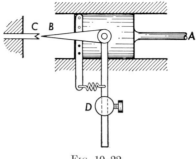

FIG. 10–22.

With full load on the engine, the gas valve would open every stroke, but
on idling the engine would fire only once in three or four strokes. The
engine thus had a characteristic intermittent putt-putt.

Hydraulic Governors

10–21. Simple Oil Impeller. It is plain that any mechanical device
which will change its configuration with changes in speed of the drive
from the engine to be controlled, will be capable of adaptation as a
governor. A governor entirely different from all those considered so far
is the hydraulic governor, which
works on oil pressure from a centrifugal pump. Such governors are used
to a considerable extent with steam
turbines.

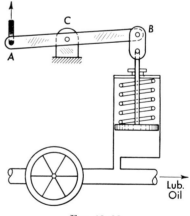

FIG. 10–23.

The governor consists essentially
of three parts, shown in simplified
form in Fig. 10–23: (a) the impeller,
which may be especially for the
governor, but is frequently the impeller used for the lubricating oil
system; (b) the governor "transformer," which is a piston in a cylinder, which acts against a spring;
(c) the valve operating mechanism,
controlled by the position of the
piston. With a decrease in load, and consequently an increase in speed
of the impeller, the oil pressure increases in proportion to the square of
the speed. The increased pressure will then move the piston up to close
the inlet steam valve.

Special precautions have to be taken to keep down turbulence, and also to avoid high velocities of the oil flow. Sufficient area must be provided in the impeller suction line to avoid oil velocities greater than 5 ft/sec under normal governing conditions. The discharge velocity should not exceed 10 ft/sec when passing oil at a rate sufficient to give full stroke of the governor-operating piston in 1/2 sec. Low velocities mean low pressure drops through the impeller and the system, so that a wide range in the rate of oil flow will not seriously disturb the pressure relations upon which the governing system is based. Low velocity through the impeller is secured by having the area of the passage through it not less than 6 or 8 times the suction area, thus giving ample time for air and vapor separation. Effective air removal is essential, so that none will lodge in the transformer and impair its immediate positive response. A vent to atmosphere with provision to return any oil to the system is always necessary. Characteristics of temperature and viscosity in the oil require a high-grade lubricating oil.

A second important matter is the provision of a trip for the quick closing of the throttle in the event of failure of the oil supply. It is to be seen that the governor would work exactly contrary to requirement in such an emergency, for loss of pressure occurs also with a drop in speed and the governor would respond by opening the throttle.

10–22. The C.A.V. Hydraulic Governor. A more complex form of governor using the principle just described is shown in Fig. 10–24. This is a simplified section of a governor developed by the C.A.V. Company;[*] it operates by directing the output of oil from a positive-displacement gear pump a through an orifice b. The pressure drop across this orifice will then be proportional to the square of the velocity.

The principal parts of the governor are the piston c and valve d which are connected. A passage e leads from the chamber between them to the upper piston f which operates the fuel-control rack. Supposing the pump delivery pressure to be P_1 and the pressure in the second chamber e (after passage through orifice b) to be P_2, then the forces tending to open the valve d are $(P_1 - P_2)A$, where A is the area of the piston c; and P_2a, where a is the area of the valve d. These are opposed by the spring g exerting a force S (this is adjustable), and by the force P_3a. Now the valve d will continually float, since the valve h is merely a high-pressure relief valve, set for say 50 psi, which is above the operating values of P_2. The pressure P_3, except at very low speeds, is a constant, say 20 psi, determined by the low-pressure relief valve j. Thus the condition of equilibrium of the valve d is that

$$S + P_3a = P_2a + (P_1 - P_2)A$$

* Messrs. C. A. V. Ltd., Acton, London, England. A full description is to be found in *Engineering*, Vol. 167 (March 18, 1949), pp. 261–64.

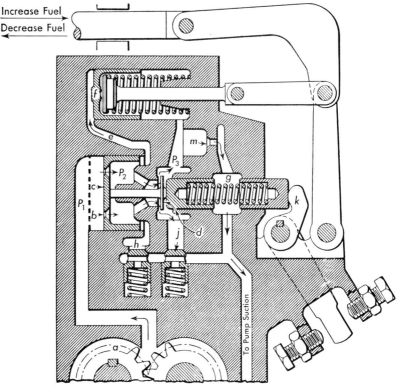

Increase Fuel

Decrease Fuel

FIG. 10–24.

The force actuating the control piston f is dependent on the difference of the two pressures P_2 and P_3; but from the above equation

$$P_2 - P_3 = \frac{S}{a} - \frac{A}{a}(P_1 - P_2)$$

Since $(P_1 - P_2)$ is proportional to the square of the speed, a curve of $(P_2 - P_3)$ plotted against speed will appear as an inverted parabola, except that P_2 cannot rise above the pressure set on the high-pressure relief valve h. With P_3 a constant, the P_2 curve is also parabolic. Such curves are shown in Fig. 10–25. The curve labeled "Max. speed" shows the condition when the accelerator controlled by the operator is fully depressed, thereby moving the pawl k for maximum compression of spring g. The P_2 curve for intermediate speed shows a lower parabola, for the spring force S is lower.

Now suppose a net pressure $P_2 - P_3$ of 20 psi fully depresses piston f for full throttle while a net pressure of 5 psi gives the idling throttle. Then for the maximum speed setting of the throttle the engine will carry full load at 2000 rpm (point x, Fig. 10–25) and will idle at 2140

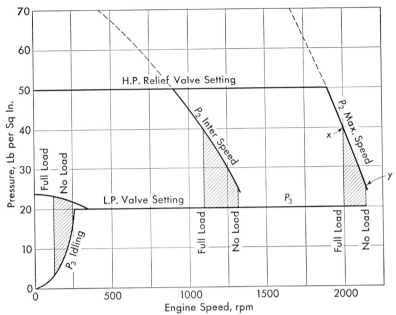

(By permission of C.A.V. Ltd. and of the Editor of *Engineering*)

FIG. 10–25.

rpm (point y on the figure). At the intermediate setting illustrated, the speed droop is from 1320 rpm to 1100 rpm. With the minimum speed setting of the accelerator control, the parabolic curve of P_2 becomes very flat (Fig. 10–25) which would give poor control. This is the reason for the incorporation of the small orifice m (Fig. 10–24). At low speeds the whole of the smaller delivery of oil by the pump may leak through this gap, with the result that the relief valve j remains closed. On the graph it appears that the valve setting of 5 psi is not reached until 250 rpm. The lower pressure P_3 is now the principal cause in moving piston f, and the speed is seen to vary between 125 and 250 rpm between full load and no load conditions.

BIBLIOGRAPHY

ANGUS, R. W. *Theory of Machines*. 2d ed. New York: McGraw-Hill Book Co., Inc., 1917, Chap. 12.

BARNARD, W. N., ELLENWOOD, F. O., and HIRSHFELD, C. F. *Heat Power Engineering*. 3d ed. New York: John Wiley & Sons, Inc., 1935, Part II, Chap. 24.

BEVAN, T. *Theory of Machines*. 2d ed. London: Longmans, Green & Co., 1943, Chap. 13.

DENT, J. D., and HARPER, A. C. *Kinematics and Kinetics of Machinery*. New York: John Wiley & Sons, Inc., 1921, Chap. 7.

HECK, R. C. H. *Mechanics of Machinery*, Part II, "Kinematics and Dynamics." New York: McGraw-Hill Book Co., Inc., 1925, Chap. 7.

LANZA, G. *Dynamics in Machinery*. New York: John Wiley & Sons, Inc., 1911, Chap. 4.

McKay, R. F. *Theory of Machines.* 2d ed. London: Edward Arnold & Co., 1929, Chap. 28.

Seeley, F. B., and Ensign, N. E. *Analytical Mechanics for Engineers.* 3d ed., and earlier editions only. New York: John Wiley & Sons, Inc., 1941, Chap. 15.

Toft, L., and Kersey, A. T. J. *Theory of Machines.* 6th ed. London: Sir Isaac Pitman & Sons, Ltd., 1949, Chap. 11.

Trinks, W. *Governors and the Governing of Prime Movers.* New York: D. Van Nostrand Co., 1919.

Also:

A.S.M.E. Test Code for Speed Responsive Governors. New York: American Society of Mechanical Engineers, 1924.

Woodward Governor Co. "Elementary Principles of Diesel Engine Governing," *Bulletin 01012.* Rockford, Ill., 1945.

PROBLEMS

10-1. Prove that an alternative form of eq. 10-2 for the conical pendulum is $h = 35{,}235/N^2$ where N is in rpm, h is in inches.

10-2. Derive the eqs. 10-8 and 10-9 by analysis of the equilibrium of the forces acting upon all links in the Porter governor of Fig. 10-4a.

10-3. The balls of a conical pendulum weigh 40 lb each. Length of arm is 20 in. At what rpm must they run in order that the radius of the path of the center of the balls may be 16 in.? What will be the value of the controlling force?

10-4. In Fig. 10-3a the central weight is 60 lb. The weight of each of the two balls is 5 lb. The arms are all equal and 12 in. long. Find the controlling force and calculate the speed when the arms meeting in the ball are at right angles.

10-5. The two balls of a Porter governor (Fig. 10-3) weigh 7.7 lb each; the arms and links are so arranged that the load rises 2 in. for a rise of 1 in. at the balls. The height of the governor at 180 rpm is 13 in. What is the central weight?

10-6. A Porter governor (Fig. 10-4) has the following dimensions: $AA_1 = DD_1 = 2$ in., $AC = CD = 8$ in., $BC = 3$ in., $W_1 = 45$ lb, and there are 3 balls weighing 3 lb each. Find the speed when the arms make 30° with the vertical. Then assuming the configuration to remain unchanged, while the speed suddenly increases 10 per cent, find the regulating force exerted at the sleeve.

10-7. A Porter governor has equal upper and lower arms, 10 in. long, with the ball at the connecting pin. Each of the two balls weighs 3 lb and the central load is 40 lb. The design is such that the radius of the balls can vary between a minimum of 4 in. and a maximum of 7 in. Find the maximum speed, and the speed regulation (per cent).

10-8. A Porter governor has 3 balls weighing 4 lb, a central weight of 30 lb, and a frictional resistance of 3 lb acting at the sleeve. The supporting and lower links are all 6 in. long with the ball at the connecting pin, and the inside ends of all links are mounted 1 in. from the axis of rotation. Find the range of speed (rpm) when the supporting arms make an angle of (a) 30°; (b) 45° with the axis of rotation.

10-9. An engine is governed to run at 240 rpm by a two-ball Watt governor driven at 80 rpm by a belt drive. At this speed the governor arms make an angle of 45° with the vertical. It is decided to replace the Watt by a Porter governor which runs at engine speed. If the Porter has the same arm lengths, and same flyballs as the Watt, and also runs with the 45° inclination at this speed, compare the regulating force exerted by the Porter for a 1 per cent speed change with that of the Watt.

10–10. A flyball governor has a controlling force of 40 lb when the balls rotate at 5-in. radius, and 45 lb at $5\frac{3}{4}$-in. radius. Is the governor stable or unstable? Why?

10–11. A Proell governor (Fig. 10–9) has the following dimensions. $AA_1 = 1\frac{1}{2}$ in., $AC = CD = 8$ in., $BC = 2\frac{1}{2}$ in., $DD' = 3$ in. The two balls weigh 5 lb and the central weight is 34 lb. When the ball arm BC is vertical, the balls rotate on a 6-in. radius. Determine the speed for this configuration.

10–12. The dimensions of a Proell governor are (Fig. 10–9) AA' coincident, $AC = CD = 12$ in., $BC = 4$ in., $DD' = 3$ in. The two balls rotate at 6.5-in. radius when the arm BC is vertical. The central weight is 120 lb and each ball weighs 10.5 lb. Determine the speed of the governor in this position.

10–13. A crossed-arm governor (Fig. 10–8) has the following dimensions: $a = 2$ in., $b = 10$ in., two 4-lb flyballs, center load and mass of links negligible. Friction is regarded as negligible. Range of movement of the arms from 30° to 45° with axis of rotation.

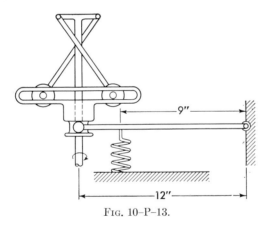

Fig. 10–P–13.

a) Find the maximum and minimum speeds. Is the governor stable?

b) If the dimension a is increased to $2\frac{1}{2}$ in. instead of 2 in. will the governor be stable?

c) If with $a = 2\frac{1}{2}$ in., a central weight is added, will this make the governor stable?

d) If a force is applied to the sleeve by a supplementary spring S, acting through a lever, as in the Fig. 10–P–13, with $a = 2\frac{1}{2}$ in., show that this can make the governor stable. The balls carry pins which slide freely in a slot perpendicular to the axis, which is integral with the sleeve. If the governor is to have a minimum speed of 120 rpm ($\theta = 30°$) find the initial spring tension required. The weight of the cross slide is 1 lb. If the speed regulation is to be 1 per cent, find the spring stiffness constant.

10–14. It is stated without proof in Art. 10–11, that the crossed-arm governor must be designed with the arms in their lowest position. Show that if the length of the arms is calculated on the basis of the highest position, the governor will be unstable.

10–15. A simple conical pendulum governor has two 25-lb balls on arms 12 in. long. The balls are connected to each other by a spring, of strength 25 lb per inch extension, and of free length 8 in. Find the speed at which the arms make an angle of 30° with the axis of rotation.

10–16. A Hartnell governor (Fig. 10–10) is required to come into action at a speed of 120 rpm, the radius of revolution of the centers of the two balls being 6 in. at this speed. If the weight of each ball is 12 lb, find the initial tension of the spring. If the lift of the sleeve is to be 1.5 in., the arms of the bell crank levers equal and $6\frac{1}{2}$ in. long, and the maximum speed of the governor 126 rpm, find the load per inch of compression of the spring. Assume the angles $\theta_1 = \theta_2$ for minimum and maximum speeds:

    a) Considering the downward gravity force of the balls.

    b) Neglecting it.

10–17. A spring-loaded governor (Fig. 10–10) has 4 right-angled arms spaced 90° apart. The arms are now in such a position that the longer radius (which is 3 units in length) is vertical with a ball weighing 3.22 lb at its upper end. The shorter radius is horizontal and 1 unit in length. The centers of the 4 balls are traveling in a circle which is 8 in. in diameter at 200 rpm. What is the compression in the central spring.

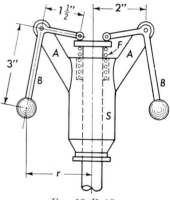

FIG. 10–P–18.

10–18. In the governor shown in Fig. 10–P–18 the 2 arms A, A are fixed to the sleeve S which is feather-keyed to the governor shaft. The light bell crank levers B, B are pivoted to A, A and bear through rollers on to the upper end of the shaft. The position of S is controlled by a spring F. The balls each weigh 1 lb, the sleeve and arms weigh 10 lb, and the spring stiffness is 20 lb per inch. Find the percentage speed regulation of the governor if the radius r is limited to 2 in. $< r <$ 3 in., the least speed of actuation being 300 rpm. Neglect friction.   (C.U.)

10–19. A spring-loaded governor is shown in the diagram. The two balls, each of weight 12 lb, are connected across by two springs A. A supplementary spring B provides an additional force at the sleeve through the medium of a lever which pivots about a fixed axis at its left-hand end. In the mean position, the radius of the governor balls is 6 in. and the speed is 600 rpm. The tension in each spring A is then 250 lb. Find the tension in the spring B for this position.

If when the sleeve moves up $\frac{3}{4}$ in. the speed is to be 630 rpm, find the necessary stiffness in spring B if the stiffness of each spring A is 45 lb per inch.

Neglect the moments produced by the weights of the balls.   (U.L.)

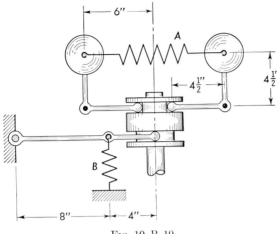

Fig. 10–P–19.

10–20. In a Hartnell governor, the two balls weighing 3 lb each revolve at a radius of 2 in. about a horizontal axis when running at the minimum operating speed of 500 rpm. At maximum speed the ball radius is 4 in. and the spring is compressed 1 in.

a) If the spring stiffness is 200 lb/in. compression, find the speed regulation.

b) What must be the spring stiffness to make the governor theoretically isochronous?

10–21. In a Hartnell governor the controlling force at maximum speed, when the radius is 1.5 in., is twice the controlling force at minimum speed (radius 1 in.). If the minimum speed is 600 rpm find the speed regulation.

10–22. A spring-loaded governor of the Hartnell type has arms of equal length. The weights rotate in a circle of $6\frac{1}{2}$-in. diameter when the sleeve is in its mid-position and the weight arms are vertical. The equilibrium speed for this position is 450 rpm, neglecting friction. The maximum sleeve movement is to be $1\frac{1}{4}$ in., and the maximum variation of speed (allowing for friction) is to be ± 5 per cent of the mid-position speed. The weight of the sleeve is $7\frac{1}{2}$ lb and friction may be considered equivalent to 6 lb at the sleeve. The governor must be sufficiently powerful to overcome the friction by a 1 per cent change of speed at mid-position.

Determine the weight of each rotating mass, the spring stiffness in lb per in., and the initial compression of the spring.   (U.L.)

10–23. For the Rites governor shown in Fig. 10–21, the bar weighs 100 lb, $r = 6$ in., $a = 5.5$ in., $b = 2$ in., $c = 10$ in., radius of gyration of bar about $G = 12$ in., rpm $= 240$. Find

a) Tension in the springs.

b) The additional torque about B due to centrifugal effect, when the speed changes from 240 rpm to 270 rpm and the position of the governor parts remains unchanged.

c) The torque about B due to inertia effect when the change in speed in (b) takes place in $\frac{1}{8}$ sec.

10–24. The figure shows the simplified arrangement of a governor. Two weighted arms A, A' are pivoted on pins B, B', $2\frac{1}{2}$ in. apart, attached to a plate C which rotates about its center. Each weighted arm weighs $\frac{1}{2}$ lb, and the centers of gravity G, G' are 2 in. from the centers of the pivots. Points S, S' in the arms, at 1-in. distance from the pivots, are connected by a spring. A linkage (not shown) ensures that the two angles θ, θ' are equal. The stiffness of the spring is 4 lb per inch.

a) Find the tension required in the spring so that the angles θ, θ' shall be 30° when the governor speed is 300 rpm.

b) If the governor, rotating in a counterclockwise direction, accelerates at the rate of 50 radians per sec², at what speed of rotation will the angles be 45°?

(U.L.)

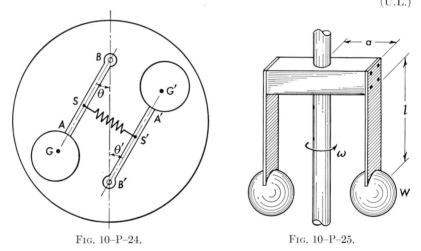

Fig. 10–P–24.   Fig. 10–P–25.

10–25. A governor consists of two flyballs of weight W attached to the ends of thin cantilever strip springs. These strips weigh w each. Derive an expression for the critical speed of rotation for radial vibrations of the balls.

10–26. A Hartnell governor with axial spring of stiffness k, two balls of mass m, bell crank lever arms equal, rotates about a horizontal axis. The masses of spring and bell cranks are negligible. Find the critical speed of the governor due to the alternating relative direction of the weight of the balls.

10–27. A Hartnell governor is driven at crankshaft speed by a four-cylinder two-stroke oil engine. The two balls of the governor weigh one lb each, the lever arms of the bell crank are equal, and the axial spring has a stiffness of 120 lb per inch compression. The governor can be set to hold any speed within the speed range of the engine by adjustment of the top end of the spring. The speed range is from 400 to 600 rpm.

Investigate the possibility of resonance of the governor.

10–28. The mechanism of a governor is designed to give straight-line radial movement only to the two equal balls. The controlling force is a linear function of the radius r of the ball path, the limiting values of r being a and b at which the equilibrium speeds of rotation are ω_a and ω_b respectively. Neglecting friction and all masses except those of the balls, show that the frequency of the free oscillations of the balls about radius r when the speed of rotation is constant, is

$$\frac{1}{2\pi}\sqrt{\frac{ab(\omega_a{}^2 - \omega_b{}^2)}{r(a - b)}}$$

(C.U.)

ANSWERS TO SELECTED PROBLEMS

CHAPTER 1

1-1. 149.5 lb.   **1-3.** 11.5 ft/sec².
1-5. Center 24 in. from A; 96.6 ft/sec².   **1-11.** $R = 10.7$ in.
1-13. 8.20 ft-lb; (top is depressed 5.17 in.).
1-15. 2.344 ft-lb (neglecting the angularity).   **1-17.** 73 in.-lb.
1-31. Roll them down any slope: the solid one will win.

CHAPTER 2

2-1. $m\ddot{x} + kx\dot{x} = w - \lambda x$ where $w - \lambda x$ is its submerged weight, x its depth below the surface.

2-3. (a) $M\ddot{x} + kx - \dfrac{kPx}{\sqrt{x^2 + P^2}} = 0$

   or $M\dot{x}^2 + k[x^2 - x_0^2 + 2P(\sqrt{x_0^2 + P^2} - \sqrt{x^2 + P^2})] = 0$

   with x_0 the maximum x.

   (b) $M(\ddot{\theta} - 2\tan\theta \cdot \dot{\theta}^2) + k(\sec\theta - 1)\sin\theta\cos^2\theta = 0$

   or $M\sec^4\theta \cdot \dot{\theta}^2 + k[(\sec^2\theta - \sec^2\theta_0) + 2P(\sec\theta_0 - \sec\theta)] = 0$.

2-5. $W\rho^2 gt \div \left\{ \left[I_A + \left(\dfrac{R}{r}\right)^2 I_B \right] g + W\rho^2 \right\}$

2-9. $x = (F_0 - \frac{1}{3}kt)t^2/2m$; $3 F_0/k$; $-3F_0/2km$.

2-11. (a) Motion in a viscous medium; (b) the heavily damped automatic door closer; (c) sine-wave (simple harmonic) motion, with amplitude 5 and a phase shift; (d) a diminishing oscillation; (e) vibration with beats.

2-13. $18m(A^2 - y^2)$.

2-15. $\{\frac{3}{2}Wr^2 + w[r^2 + a^2 - 2ar\cos(\theta - \phi)]\}\dot{\theta}^2/2g = (W + w)r\theta \sin\phi$
   $- wa(1 - \cos\theta)$.   **2-17.** $k = 0.0108$; $s = 1897$ ft.

2-19. Approx. $0.36WL$ (graphical solution of $\theta \sin\theta = 1 - \cos\theta$ yields about 2.34 radians).

2-23. (a) 38 rad/sec; (b) 9.34 sec; (c) 3.48 sec; (d) 3.52 turns.

2-25. 3.61 ft/sec; high.

2-33. 24 lb/in.; no.

2-35. 40.2 in./sec; 35.3 in.-lb.

2-41. $\phi = \dfrac{2r}{d}\int r\, d\theta = \dfrac{2Ar}{d}(1 - \cos\omega t)$

CHAPTER 3

3-1. 13 in.; 52 in./sec; 208 in./sec².   **3-3.** 0.069 lb.

3-5. $\dfrac{1}{2\pi} \sqrt{\dfrac{(k_1 + k_2)r^2}{I}}$ **3-7.** 3.13 sec.   **3-9.** 0.113 sec.

3-11. 1.70 sec.   **3-13.** 0.72 sec.   **3-15.** 23 cps.

3-17. 0.122 lb in.²; 2.19 rad/sec.

3-19. (a) $\dfrac{1}{2\pi}\dfrac{s}{L}\sqrt{\dfrac{kg}{W}}$; (b) $\dfrac{wL^2}{ks^2}\sqrt{1 + \dfrac{s^2}{L^2} \cdot \dfrac{2kh}{(W + w)}}$

3–21. 1.5 in.; 1.81 cps.   **3–23.** Lengthened by $1/1080$ ($1/1079$ is wrong).
3–25. $\pm 0.98\%$.   **3–27.** 0.328 cps ($\omega^2 = 386/91$).   **3–29.** 2.39 cps.

3–31. $\dfrac{1}{2\pi}\sqrt{\dfrac{3EIg}{(WL^2 + 4Jg)L}}$.   **3–33.** $2\pi\sqrt{l/2g}$.   **3–39.** 0.282 sec.; $^4/_9$ in.

3–43. 26.67 and 0; 20 and 6.67 ft/sec.
3–45. 639 rpm.   **3–47.** 295 cps approx.   **3–49.** 2.575 cps.

CHAPTER 4

4–1. 14.14 lb, at 45° between the 5- and 10-lb weights.
4–3. 110 lb, at 49° 6′ from W_3 away from W_2.   **4–5.** 6.30 (mph)².
4–7. Two 1-oz weights will do, one at 5° 11′, the other at 11° 51′ from 3 oz.
    toward 2 oz.   **4–9.** 4 lb each.   **4–11.** 171 lb each.
4–13. $W = 4.26$; $\phi = 0°$; $x = 1.1$.   **4–15.** $e = 0.384$ in.; 174 lb in.
4–17. $W_D = 0.785$ lb at 45° 47′; $W_E = 0.621$ lb at 92° 46′.
4–19. 2.18 lb at $\theta = 203\frac{1}{2}°$, with $d = -1.787$.   **4–23.** 4410 rpm.

4–25. $N = \dfrac{235}{\sqrt{\Delta}}$rpm.   **4–27.** 9240 rpm.   **4–29.** Approx. 1000 rpm.

4–31. Over 2 in.   **4–33.** (a) 1382, 5540, and 12,450 rpm.
4–35. 700 rad/sec. (See J. P. Den Hartog, *Mechanical Vibrations*, 3d ed: p. 197.)
4–39. 233 rpm.

CHAPTER 5

5–1. $x = e^{-2t} - 4e^{-8t}$ **5–3.** 0.213; 20.5 cps; 58 lb (weight).
5–5. Reduce W by 11.1%.
5–9. $y = \frac{8}{9}(\sin \frac{5}{2}\pi t_1 - \cos \frac{5}{2}\pi t_1)$ where $t_1 = (t - 3)$.
5–11. 0.31 in.   **5–13.** Resonance with universal joint at 1840 rpm.
5–15. $100{,}000 < k < 102{,}000$ lb/in. or $k > 306{,}000$

5–17. Transmissibility $= \dfrac{F_T}{F} = \sqrt{\dfrac{1 + 4\gamma^2\rho^2}{(1 - \rho^2)^2 + 4\gamma^2\rho^2}}$ where $\begin{cases} \gamma = c/c_c \\ \rho = \omega/\omega_n \end{cases}$

5–19. 0.067 in.
5–21. Between M and m provided $\omega^2 \geq 2k/M$.
5–23. Constant c cannot be found, but c/c_c ratio $= \gamma = 0.0355$.

CHAPTER 6

6–1. 1003 in./sec ($v_x = 80$; $v_y = -800$; $v_z = 600$).
6–3. $W_A = 0.309$ oz, 75° 58′ from y-axis toward z-axis;
    $W_B = 0.075$ oz in the $-y'$ direction.
6–5. 0.230 lb at eccentric end, on heavy side, 0.128 lb at other end.
6–7. Horizontal maxima 67 lb; vertical maxima 72 lb.
6–11. -6 lb in.²; $\theta = 28° 10′$; $I_X = 18.09$, $I_Y = 3.666$, $I_Z = 18.75$ lb. in.².
6–15. 15.6 lb-in-sec at 33.6°.
6–17. Design not suitable; AB would have to be over 2.56 diam. Needs higher
    permissible stress or reinforcing rib.
6–19. Will make the plane veer to the right.
6–21. (a) None; (b) horizontal forces appear on turbine shaft bearings.
6–23. 10,300 lb ft; rear bearing 5344 lb, front bearing 656 lb, both downward.
6–25. (a) Turns right, helping caster; (b) 14.8 lb in.
6–27. Centrifugal 6 lb down; gyro 0.118 lb sideways.
6–29. 30.1 tons.   **6–31.** 39.7°.   **6–35.** 13° 12′.

CHAPTER 7

7–1. $F_P = F_O = 73$ lb; at tooth $26\frac{1}{2}$ lb.   **7–7.** 112 lb.

7–11. (a) $F_A = 251$ lb; $F_C = 305$ lb; $F_D = 223$ lb; torque $= 312$ lb in.

7–13. Representative points on the curve of F lb against distance x in. from B are:

$F =$	0	3.53	2.56	1.52	0.65	-0.15	-0.23	-0.18	0
$x =$	1.25	1.35	1.55	1.75	2.0	2.5	3.0	3.5	3.75

7–15. At $\theta = 0°, 30°, \ldots$ normal force $= 0, 73.2, 52.1, 17.5, 7.4, 1.2, 0$ lbs.

7–17. 658 ft-lb.   **7–19.** 1.082 oz in.; 2.37/1000 hp; 126.4%.

CHAPTER 8

8–1. 28.56 hp; 1.76%.   **8–3.** 889 lb.   **8–5.** 2240 lb; 4.76 in.

8–7. 6.9%.   **8–9.** $\Delta E = 1530$ ft-lb approx.; 0.52%.   **8–11.** 0.5% approx.

8–13. 150 ft-lbs.

8–15. Primary couple $= mr\omega^2 a\,(0.866 \sin\theta - 1.5 \cos\theta)$; secondary couple $= -m(r^2/l)\omega^2 a\,(0.866 \sin 2\theta + 1.5 \cos 2\theta)$; remove primary by a pair of Lanchesters.

8–17. (a) Unbalanced primary couple $= -mr\omega^2 a\,(0.172 \cos\theta + 0.414 \sin\theta)$; (b) two Lanchesters, $8a$ apart, producing $0.0560\ mr\omega^2$ each, the one nearer Crank No. 1 to produce its maximum downward force when first crank angle is $67° \, 26'$.

8–19. Still perfectly balanced.

8–21. Primary force 5260 lb; secondary couple 9150 lb ft.

8–23. Only secondary couple unbalanced.

8–25. Two rotating vectors unbalanced—a force $\frac{3}{2} mr\omega^2$ in direction θ of crank, and a force $\frac{3}{2} m(r^2/l)\omega^2$ in direction -2θ (counter-rotating).

8–27. All couples balanced. Unbalanced forces of 6th, 12th, 18th, etc., harmonics, in which all six cylinders act in phase.

8–29. Net force zero (accelerations $r\omega^2$ produce constant force $2\ me\omega^2$ to the left, $\ddot{r}$ produce the same, but Coriolis' produce $4\ me\omega^2$ to the right).

8–31. See Art. 7–6, Example 2.

CHAPTER 9

9–1. $F = 2180$ lb; $s_t = 11,620$ psi.   **9–3.** 434 psi.   **9–5.** 20,400 psi; 8000 psi.

9–7. 175 lb ft.   **9–9.** 7300 psi.

9–13. The second differences show an imposed frequency of accelerations of 4.5 cps; natural frequency is 4.55 cps.

9–15. $k \gg \dfrac{4\pi^2 n^2 (I + \frac{1}{2} mr^2)}{225 D^2}$ when D is assumed diameter of pulley.

CHAPTER 10

10–3. 54.2 rpm; 53.33 lb.   **10–5.** 84.3 lb.   **10–7.** 233 rpm; $12\frac{1}{2}\%$.

10–9. The Porter has nine times the force of the Watt.   **10–11.** 161.9 rpm.

10–13. (a) 83.3 and 82.3 rpm; stable; (b) no; (c) no; (d) 6.85 lb; 1.27 lb/in.

10–15. 164 rpm.   **10–17.** 175.5 lb.   **10–19.** (a) 705 lb; (b) 246 lb/in.

10–21. 14.4%.   **10–23.** (a) 539 lb; (b) 118 lb ft; (c) 52.8 lb ft.

10–25. $16.66 \sqrt{\dfrac{EIg}{(W + 0.226w)l^3}}$ or $16.5 \sqrt{\dfrac{EIg}{(W + 0.375w)l^3}}$

10–27. Critical speed 353 rpm; design is poor.

INDEX